MAHABHARATA

Mahabharata 3

On the Battlefield of Kurukshetra

Editor: Anant Pai

Illustrations: Dilip Kadam

This volume of Mahabharata contains the following titles:

Amar Chitra Katha Pvt Ltd

© Amar Chitra Katha Pvt Ltd, 1998, Reprinted July 2012, ISBN 978-81-905990-4-7
Published & Printed by Amar Chitra Katha Pvt. Ltd., Krishna House, 3rd Floor,
Raghuvanshi Mill Compound, S.B.Marg, Lower Parel (W), Mumbai- 400 013. India
For Consumer Complaints Contact Tel : +91-22 40497436
Email: customerservice@ack-media.com

Mahabharafa—29
KRISHNA'S PEACE MISSION

O MONARCH, HAVING TAKEN LEAVE OF YUDHISHTHIRA, KRISHNA SET OFF ON HIS PEACE MISSION FOR HASTINAPURA.

" AND STRANGE OMENS WERE SEEN ON THE OCCASION. THOUGH THERE WERE NO CLOUDS, THERE WERE THUNDER AND LIGHTNING.

" THE SKY WAS CLEAR AND YET THERE WAS TORRENTIAL RAIN.

" THE RIVERS FLOWED UPSTREAM.

" THE WELLS SPEWED OUT THEIR CONTENTS.

"BUT, ALONG THE ROUTE TAKEN BY KRISHNA, NATURE WAS REVEALED IN ALL ITS SPLENDOUR AND BEAUTY.

" WHEREVER HE WENT, HE RECEIVED AN ENTHUSIASTIC RECEPTION.

"AT VRIKASTHALA, ON THE WAY TO HASTINAPURA—

WE WILL SPEND THE NIGHT IN THIS DELIGHTFUL PLACE.

"MEANWHILE, AT HASTINAPURA, A SPY PRESENTED HIMSELF BEFORE KING DHRITARASHTRA.

O GREAT KING, KRISHNA IS ON HIS WAY HERE.

"DHRITARASHTRA IMMEDIATELY CALLED VIDURA.

O VIDURA, WE MUST SPARE NO EFFORT IN GIVING A BIG WELCOME TO KRISHNA. HE IS THE FOREMOST AMONG MEN AND WORTHY OF WORSHIP.

HAVE A GRAND MANSION BUILT ON HIS WAY HERE. I WILL HONOUR HIM WITH SIXTEEN GOLDEN CHARIOTS, EIGHT ELEPHANTS AND MANY OTHER PRECIOUS GIFTS. I WILL PERSONALLY GO WITH ALL MY SONS AND GRANDSONS TO WELCOME HIM. DURYODHANA WILL NOT COME WITH ME.

"HEARING THIS, VIDURA SAID —

O KING, NO DOUBT KRISHNA DESERVES ALL THIS. INDEED HE DESERVES THE WHOLE EARTH. BUT I KNOW YOUR MIND. YOU DO NOT REALLY WISH TO HONOUR HIM. THE TRUTH IS THAT YOU THINK YOU COULD BRIBE KRISHNA WITH YOUR GIFTS AND DRIVE A WEDGE BETWEEN HIM AND THE PANDAVAS.

THAT, O KING, WILL NEVER BE POSSIBLE. KRISHNA WILL NEVER ACCEPT ANY OF YOUR GIFTS. IF YOU REALLY WISH TO MAKE HIM HAPPY, AGREE TO WHAT HE IS COMING HERE FOR — A PEACEFUL SETTLEMENT BETWEEN YOUR SONS AND THE PANDAVAS.

"DURYODHANA SAID—

O KING, I TOO THINK YOU WILL NOT SUCCEED IN ALIENATING KRISHNA FROM THE PANDAVAS. DO NOT GO TOO FAR TO PLEASE HIM. HE MAY THINK WE ARE AFRAID OF HIM.

"BHEESHMA INTERPOSED—

WE MUST PAY HEED TO WHAT KRISHNA SAYS AND ACCEPT HIS ADVICE WITHOUT QUESTION. HE IS VIRTUOUS AS WELL AS INTRANSIGENT.

"BUT DURYODHANA PERSISTED.

O GRANDSIRE, THERE IS NOT THE LEAST LIKELIHOOD OF MY SHARING THE KINGDOM WITH THE PANDAVAS. LISTEN, EVERYBODY, TO MY PLAN. I WANT TO IMPRISON KRISHNA ON WHOM THE PANDAVAS RELY SO MUCH. WITHOUT HIM, THE PANDAVAS AND THEIR ALLIES WILL BE EASILY OVERCOME BY US. DO SUGGEST HOW TO GO ABOUT MY PLAN.

"DHRITARASHTRA WAS SHOCKED:—

O DURYODHANA! NEVER SAY SUCH A THING AGAIN! KRISHNA COMES TO US AS AN AMBASSADOR AND SHOULD BE TREATED AS SUCH!

"BHEESHMA SAID—

O KING, DURYODHANA'S HOUR HAS COME. DISREGARDING THE ADVICE OF HIS WELL-WISHERS HE CHOOSES THE PATH OF DESTRUCTION. I DO NOT WISH TO HEAR ANY MORE OF HIS RAVINGS.

"AND A FURIOUS BHEESHMA STALKED OUT OF THE COURT.

" THE NEXT DAY KRISHNA WAS GIVEN A WARM WELCOME ON HIS ARRIVAL AT THE COURT OF HASTINAPURA.

WELCOME TO OUR ABODE, O KRISHNA.

PLEASE SIT DOWN FOR A WHILE YOU MUST BE TIRED AFTER YOUR LONG JOURNEY.

" AND, KRISHNA SAT AND CHATTED WITH THE KAURAVAS.

AFTER SPENDING SOME TIME EXCHANGING PLEASANTRIES WITH THE KAURAVAS, KRISHNA WENT TO PAY HIS RESPECTS TO KUNTI, HIS PATERNAL AUNT AND MOTHER OF THE PANDAVAS.

"HER VOICE CHOKED WITH GRIEF, KUNTI SAID TO KRISHNA—

HOW ARE MY SONS? THEY WERE USED TO A LIFE OF COMFORT IN PALATIAL MANSIONS. HOW ARE THEY FARING IN THE FORESTS INFESTED WITH SAVAGE BEASTS?

HOW IS MY VIRTUOUS YUDHISHTHIRA AND HOW IS MY POWERFUL BHEEMA WHO IS EASILY AROUSED TO ANGER? HOW IS MY ARJUNA, THAT DEARLY LOVED COUSIN AND FRIEND OF YOURS? ARE THE TWINS IN GOOD HEALTH? AND MY DEAREST DAUGHTER-IN-LAW, THE BEAUTIFUL PANCHALI, IS SHE WELL?

HOW SHE HAS SUFFERED AT THE HANDS OF THE VILE KAURAVAS! O KRISHNA, NEVER IN MY LIFE HAVE I FELT AS GRIEVED AS WHEN I SAW DRAUPADI BEING DRAGGED INTO THE KAURAVA ASSEMBLY AND DISGRACED IN FRONT OF EVERYBODY.

WIDOWHOOD, POVERTY, DEPENDENCE ON CHARITY AND PROLONGED SEPARATION FROM MY SONS HAVE CAUSED ME GREAT SUFFERING.

I WAS DISTRESSED AT MY NOBLE SONS BEING DRIVEN INTO THE FOREST. AND NOW THEY HAVE EVEN BEEN DEPRIVED OF THEIR LIVELIHOOD. WE DESERVE HAPPINESS, O KRISHNA, AFTER LONG YEARS OF AGONY.

O KRISHNA, TELL MY SONS THAT THE TIME HAS COME FOR THEM TO SHOW THEMSELVES AS TRUE KSHATRIYAS. TELL THEM THAT IF THEY DO NOT UPHOLD THEIR DHARMA NOW, I SHALL FORSAKE THEM FOR EVER.

"KRISHNA ROSE—

O DURYODHANA, ONE ACCEPTS AN INVITATION TO A MEAL EITHER OUT OF FRIENDSHIP AND GOODWILL OR OUT OF DIRE NEED. YOU HAVE NEVER BY ANY ACT OF YOURS INSPIRED FRIENDSHIP IN ME. NOR AM I IN EXTREME NEED. YOUR FOOD IS DEFILED BY YOUR WICKEDNESS.

"SO SAYING, HE WENT TO VIDURA'S PLACE AND TOOK HIS FOOD THERE.

LATER—

I DO NOT BELIEVE YOU HAVE DONE THE RIGHT THING IN COMING HERE. DURYODHANA AND HIS FRIENDS ARE EVIL. HE WILL DISREGARD YOUR COUNSEL. DO NOT GO IN THEIR MIDST, O KRISHNA.

I KNOW THAT, VIDURA. I WILL STRIVE WITH IMPARTIALITY FOR THE WELFARE OF BOTH SIDES. EVEN IF DURYODHANA MISTRUSTS ME, I WILL HAVE THE SATISFACTION OF HAVING DONE MY DUTY.

I DO NOT WISH TO BE ACCUSED OF NOT HAVING ATTEMPTED TO STOP A POSSIBLE WAR.

NEXT MORNING, KRISHNA ARRIVED AT THE COURT OF KING DHRITARASHTRA TO MAKE PROPOSALS FOR A PEACEFUL SETTLEMENT OF THE PANDAVA-KAURAVA RIVALRY.

O KING, I COME HERE TO PREVENT BLOODSHED AND DESTRUCTION AND TO ESTABLISH LASTING PEACE BETWEEN THE KAURAVAS AND THE PANDAVAS.

A GREAT CALAMITY IS ABOUT TO BEFALL THE KAURAVAS. IF STEPS ARE NOT TAKEN TO PREVENT IT, THE WHOLE WORLD WILL BE DESTROYED.

IF YOU SO DESIRE, O DHRITARASHTRA, IT IS YET POSSIBLE TO PREVENT THIS DESTRUCTION.

YOU KEEP YOUR SONS UNDER CHECK AND I WILL RESTRAIN THE PANDAVAS. THEREBY WE WILL INSURE THE WELFARE OF BOTH SIDES.

O KING, PEACE WITH THE PANDAVAS WILL BE OF BENEFIT TO YOU. IF YOU RESTORE THEIR KINGDOM TO THEM AND HONOUR THEM AS BEFORE, YOU WILL CONTINUE TO RULE THE EARTH UNDER THEIR PROTECTION.

THEY ARE EVER RESPECTFUL TO YOU. IN SPITE OF THE FACT THAT YOU HAVE BEEN UNJUST TO THEM, THEY SEEK YOUR PROTECTION AND ARE READY TO SERVE YOU. BUT THEY WILL FIGHT FOR THEIR RIGHTS. SO DO WHAT YOU DEEM FIT.

"THE WHOLE ASSEMBLY LISTENED TO KRISHNA'S PROPOSAL IN RESPECTFUL SILENCE.

"DHRITARASHTRA THEN SAID—

O KRISHNA, THERE IS TRUTH AND WISDOM IN YOUR WORDS. BUT, ALAS, I AM UNABLE TO CHECK MY SON. IT IS FOR YOU NOW TO BRING HIM ON TO THE RIGHT PATH.

"KRISHNA SAID—

O DURYODHANA, LISTEN TO ME, FOR I SPEAK FOR THE GOOD OF YOU AND YOUR KIN.

LOOK AT YOUR SONS, BROTHERS AND KINSMEN. LET THEM NOT PERISH ON YOUR ACCOUNT. MAKE PEACE WITH THE PANDAVAS.

IT WILL BE TO YOUR EVERLASTING GOOD. THE PANDAVAS WILL MAKE YOU THE YUVARAJA* AND YOUR FATHER DHRITARASHTRA WILL REMAIN THE KING.

DURYODHANA, DO NOT SPURN THIS OPPORTUNITY OF PRESERVING YOUR WEALTH AND WELL-BEING. GIVE AWAY HALF YOUR KINGDOM TO THE PANDAVAS AND REIGN IN PEACE.

"BHEESHMA SAID —

KRISHNA SPEAKS THE TRUTH. DO NOT IGNORE THE WORDS OF DHRITARASHTRA. SAVE YOURSELF FROM THE SIN OF DESTRUCTION OF YOUR RACE AND PLUNGING YOUR PARENTS INTO SORROW.

"DRONA SAID —

KRISHNA AND BHEESHMA ARE RIGHT. DO NOT RELY ON PEOPLE WITH A LOW LEVEL OF INTELLIGENCE. DO NOT DESPISE KRISHNA, O DURYODHANA.

"THEN VIDURA SAID —

I DO NOT FEEL SORRY FOR YOU. I FEEL SORRY FOR YOUR AGED PARENTS WHO WILL BECOME HELPLESS AND INSECURE ON YOUR ACCOUNT. LIKE BEGGARS THEY WILL ROAM THE EARTH IN DEEP SORROW.

* CROWN PRINCE.

"HEARING ALL THIS, DURYODHANA SAID TO KRISHNA.

HOW UNJUST THAT EACH OF YOU SHOULD FIND FAULT WITH ME ALONE! THERE IS NOTHING REPREHENSIBLE IN MY BEHAVIOUR.

I DID NOT FORCE YUDHISHTHIRA TO PLAY DICE. THE PROPERTY THEY LOST BY PLAYING THE GAME WAS RETURNED TO THEM. IF THEY LOST AGAIN, HOW AM I TO BLAME? WHY DO THEY WISH TO KILL US?

THE KINGDOM BEQUEATHED TO ME BY MY FATHER WILL NEVER BE GIVEN AWAY SO LONG AS I AM ALIVE. WHILE KING DHRITARASHTRA IS ALIVE, WE AND THE PANDAVAS SHOULD LIVE PEACEFULLY, WITHOUT RESORTING TO AN ARMED CONFLICT.

OUT OF FEAR AND IGNORANCE, I GAVE TO THE PANDAVAS WHAT WAS NEVER THEIRS. BUT NOW I WILL NOT GIVE THEM EVEN THAT MUCH LAND AS CAN BE PIERCED BY THE POINT OF A NEEDLE.

"KRISHNA REPLIED, HIS EYES FLASHING WITH ANGER—

DURYODHANA, THE TRUTH IS THAT YOU GOT SHAKUNI TO PLAY A DECEITFUL GAME. AND YOU HAVE ALWAYS PLAYED FOUL WITH THE PANDAVAS.

YOU WISH FOR THE DEATH OF HEROES? THEN YOU SHALL HAVE IT. SOON THERE WILL BE A FEARFUL SLAUGHTER OF THE KAURAVAS AT THE HANDS OF THE PANDAVAS.

"DUHSHASANA SAID—

O DURYODHANA, I SUSPECT THAT IF YOU DO NOT GIVE IN TO KRISHNA'S PROPOSAL, THEN YOU, KARNA AND I WILL BE BOUND HAND AND FOOT AND TURNED OVER TO THE PANDAVAS.

"DURYODHANA ROSE, SPEECHLESS WITH RAGE...

"... AND WITHOUT A WORD, HE STALKED OUT OF THE COURT, FOLLOWED BY ALL HIS BROTHERS AND COUNSELLORS.

"THEN KRISHNA SAID— LISTEN TO ME, O VENERABLE MEN OF THE KURU RACE. FOR THE GREATER GOOD OF ALL, EACH MUST LEARN TO SACRIFICE A LITTLE OF HIS OWN. ARREST DURYODHANA, MAKE PEACE WITH THE PANDAVAS AND SAVE THE KSHATRIYAS FROM DESTRUCTION.

DHRITARASHTRA SAID—

VIDURA, PLEASE BRING GANDHARI HERE. PERHAPS SHE WILL BE ABLE TO PERSUADE MY SON TO FOLLOW THE RIGHT PATH.

"GANDHARI WAS BROUGHT TO THE COURT—

O GANDHARI, YOUR WICKED SON IS BENT UPON BRINGING ABOUT TOTAL DESTRUCTION. DISREGARDING THE ADVICE OF ELDERS, HE HAS INSULTED ALL OF US BY STALKING OUT WITHOUT A WORD.

"GANDHARI REPLIED—

O KING, YOU INDULGED YOUR SON TOO MUCH AND ARE HENCE RESPONSIBLE FOR THE PRESENT SITUATION.

ON DHRITARASHTRA'S INSTRUCTION VIDURA SUMMONED DURYODHANA BACK INTO COURT.

WHEN DURYODHANA ARRIVED—

O DURYODHANA, LISTEN TO ME FOR I SPEAK FOR YOUR WELFARE.

IT IS NOT TRUE THAT KRIPA, BHEESHMA AND DRONA WILL EMPLOY THEIR FULL MIGHT AGAINST THE PANDAVAS, BECAUSE THEY LOVE THE PANDAVAS AS MUCH AS THEY LOVE YOU. THEY MAY FIGHT ON YOUR SIDE AND DIE ON THE BATTLEFIELD BECAUSE THEY HAVE BEEN YOUR DEPENDANTS. BUT THEY WILL NEVER DESPISE YUDHISHTHIRA.

"DURYODHANA ONCE AGAIN STORMED OUT OF THE COURT.

" THEN HE GOT TOGETHER WITH SHAKUNI, KARNA AND DUHSHASANA...

"... AND HATCHED A CONSPIRACY.

BEFORE KRISHNA, BHEESHMA AND DHRITARASHTRA HAVE US ARRESTED, WE MUST TAKE KRISHNA CAPTIVE. IT WILL DEMORALISE AND PARALYSE THE PANDAVAS.

"THE ASTUTE SATYAKI FORESAW THE SCHEME. HE CALLED KRITAVARMAN AND SAID—

GET OUR TROOPS READY FOR BATTLE. MEANWHILE I SHALL INFORM KRISHNA OF THE CONSPIRACY.

"SATYAKI THEN ENTERED THE KAURAVA COURT AND ANNOUNCED—

I HAVE JUST COME TO KNOW THAT DURYODHANA, SHAKUNI, KARNA AND DUHSHASANA ARE PLANNING TO TAKE THE UNCONQUERABLE KRISHNA CAPTIVE.

O KING, YOUR SON BELIEVES HE CAN TAKE ME PRISONER. I CAN TAKE ALL KAURAVAS PRISONER SINGLE-HANDED. BUT REST ASSURED, I SHALL NOT DO ANYTHING DISHONOURABLE.

KNOW, O KING, THAT I CAN IF I WISH HAND OVER THIS KINGDOM TO YUDHISHTHIRA HERE AND NOW. HOW LONG WILL IT TAKE ME TO SEIZE YOUR SONS AND TURN THEM OVER TO YUDHISHTHIRA.

"DURYODHANA WAS BROUGHT BACK TO COURT. KRISHNA ADDRESSED HIM.

O DURYODHANA, YOU ARE MISTAKEN IF YOU BELIEVE THAT I AM ALONE AND WITHOUT POWER. LOOK AT ME.

"AND KRISHNA REVEALED HIMSELF IN HIS CELESTIAL FORM BEFORE AN AWE-STRUCK COURT.

"SEEING THE DIVINE FORM, THE GODS SHOWERED FLOWERS FROM ABOVE.

"THE WHOLE EARTH TREMBLED AND THE OCEANS BECAME AGITATED.

"THEN ASSUMING HIS NORMAL FORM, KRISHA ROSE AND WALKED OUT OF THE COURT.

"AT THE GATE, DHRITARASHTRA ADDRESSED KRISHNA —

O KRISHNA, YOU HAVE SEEN THE POWER I WIELD OVER MY SONS. YOU HAVE SEEN WITH YOUR OWN EYES HOW I HAVE MADE EVERY EFFORT TO BRING ABOUT PEACE.

"KRISHNA REPLIED —

ALL OF YOU HAVE SEEN DURYODHANA'S IMPROPER BEHAVIOUR. NOW EVEN DHRITARASHTRA PLEADS HIS INABILITY TO RESTRAIN HIS SON. WITH YOUR PERMISSION I WILL NOW GO BACK TO YUDHISHTHIRA.

"THEN KRISHNA WENT AND PAID HIS RESPECTS TO KUNTI.

O AUNT, WE TRIED IN VAIN TO PERSUADE DURYODHANA FOR A PEACEFUL UNDERSTANDING. BUT HE REFUSED TO SEE REASON. I AM NOW GOING BACK TO YOUR SONS. DO YOU HAVE ANY MESSAGE FOR THEM?

"KUNTI SAID —

TELL YUDHISHTHIRA, THE KINGDOM THAT RIGHTFULLY BELONGS TO HIM LIES IN THE HANDS OF THE ENEMY. HE MUST TRY EVERY MEANS TO RECOVER IT — IF NOT BY CONCILIATION, GENEROSITY, THEN BY INCITING DISSENSION IN HIS RANKS OR BY INFLICTING PUNISHMENT.

TELL HIM THAT HE MUST FIGHT SINCE THAT IS IN ACCORDANCE WITH HIS DHARMA. OR ELSE, HE WILL BRING DISGRACE TO THE FAMILY'S NAME.

O KRISHNA, TELL THE MIGHTY ARJUNA THAT THE TIME HAS COME TO VANQUISH HIS ENEMIES IN BATTLE AND WIN BACK THE KINGDOM.

YOU KNOW BHEEMA'S MIND HE WILL NOT REST TILL HE HAS DESTROYED HIS FOES.

TELL DRAUPADI THAT I AM PLEASED WITH HER FOR HER BEING FAITHFUL TO HER HUSBANDS AND FOR TREATING ALL OF THEM IMPARTIALLY. O KRISHNA, WHAT GRIEVED ME EVEN MORE THAN THE PANDAVAS LOSING THE KINGDOM WAS THE WAY IN WHICH DRAUPADI WAS DISGRACED IN THE ASSEMBLY.

REMIND THE PANDAVAS OF THAT SHAMEFUL INCIDENT. REMIND THEM ABOUT THE CRUEL INSULTS WE SUFFERED AT THEIR HANDS AND ROUSE THEIR IRE. LOOK AFTER MY SONS AND DRAUPADI, O KRISHNA.

"KRISHNA SAID—

O NOBLE LADY, I SHALL DELIVER YOUR MESSAGES TO THE PANDAVAS AND DRAUPADI.

AND WITH THAT, HE LEFT.

"AND TAKING KARNA WITH HIM, KRISHNA DEPARTED FOR UPAPLAVYA.

"BACK AT THE COURT OF HASTINAPURA, BHEESHMA SAID TO DURYODHANA—

O DURYODHANA, YOU MUST HAVE HEARD KUNTI'S MESSAGE TO THE PANDAVAS. THEY WILL NEVER DISOBEY HER WORDS.

THEREFORE, O KING, MAKE PEACE WITH THE PANDAVAS AND SAVE THE EARTH FROM CONFLICT. YUDHISHTHIRA IS YOUR ELDER BROTHER. HE IS VIRTUOUS AND AFFECTIONATE TOWARDS YOU. HAND OVER THE KINGDOM TO HIM.

IF YOU DO NOT LISTEN TO OUR WORDS OF WISDOM, ARJUNA WILL DESTROY YOUR ARMY.

"DRONA SAID—

I LOVE ARJUNA EVEN MORE THAN I LOVE MY SON, ASHWATTHAMA. ALAS! I WILL HAVE TO FIGHT HIM IN ACCORDANCE WITH MY DHARMA.

I AGAIN ENTREAT YOU, O DURYODHANA, THERE IS NO NEED FOR WAR. MAKE PEACE WITH THOSE HEROES FOR THE PROSPERITY AND WELL-BEING OF THE WHOLE KURU RACE.

BUT THE ENTREATIES OF BHEESHMA AND DRONA FELL UPON DEAF EARS. DURYODHANA GLOWERED AT THEM AND REFUSED TO SAY A WORD IN REPLY.

"DHRITARASHTRA SAID TO SANJAYA —

O SANJAYA, I HEAR THAT KRISHNA TOOK KARNA WITH HIM IN HIS CHARIOT AND WENT OUT OF THE CITY. TELL ME, O SANJAYA, WHAT KRISHNA SPOKE TO KARNA AND WHAT THE LATTER SAID IN REPLY.

"SANJAYA SAID —

THEN LISTEN, O KING, WHILE I RECOUNT THE DIALOGUE BETWEEN KRISHNA AND KARNA.

O KARNA, YOU ARE THE SON OF KUNTI, BORN TO HER WHEN SHE WAS A MAIDEN. YOU ARE THUS THE ELDEST AMONG THE PANDAVAS. FORSAKE DURYODHANA AND JOIN YOUR BROTHERS, THE PANDAVAS.

amar chitra katha

"KRISHNA SAID—

O KARNA, YOU DO NOT WISH TO RULE THE EARTH WITH THE PANDAVAS AND MYSELF AS YOUR ALLIES. GO THEN BACK TO THE KAURAVAS AND TELL THEM THAT THE PRESENT MONTH IS AUSPICIOUS FOR BATTLE.

SUPPLIES ARE IN PLENTY AND THE WEATHER IS DELIGHTFUL SEVEN DAYS FROM NOW IS THE NEW-MOON DAY. LET THE BATTLE COMMENCE THEN. THIS BATTLE WILL BE PRESIDED OVER BY INDRA HIMSELF.

"KARNA SAID— O KRISHNA, YOU KNOW THE PAST, PRESENT AND FUTURE. YOU KNOW THAT ALL KAURAVAS AND MYSELF ARE DESTINED TO BE DESTROYED.

IF WE COME OUT OF THIS GREAT BATTLE ALIVE, THEN WE SHALL MEET AGAIN HERE ON EARTH. OTHERWISE, CERTAINLY, WE SHALL MEET IN HEAVEN.

" KARNA THEN EMBRACED KRISHNA FONDLY...

"...AND LEFT FOR HASTINAPURA.

MEANWHILE, BACK IN HASTINAPURA, VIDURA INFORMED KUNTI OF THE FAILURE OF KRISHNA'S MISSION AS A RESULT OF DURYODHANA'S OBSTINACY.

"KUNTI BEMOANED—

OF WHAT USE ARE WEALTH AND POWER GAINED THROUGH LARGE-SCALE DESTRUCTION? THE FACT THAT BHEESHMA, DRONA AND KARNA WILL JOIN THE RANKS OF THE KAURAVAS FILLS ME WITH GREATER FEAR.

BHEESHMA AND DRONA WILL NOT WILLINGLY SLAY THE PANDAVAS WHO ARE VERY DEAR TO THEM. BUT KARNA? HE IS MIGHTY AND WILL SURELY TRY TO KILL MY SONS. I WILL GO AND APPEAL TO HIM AS A MOTHER.

"SO KUNTI ARRIVED ON THE BANKS OF THE GANGA WHERE KARNA WAS WORSHIPPING SURYA, THE SUN GOD.

"HAVING FINISHED HIS PRAYERS, KARNA TURNED AND SAW KUNTI. HE BOWED TO HER AND SAID—

I AM KARNA, THE SON OF RADHA AND ADHIRATHA. TELL ME, O LADY, WHAT I CAN DO FOR YOU.

"KUNTI SAID —

YOU ARE MY SON. I BORE YOU WHEN I WAS YET A MAIDEN BY THE GRACE OF THE DIVINE AND BLAZING SURYA.

"JUST THEN, SURYA'S VOICE RANG OUT FROM THE HEAVENS.

O KARNA, KUNTI IS RIGHT. SHE IS YOUR MOTHER. FOLLOW HER WORDS AND BE WITH VIRTUE.

"KUNTI CONTINUED —

O KARNA, BEING MY SON, IT IS NOT PROPER FOR YOU TO SERVE DURYODHANA.

JOIN HANDS WITH ARJUNA. YOU WILL MAKE AN INVINCIBLE PAIR, CAPABLE OF ACCOMPLISHING ANYTHING ON EARTH. SHED THE ROLE OF CHARIOTEER'S SON AND JOIN THE PANDAVAS AS A KING.

"KARNA SAID —

O MOTHER, I WAS ABANDONED BY YOU AS I WAS BORN. I HAVE BEEN DEPRIVED OF THE LIFE OF A KSHATRIYA. AFTER CASTING ME AWAY, HOW CAN YOU COMMAND ME THUS?

YOU HAVE NEVER BEFORE SOUGHT MY GOOD. AND EVEN TODAY, IT IS NOT MY GOOD YOU SEEK, BUT YOUR OWN. HOW CAN I JOIN THE CAMP OF THE PANDAVAS? WILL I NOT BE ACCUSED OF DOING SO OUT OF FRIGHT?

HOW CAN I BETRAY A FRIENDSHIP? DURYODHANA IS RELYING ON ME TO VANQUISH THE PANDAVAS. O MOTHER, I CANNOT CARRY OUT YOUR WISHES. HOWEVER, I WILL MAKE YOU ONE PROMISE.

THOUGH I CAN EASILY SLAY YUDHISHTHIRA, BHEEMA, NAKULA AND SAHADEVA IN SINGLE COMBAT, I WILL NOT DO SO. MY TARGET IS ARJUNA ALONE. EITHER HE PERISHES OR I WILL. THUS THE NUMBER OF YOUR SONS WILL ALWAYS REMAIN FIVE.

"KUNTI SAID—

O KARNA, REMEMBER YOUR VOW ON THE BATTLE-FIELD. YOU WILL SPARE FOUR OF MY SONS. I WISH YOU WELL, O SON.

THEN, O MONARCH, MOTHER AND SON PARTED. MEANWHILE, KRISHNA WAS ON HIS WAY BACK TO THE PANDAVAS.

ARRIVING AT UPAPLAVYA, KRISHNA WAS GIVEN AN AFFECTIONATE WELCOME BY THE PANDAVAS.

LATER —

O KRISHNA, TELL US ALL THAT HAPPENED AT THE COURT OF DHRITARASHTRA. WHAT DID YOU SAY TO DURYODHANA? WHAT WAS HIS REACTION AND THAT OF THE ELDERS?

"KRISHNA SAID —

O YUDHISHTHIRA I MADE AN APPEAL TO DURYODHANA'S REASON. BUT HE LAUGHED SCORNFULLY. INCENSED AT THIS, BHEESHMA CHIDED HIM AND EXHORTED HIM TO SURRENDER HALF THE KINGDOM TO YOU.

"THEN DRONA SAID —

O DURYODHANA, FOLLOW THE TRADITION OF HUMILITY IN YOUR FAMILY. AS PANDU SERVED DHRITARASHTRA, BHEESHMA SERVED THE KING, AND VIDURA IS SERVING DHRITARASHTRA, YOU TOO MUST SERVE YUDHISHTHIRA. RESPECT BHEESHMA AS I DO. DHARMA WILL TRIUMPH.

"BUT DURYODHANA WOULD NOT YIELD. THE WORDS OF DHRITARASHTRA AND GANDHARI ALSO PROVED IN VAIN.

"DURYODHANA SAID TO HIS SUPPORTERS—

GET READY FOR WAR. MARCH THIS VERY DAY TO KURUKSHETRA.

"THEN THE TROOPS MARCHED OUT WITH BHEESHMA AT THEIR HEAD.

THIS, THEN, IS WHAT HAPPENED AT THE COURT OF HASTINAPURA. I HAVE DONE ALL I COULD TO AVERT A WAR. I TRIED TO INSTIL TERROR INTO THE HEART OF DURYODHANA BY ASSUMING MY COSMIC FORM, I CAJOLED HIM, I REBUKED HIM, BUT TO NO AVAIL. THE KAURAVAS ARE PREPARING FOR WAR.

AND THUS ENDS THE TWENTY-NINTH SESSION OF OUR RENDERING OF VAISHAMPAYANA'S RECITAL OF VYASA'S IMMORTAL ITIHASA, MAHABHARATA.

Mahabharata-30
THE WAR BEGINS

O MONARCH, WHEN KRISHNA REPORTED ON THE FAILURE OF HIS PEACE MISSION AT THE COURT OF HASTINAPURA, YUDHISHTHIRA BEGAN PREPARATIONS FOR WAR.

"YUDHISHTHIRA SAID —

SO HERE WE ARE, PREPARED FOR BATTLE, WITH EACH OF OUR AKSHAUHINIS* BEING LED BY GREAT HEROES LIKE DRUPADA, VIRATA, DHRISHTADYUMNA, SHIKHANDI, SATYAKI, CHEKITANA, AND BHEEMA. TELL US, OH SAHADEVA, WHO DO YOU CONSIDER TO BE WORTHY OF BEING APPOINTED AS THE COMMANDER-IN-CHIEF?

* A COMPLETE ARMY CONSISTING OF 21870 ELEPHANTS, 21870 CHARIOTS, 65610 CAVALRY AND 109350 INFANTRY.

"SAID SAHADEVA*—

IN MY OPINION, VIRATA THE MIGHTY KING OF MATSYA SHOULD BE THE COMMANDER-IN-CHIEF OF OUR FORCES.

"NAKULA SAID—

DRUPADA SHOULD BE OUR COMMANDER-IN-CHIEF.

"ARJUNA SAID—

DHRISHTADYUMNA IS DESTINED TO KILL DRONA. HE IS FULLY CONVERSANT WITH ALL ASPECTS OF WARFARE AND WILL BE ABLE TO WITH-STAND THE ARROWS OF BHEESHMA. HE ALONE IS FIT TO BE OUR COMMANDER-IN-CHIEF.

"BHEEMA SAID—

SHIKHANDI IS BORN TO KILL BHEESHMA. HENCE SHIKHANDI SHOULD BE OUR COMMANDER-IN-CHIEF.

"YUDHISHTHIRA SAID—

KRISHNA IS ALL-KNOWING. HE IS AWARE OF OUR STRENGTHS AND WEAKNESSES. SO LET HIM NAME OUR COMMANDER-IN-CHIEF.

* IN THE OLDEN DAYS, IT WAS THE PRACTICE TO ASCERTAIN THE VIEWS OF THE YOUNGER PEOPLE BEFORE CONSULTING THE ELDERS

"KRISHNA SAID —

O KING, I FULLY APPROVE OF THE HEROES YOU HAVE CHOSEN TO LEAD YOUR SEVEN AKSHAUHINIS. AS FOR THE COMMANDER-IN-CHIEF I THINK THE CHOICE OF DHRISHTA-DYUMNA IS THE RIGHT ONE.

O KING, ONCE KRISHNA HAD NAMED THE COMMANDER-IN-CHIEF, THE TROOPS ENTHUSIASTICALLY BEGAN TO GET READY.

"AS THE PANDAVA ARMY IN MARTIAL ARRAY SET OUT FOR KURUKSHETRA, THE ATMOSPHERE RESOUNDED WITH THE LION-ROAR OF WARRIORS, THE BLOWING OF CONCH SHELLS, THE NEIGHING OF HORSES AND THE TRUMPETING OF ELEPHANTS.

"WHEN THEY REACHED A COOL AND SHADY STRETCH OF FLAT LAND, YUDHISHTHIRA SIGNALLED THE ARMY TO STOP.

WE SHALL CAMP HERE.

"AND SO, THE PANDAVA ARMY PITCHED TENTS AND CAMPED THERE.

"MEANWHILE, AT HASTINAPURA, DURYODHANA CALLED KARNA, DUHSHASANA AND SHAKUNI AND SAID —

HAVING FAILED IN HIS PEACE MISSION, KRISHNA IS SURE TO INCITE THE PANDAVAS TO FIGHT. THEIR ALLIES, VIRATA AND DRUPADA, ARE OUR OLD ENEMIES. HENCE THIS WAR IS GOING TO BE A VERY FEARSOME ONE.

SO LET US PREPARE FOR WAR IMMEDIATELY. LET OUR ALLIES WITH THEIR ARMIES PROCEED TO KURUKSHETRA AND CAMP THERE.

LET THE ROADS FROM OUR CITY TO THE CAMP BE LEVELLED. LET THE TENTS BE WELL-EQUIPPED WITH ARMS AND WEAPONS AND DECKED WITH STREAMERS AND FLAGS.

"AND SO, DURYODHANA'S FORCES GOT READY AND SET OFF FOR THE BATTLE-FIELD OF KURUKSHETRA.

amar chitra katha

"ON THE EVE OF THE BATTLE, THE PANDAVAS SPENT LONG HOURS IN DISCUSSION.

O KRISHNA, WHAT DO YOU THINK SHOULD BE OUR STANCE IN THE PRESENT SITUATION? WHAT DO YOU FEEL WE SHOULD DO SO THAT WE DO NOT STRAY FROM THE PATH OF DHARMA*?

"KRISHNA SAID—

O YUDHISHTHIRA, DURYODHANA IS BEING UNJUST TO YOU. YOU HAVE NO CHOICE BUT TO DECLARE WAR.

" THE PANDAVA WARRIORS WERE JUBILANT AT THIS STATEMENT OF KRISHNA'S.

"BUT YUDHISHTHIRA SIGHED.

MUCH AS I HAVE TRIED TO AVOID IT, THAT WE MUST FIGHT OUR KINSMEN AND ELDERS SEEMS INEVITABLE.

"ARJUNA SAID—

O KING, YOU HAVE HEARD THE ADVICE OF VIDURA AND KUNTI CONVEYED TO YOU BY KRISHNA. NEITHER OF THEM WOULD STRAY FROM THE PATH OF RIGHTE-OUSNESS. NOW IT IS NOT PROPER FOR US TO WITHDRAW FROM WAR.

"KRISHNA SAID—

ARJUNA IS RIGHT, YUDHISHTHIRA.

THE MATTER WAS THUS SETTLED.

* DUTY

amar chitra katha

5

"IN THE KAURAVA CAMP, DURYODHANA DIVIDED HIS ARMY INTO ELEVEN AKSHAUHINIS AND HE PLACED KRIPA, DRONA, SHALYA, JAYADRATHA, SUDAKSHINA, KRITAVARMA, ASHWATTHAMA, KARNA, SHAKUNI AND BAHLIKA* IN CHARGE OF ONE EACH.

"EACH CHARIOT WAS PULLED BY FOUR EXCELLENT HORSES AND WAS EQUIPPED WITH A HUNDRED BOWS. THERE WERE TWO WARRIORS, TWO ATTENDANTS AND ONE CHARIOTEER ON EVERY CHARIOT.

"EACH ELEPHANT WAS DECKED WITH ORNAMENTS AND CARRIED SEVEN WARRIORS AND LOADS OF WEAPONS AND QUIVERS OF ARROWS.

"APART FROM THESE THERE WERE THOUSANDS OF CAVALRYMEN...

"...AND HUNDREDS OF THOUSANDS INFANTRYMEN.

* KING OF BAHLIK, THE ANCIENT NAME FOR BALAKH

"DURYODHANA THEN ADDRESSED BHEESHMA —

O GREAT SIRE, YOU ARE MY WELL-WISHER AND A PAST MASTER OF WARFARE. IT IS DESTINED THAT YOU WILL MEET YOUR DEATH ONLY WHEN YOU ARE READY FOR IT. BE, THEREFORE, THE COMMANDER OF OUR VAST FORCES. LEAD US INTO BATTLE.

"BHEESHMA SAID —

O DURYODHANA, I SHALL CERTAINLY FIGHT FOR YOU AS I HAVE PLEDGED, AND COMMAND YOUR FORCES. HOWEVER, I CANNOT SLAY THE PANDAVAS. I SHALL, THEREFORE, KILL TEN THOUSAND OF THEIR WARRIORS EVERY DAY.

THERE IS ANOTHER CONDITION BEFORE I ACCEPT COMMAND. KARNA WILL NOT SHARE THE BATTLE-FIELD WITH ME. EITHER HE SHALL FIGHT OR I SHALL.

"HEARING THIS, KARNA SAID —

AS LONG AS BHEESHMA IS ALIVE, I SHALL NOT FIGHT. ONLY AFTER HIS DEATH SHALL I FACE ARJUNA IN BATTLE.

"WHEN THE NEWS OF BHEESHMA HAVING TAKEN THE COMMAND OF THE KAURAVA ARMY REACHED THE PANDAVA CAMP, YUDHISHTHIRA SAID —

ENSURE THAT THE ARMY IS ALERT AND READY FOR COMBAT. OUR FIRST ENCOUNTER WILL BE WITH OUR GRANDSIRE, BHEESHMA. LET SKILLED WARRIORS LEAD OUR FORCES INTO BATTLE.

"AND SO, THE SEVEN DIVISIONS OF THE PANDAVA ARMY WERE ARRAYED FOR BATTLE UNDER THE COMMAND OF DHRISHTADYUMNA. THE OVERALL COMMAND WAS BESTOWED ON ARJUNA, WHO HAD KRISHNA AS HIS GUIDE AND CHARIOTEER.

"AS THEY SAT DISCUSSING THE STRATEGY OF WAR, KRISHNA'S BROTHER, BALARAMA, ARRIVED THERE.

"HE SAID —

THIS FIERCE AND TERRIBLE SLAUGHTER APPEARS INEVITABLE. I LOOK FORWARD TO SEE-ING YOU ALL EMERGE SAFE AND SOUND FROM THIS STRIFE.

AS BHEEMA AND DURYODHANA ARE BOTH MY DISCIPLES AND EQUALLY DEAR TO ME, I SHALL NOT TAKE SIDES IN THIS BATTLE.

I CANNOT BEAR TO SEE THE DESTRUCTION OF ALL THE KAURAVAS. I SHALL GO ON A PILGRIMAGE FAR AWAY FROM HERE TO THE BANKS OF THE RIVER SARASWATI.

"AND WITH THAT, BALARAMA LEFT.

"THEN YUDHISHTHIRA HAD ANOTHER VISITOR, KING RUKMI, BROTHER-IN-LAW OF KRISHNA. ADDRESSING ARJUNA, HE SAID —

IF YOU ARE NERVOUS, I AM HERE TO HELP YOU. I SHALL SINGLE-HANDEDLY KILL ALL YOUR FOES.

"ARJUNA SAID —

O GREAT KING, DO NOT FORGET I AM A SON OF PANDU AND A DISCIPLE OF DRONA. NOW WITH KRISHNA AS MY ALLY, WHAT HAVE I TO FEAR? YOU MAY STAY WITH US OR GO, AS YOU WISH.

"RUKMI THEN OFFERED HIS ASSISTANCE TO DURYODHANA.

O DURYODHANA, I AM HERE TO HELP YOU IF YOU NEED ME.

O KING, I DO NOT NEED YOUR HELP. I HAVE MANY INVINCIBLE HEROES AMONG MY RANKS.

"AND SO TWO GREAT WARRIORS — BALARAMA AND RUKMI ABSTAINED FROM THE GREAT WAR.

amar chitra katha

9

amar chitra katha

THEN, O KING, TO ARJUNA, DURYODHANA ASKED ME TO CONVEY THIS: O ARJUNA, DO NOT BRAG! FIGHT! FOR THIRTEEN YEARS I ENJOYED SOVEREIGNTY WHILE YOU SUFFERED IN THE FOREST. NEITHER THE FEAR OF KRISHNA, NOR OF YOU WILL MAKE ME GIVE UP THE KINGDOM.

"HEARING THESE WORDS, ALL THE PANDAVAS STOOD UP SHAKING WITH RAGE.

"SEEING BHEEMA'S FURY, KRISHNA SAID TO ULOOKA —

O ULOOKA, TELL THIS TO DURYODHANA: YOUR MESSAGE HAS BEEN HEARD AND UNDERSTOOD. NOW, AS YOU SO ARDENTLY DESIRE, LET THERE BE A WAR.

"BHEEMA'S FURY BURST FORTH.

O FOOL! REPEAT MY WORDS TO THE VILE DURYO-DHANA: IT IS IN DEFERENCE TO THE WISHES OF OUR ELDER BROTHER THAT WE TOLERATED YOUR MISDEEDS. BUT NO MORE! I WILL SLAY YOU AND YOUR BROTHERS AS I HAVE VOWED!

"SAHADEVA SAID —

TELL SHAKUNI, YOUR WICKED FATHER, THAT HE HAS CAUSED OUR ANIMOSITY WITH THE KAURAVAS. LET THE BATTLE START, I WILL SLAY YOU FIRST AND THEN YOUR FATHER.

"ARJUNA SAID —

OH ULOOKA! WORDS ARE WASTED NOW. I WILL CONVEY THE REST OF MY REPLY THROUGH MY GANDEEVA ON THE MORROW.

"YUDHISHTHIRA SAID —

GO AND TELL THIS TO DURYODHANA: O SINFUL WRETCH, YOU HAVE ALWAYS ACTED BASELY TOWARDS US. BE A KSHATRIYA! DO NOT HIDE BEHIND REVERED PRECEPTORS! RELY ON YOUR OWN MIGHT AND FIGHT.

"KRISHNA SAID —

TAKE MY ANSWER TO DURYODHANA: O FOOL, DON'T THINK I'LL BE A MERE CHARIOTEER TO ARJUNA. IF PROVOKED, I CAN ANNIHILATE THE ENTIRE KAURAVA ARMY.

"SHIKHANDI SAID—

TELL DURYODHANA: I SHALL SLAY HIS GRANDSIRE, BHEESHMA! FOR I HAVE BEEN CREATED SPECIFICALLY FOR THAT TASK...

"DHRISHTADYUMNA SAID—

...AND I SHALL SLAY DRONA!

"THEN ULOOKA LEFT THE PANDAVAS...

"...AND, RETURNING TO DURYODHANA, HE REPEATED THE PANDAVAS' REPLIES.

"DURYODHANA CALLED DUHSHASANA, KARNA AND SHAKUNI.

PREPARE THE TROOPS FOR BATTLE AT SUNRISE!

"THEN DURYODHANA CALLED BHEESHMA AND SAID —

O GRANDSIRE! WITH YOUR LEADERSHIP AND DRONA'S SUPPORT, OUR VICTORY IS ENSURED. WOULD YOU CLASSIFY THE RATHIS, ATIRATHIS AND MAHARATHIS* IN THE TWO ARMIES?

"BHEESHMA SAID —

O DURYODHANA, YOU AND YOUR BROTHERS, SKILLED AND ACCOMPLISHED WARRIORS, ARE RATHIS, FOR CERTAIN.

"THE MIGHTY DRONA, ENDUED WITH GREAT PROWESS, IS A MAHARATHI.

"DRONA'S SON, ASHWATTHAMA, A MASTER AT WARFARE, IS A MAHARATHI.

THIS VILE BRAGGART, KARNA, IS NEITHER A RATHI NOR AN ATIRATHI. IN MY JUDGEMENT HE IS ONLY HALF A RATHI!

* WARRIORS ON CHARIOT WERE CLASSIFIED AS RATHI, ATIRATHI OR MAHARATHI, DEPENDING ON THEIR SKILL AND VALOUR

"TOUCHED TO THE QUICK, KARNA REPLIED —

O GRANDSIRE, YOU NEVER FAIL TO INSULT ME AT THE SLIGHTEST OPPORTUNITY! THE KAURAVAS DO NOT REALISE THAT YOU ARE IMPAIRING THEIR INTERESTS BY DEMORALISING ME AT THIS HOUR!

"HE TURNED TO DURYODHANA —

O DURYODHANA! BHEESHMA WILL ONLY MISGUIDE YOU! ABANDON HIM! I CAN DEFEAT THE ENTIRE PANDAVA ARMY SINGLE-HANDED! BUT I WILL NOT FIGHT AS LONG AS BHEESHMA LIVES!

"BHEESHMA RETORTED —

O SON OF A CHARIOTEER, YOU ARE NO MATCH FOR ME! BE A MAN AND FIGHT ARJUNA WHOM YOU SO OFTEN CHALLENGE! LET ME SEE HOW YOU SURVIVE THAT ENCOUNTER!

"DURYODHANA INTERVENED —

O GRANDSIRE! NOW TELL ME ABOUT THE MIGHT OF THE PANDAVAS!

"BHEESHMA SAID —

THEN LISTEN, O DURYODHANA. YUDHISHTHIRA IS, WITHOUT DOUBT, A RATHI. THE MIGHTY BHEEMA IS EQUAL TO EIGHT RATHIS. NAKULA AND SAHADEVA ARE BOTH RATHIS.

"WITH KRISHNA AS HIS CHARIOTEER AND WITH HIS CELESTIAL WEAPONS, THERE IS NO ONE TO MATCH THE VALOUR OF ARJUNA.

"VIRATA AND DRUPADA ARE BOTH MAHARATHIS.

"SHIKHANDI IS A RATHI AND DHRISHTADYUMNA IS AN ATIRATHI.

I HAVE NOW TOLD YOU WHO ARE THE RATHIS, ATIRATHIS AND MAHARATHIS IN BOTH THE ARMIES. I WILL FIGHT ARJUNA AND KRISHNA AND OTHER MIGHTY HEROES. BUT I WILL NOT KILL SHIKHANDI EVEN IF HE OPPOSES ME.

YOU MUST HAVE HEARD THAT SHIKHANDI WAS BORN A FEMALE AND LATER BECAME A MALE. I WILL NOT FIGHT A WOMAN OR ONE WHO WAS FORMERLY A WOMAN. THIS IS MY VOW.*

* ACK ON BHEESHMA, NO. 34

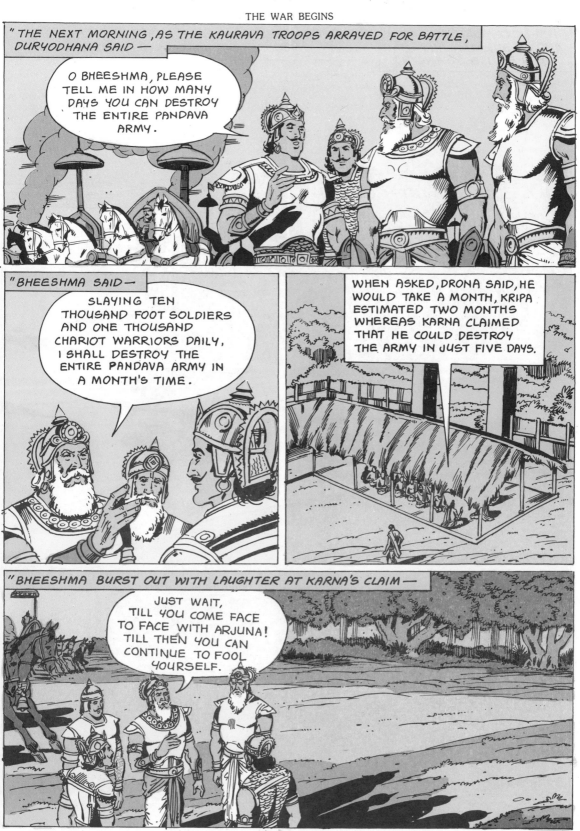

"THE NEXT MORNING, AS THE KAURAVA TROOPS ARRAYED FOR BATTLE, DURYODHANA SAID —

O BHEESHMA, PLEASE TELL ME IN HOW MANY DAYS YOU CAN DESTROY THE ENTIRE PANDAVA ARMY.

"BHEESHMA SAID —

SLAYING TEN THOUSAND FOOT SOLDIERS AND ONE THOUSAND CHARIOT WARRIORS DAILY, I SHALL DESTROY THE ENTIRE PANDAVA ARMY IN A MONTH'S TIME.

WHEN ASKED, DRONA SAID, HE WOULD TAKE A MONTH, KRIPA ESTIMATED TWO MONTHS WHEREAS KARNA CLAIMED THAT HE COULD DESTROY THE ARMY IN JUST FIVE DAYS.

"BHEESHMA BURST OUT WITH LAUGHTER AT KARNA'S CLAIM —

JUST WAIT, TILL YOU COME FACE TO FACE WITH ARJUNA! TILL THEN YOU CAN CONTINUE TO FOOL YOURSELF.

"THE NEXT MORNING, LED BY BHEESHMA AND DRONA, DURYODHANA, ASHWATTHAMA AND JAYADRATHA AND OTHER MIGHTY WARRIORS, THE KAURAVA ARMY MARCHED OUT IN ALL ITS STRENGTH.

"LIKEWISE, THE PANDAVA ARMY ALSO MARCHED OUT, HEADED BY DHRISHTADYUMNA. AND THE OTHER HEROES LEADING THE TROOPS INCLUDED ARJUNA AND BHEEMA, VIRATA AND DRUPADA, AND SHIKHANDI.

THEN WARRIORS REPRESENTING THE TWO SIDES MET TO DECIDE THE CODE OF CONDUCT. EACH DAY AT SUNSET, THE ARMIES WOULD CEASE TO FIGHT AND BEHAVE AS FRIENDS. AT SUNRISE THE BATTLE WOULD BEGIN ANEW. SINGLE COMBAT SHOULD BE BETWEEN EQUALS. A HORSEMAN TO FIGHT A HORSEMAN, LIKEWISE CHARIOTEERS, ELEPHANT TROOPS AND CAVALRY WOULD ATTACK ONLY THEIR EQUALS.

THOSE WHO HAD LEFT THE FIELD, WHO WERE UNARMED, OR HAD SURRENDERED WERE TO BE SPARED FROM ATTACK. THE NON-COMBATANT ATTENDANTS, COURIERS AND CONCH-BLOWERS WERE ALSO TO BE LEFT ALONE.*

"WHILE THE TWO ARMIES WERE ARRAYED FOR BATTLE, VEDA VYASA VISITED KING DHRITARASHTRA.

O KING, THE HOUR OF DEATH IS NIGH FOR ALL YOUR SONS AND THEIR ALLIES. I COULD BESTOW DIVINE VISION ON YOU TO ENABLE YOU TO FOLLOW THE BATTLE, IF YOU SO WISH.

"DHRITARASHTRA SAID—

I CANNOT BEAR THE THOUGHT OF SEEING MY NEAR ONES KILLED BUT I WOULD LIKE TO HEAR THE FULL ACCOUNT OF THE BATTLE.

* THIS CODE OF WARFARE IS REFRESHINGLY DIFFERENT FROM PRESENT-DAY PRACTICES WHICH SPARE NO ONE

SO BE IT! I SHALL BESTOW DIVINE VISION ON SANJAYA. HE WILL BE ABLE TO SEE EVERY-THING THAT HAPPENS ON THE BATTLE-FIELD AND NARRATE IT TO YOU.

"DHRITARASHTRA SAID—

O SANJAYA, NOW THAT THE VENERABLE SAGE HAS BESTOWED DIVINE VISION ON YOU, TELL ME WHAT IS HAPPENING ON THE BATTLE-FIELD, HOW THE TWO ARMIES HAVE ARRAYED THEMSELVES.

O KING, AS SOON AS THE SUN ROSE, THE AIR REVER-BERATED WITH THE BLARE OF CONCHES, THE SOUND OF DRUMS, THE NEIGH-ING OF HORSES AND THE WAR-CRIES OF THE ARMIES.

"THE KAURAVA ARMY SURGED FORTH, LED BY BHEESHMA. BEHIND HIM WERE THE MIGHTY DRONA, KRIPA AND ASHWATTHAMA.

"SEEING THE MAMMOTH KAURAVA ARMY IN BATTLE ARRAY ADVANCING TOWARDS THEM, YUDHISHTHIRA SAID TO ARJUNA —

O ARJUNA, COMPARED TO THE KAURAVAS, OUR ARMY IS MUCH SMALLER. KEEPING THIS IN MIND WE SHOULD ARRANGE OUR TROOPS IN A SUITABLE FORMATION.

"ARJUNA REPLIED —

O KING, LET US THEN ORGANISE OUR TROOPS TO FORM THE ARRAY CALLED THE VAJRA*. DESIGNED BY INDRA HIMSELF, IT IS AN INVINCIBLE FORMATION.

✻ THUNDERBOLT, INDRA'S WEAPON

21

"AND THUS ARRAYED, THE PANDAVA ARMY BEGAN TO MARCH FORWARD, LED BY DHRISHTADYUMANA, BHEEMA AND ARJUNA.

"AND ON THE BATTLEFIELD OF KURUKSHETRA, RAIN FELL FROM A CLOUDLESS SKY AND THE ROLL OF THUNDER WAS HEARD.

"A MIGHTY WIND BLEW ACROSS THE FIELD THROW-ING SAND AND PEBBLES IN ALL DIRECTIONS. SO THICK WAS THE DUST CLOUD, THAT DARKNESS DESCENDED AT SUNRISE.

"WHEN YUDHISHTHIRA SAW THE VAST KAURAVA ARMY, HIS HEART SANK. HE ADDRESSED ARJUNA —

O ARJUNA, BHEESHMA HAS ARRAYED THE VAST KAURAVA ARMY IN AN INVINCIBLE FORMATION. HOW CAN WE HOPE TO FIGHT THEM?

"ARJUNA SAID —

O KING, IT IS POSSIBLE FOR A SMALL ARMY TO DEFEAT A VAST FORCE. FOR VICTORY DOES NOT DEPEND ON MIGHT AND NUMBERS, BUT ON RIGHTEOUSNESS.* WHERE THERE IS KRISHNA, THERE IS VICTORY.

"MEANWHILE, DURYODHANA, ON SEEING THE PANDAVA ARMY ARRAYED FOR WAR, APPROACHED DRONA AND SAID —

SIRE, JUST LOOK AT THE BATTLE FORMATION OF THE PANDAVAS! BHEESHMA WILL BE THEIR IMMEDIATE TARGET. ORDER THE MIGHTIEST OF WARRIORS TO SURROUND AND PROTECT BHEESHMA.

"THEN BHEESHMA BLEW ON HIS CONCH, SIGNALLING THE START OF THE WAR.

"AT THE PALACE DHRITARASHTRA ASKED SANJAYA —

O SANJAYA, WHAT DID MY SONS AND THOSE OF PANDU DO AT THE FIELD OF KURUKSHETRA?

O KING! KRISHNA BLEW ON THE PANCHAJANYA AND ARJUNA ON THE DEVADATTA CONCHES SIGNALLING THEIR READINESS FOR WAR.

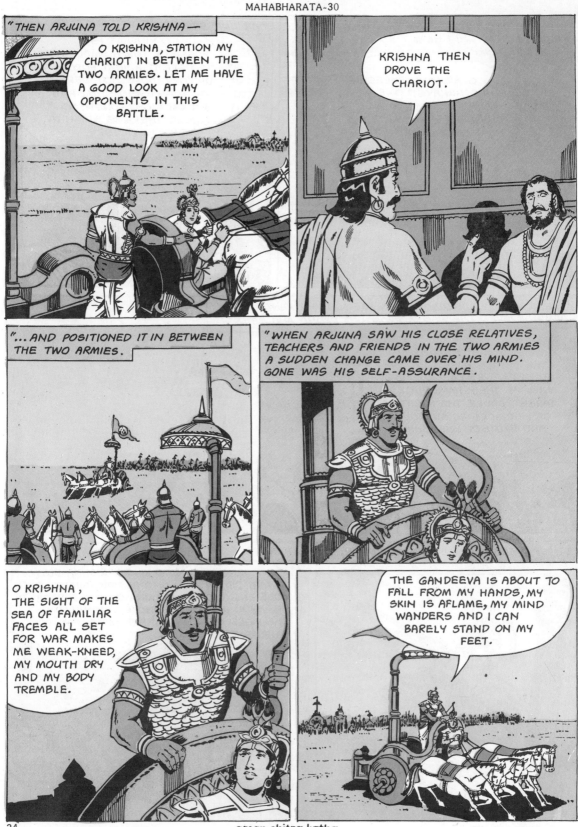

"THEN ARJUNA TOLD KRISHNA —

O KRISHNA, STATION MY CHARIOT IN BETWEEN THE TWO ARMIES. LET ME HAVE A GOOD LOOK AT MY OPPONENTS IN THIS BATTLE.

KRISHNA THEN DROVE THE CHARIOT.

"... AND POSITIONED IT IN BETWEEN THE TWO ARMIES.

"WHEN ARJUNA SAW HIS CLOSE RELATIVES, TEACHERS AND FRIENDS IN THE TWO ARMIES A SUDDEN CHANGE CAME OVER HIS MIND. GONE WAS HIS SELF-ASSURANCE.

O KRISHNA, THE SIGHT OF THE SEA OF FAMILIAR FACES ALL SET FOR WAR MAKES ME WEAK-KNEED, MY MOUTH DRY AND MY BODY TREMBLE.

THE GANDEEVA IS ABOUT TO FALL FROM MY HANDS, MY SKIN IS AFLAME, MY MIND WANDERS AND I CAN BARELY STAND ON MY FEET.

O KRISHNA, IF I MUST KILL MY KINSMEN, I CARE NOT FOR VICTORY NOR PLEASURE, NAY NOT EVEN FOR LIFE ITSELF.

THOSE ON WHOM WE WANT TO BESTOW OUR KINGDOM, WEALTH AND HAPPINESS ARE THEMSELVES HERE RISKING LIFE ITSELF. FIE ON US! I WOULD RATHER DIE UNARMED AT THE HANDS OF THE SONS OF DHRITARASHTRA.

"WITH THIS, ARJUNA DROPPED THE GANDEEVA AND SAT DOWN IN DEEP SORROW.

"KRISHNA THEN SAID —

O ARJUNA! WHAT HAS COME OVER YOU AT THIS CRUCIAL MOMENT? SUCH BEHAVIOUR DOES NOT BEHOVE GREAT MEN.

YOU WILL NEITHER MERIT HEAVEN NOR ACHIEVE FAME WITH SUCH THOUGHTS. DESIST FROM THIS WEAKNESS AND GET READY TO FIGHT.

HOW CAN I FIGHT BHEESHMA AND DRONA, BOTH OF WHOM I HONOUR SO MUCH? WE DON'T EVEN KNOW WHETHER OR NOT WE SHOULD FIGHT THIS WAR. OR EVEN WHO WILL WIN THE BATTLE.

HERE, STAND BEFORE US THE SONS OF DHRITARASHTRA. WILL WE BE ABLE TO LIVE HAPPILY AFTER KILLING THEM?

ARJUNA! YOU SPEAK LIKE A WISE MAN AND YET GRIEVE NEEDLESSLY.

JUST AS THE SOUL PASSES THROUGH THE STAGES OF CHILDHOOD, YOUTH AND OLD AGE, SO DOES IT THROUGH DEATH AND WISE MEN DO NOT GRIEVE OVER THIS PHENOMENON.

THE BODY IS MORTAL BUT THE SOUL IS IMMORTAL. JUST AS A MAN DISCARDS OLD CLOTHES AND WEARS NEW ONES, SO DOES THE ETERNAL SOUL DISCARD AN OLD BODY AND ENTER A NEW ONE.

THE SOUL IS INDESTRUCTIBLE. NO WEAPON CAN PIERCE IT, NO FIRE BURN IT, AIR CANNOT DRY IT AND WATER CANNOT DISSOLVE IT.

ONE WHO IS BORN IS CERTAIN TO DIE AND ONE WHO DIES IS CERTAIN TO BE REBORN. THERE IS NOTHING TO GRIEVE OVER.

O ARJUNA, IF YOU DIE FIGHTING, YOUR PLACE IN HEAVEN IS ASSURED. IF YOU WIN, THE WHOLE EARTH IS YOURS TO RULE FOR EVER.

RISE UP. WITHOUT MAKING ANY DISTINCTION BETWEEN VICTORY AND DEFEAT, PAIN AND PLEASURE, GAIN AND LOSS, RESOLVE TO FIGHT.

YOUR RIGHT IS ONLY TO WORK, BUT NEVER TO ITS FRUIT. LET NOT THE FRUIT OF ACTION BE YOUR MOTIVE, NOR LET YOUR ATTACHMENT BE TO INACTION.

PERFORM YOUR DUTY WITH AN EVEN-NESS OF MIND O ARJUNA!

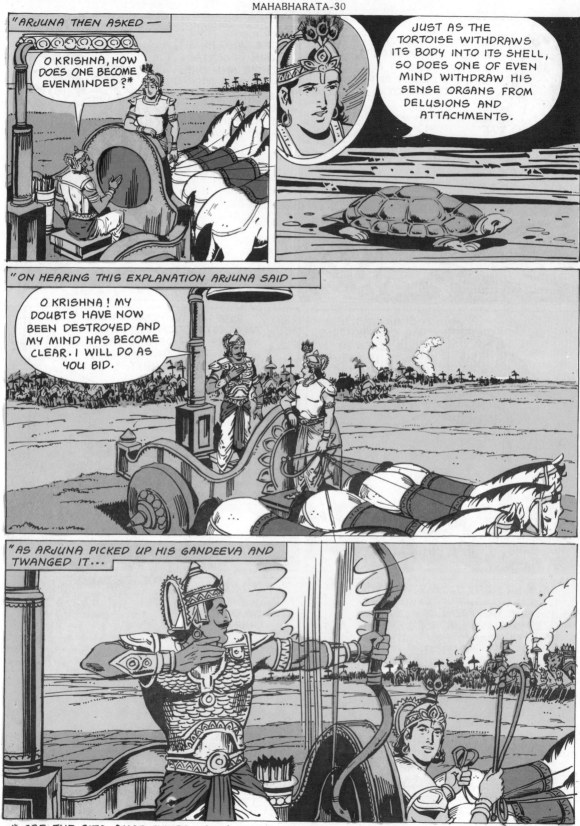

"ARJUNA THEN ASKED —

O KRISHNA, HOW DOES ONE BECOME EVENMINDED ?*

JUST AS THE TORTOISE WITHDRAWS ITS BODY INTO ITS SHELL, SO DOES ONE OF EVEN MIND WITHDRAW HIS SENSE ORGANS FROM DELUSIONS AND ATTACHMENTS.

"ON HEARING THIS EXPLANATION ARJUNA SAID —

O KRISHNA ! MY DOUBTS HAVE NOW BEEN DESTROYED AND MY MIND HAS BECOME CLEAR. I WILL DO AS YOU BID.

"AS ARJUNA PICKED UP HIS GANDEEVA AND TWANGED IT...

* SEE THE GITA, AMAR CHITRA KATHA TITLE NO. 127

Mahabharata – 31
BHEESHMA IN COMMAND

O JANAMEJAYA, SUCH IS THE GLORY OF THE GITA THAT ONE WHO RECITES IT WITH DEVOTION IS FREED FROM REBIRTH.

O KING, THE PANDAVA WARRIORS WERE HEARTENED BY THE FACT THAT ARJUNA ONCE AGAIN PICKED UP THE GANDEEVA BOW AND BECAME READY FOR THE BATTLE. WITH GUSTO THEY BLEW ON THEIR CONCH-SHELLS.

"AS THE TWO ARMIES WERE POISED FOR COMBAT, YUDHISHTHIRA SUDDENLY DESCENDED FROM HIS CHARIOT...

"...AND WALKED TOWARDS THE CHARIOT OF BHEESHMA.

"SURPRISED, ARJUNA FOLLOWED HIM.

WHERE ARE YOU GOING, O KING? WHAT IS IN YOUR MIND AT THIS HOUR?

"BUT YUDHISHTHIRA DID NOT REPLY. THE KAURAVAS FELT HAPPY.

HE IS FRIGHTENED OF OUR MIGHT.

HA HA!

COWARD!

"YUDHISHTHIRA TOUCHED THE FEET OF BHEESHMA AND SAID —

O GRANDSIRE! I WISH TO FIGHT WITH YOU. GIVE ME YOUR BLESSINGS.

"BHEESHMA REPLIED —

I AM PLEASED, SON. MY BLESSINGS ARE WITH YOU. VICTORY WILL BE YOURS.

"YUDHISHTHIRA THEN APPROACHED DRONA, HIS TEACHER IN THE MARTIAL ARTS.

I SEEK YOUR BLESSINGS AND ADVICE, O LORD. HOW WILL I BE ABLE TO CONQUER THE KAURAVAS WHEN THE INVINCIBLE, YOU ARE ON THEIR SIDE?

O KING, YOU HAVE MY BLESSINGS. YOU ARE SURE TO BE VICTORIOUS. I DO NOT WISH TO FIGHT AGAINST YOU, BUT AM HELPLESS. BUT I WILL TELL YOU HOW YOU MAY SLAY ME IN BATTLE.

amar chitra katha

I CAN ONLY BE SLAIN WHEN I HAVE DROPPED MY ARMS. AND I WILL DO SO ONLY IF A MAN I TRUST BRINGS ME UN-PLEASANT TIDINGS.

AFTER THIS, YUDHISHTHIRA APPROACHED KRIPA, SHALYA AND OTHER SENIOR WARRIORS AND OBTAINED THEIR BLESSINGS.

"THEN HE STOOD BETWEEN THE TWO ARMIES AND CALLED OUT—

I MAKE AN APPEAL TO ALL KAURAVA WARRIORS. IF ANY OF YOU WISH TO COME OVER TO MY SIDE HE IS WELCOME.

"YUYUTSU, ONE OF DURYODHANA'S BROTHERS, SPOKE UP.

O KING, IF YOU WILL ACCEPT ME, I WILL JOIN YOU.

YOU ARE WELCOME, YUYUTSU.

"THE WAR-DRUMS, THE TRUMPETING OF THE ELEPHANTS, THE NEIGHING OF THE HORSES AND THE BLOWING OF THE CONCH-SHELLS MADE A FEARSOME NOISE.

"THE TWO ARMIES FELL UPON EACH OTHER.

amar chitra katha

"INTENSE WARFARE ENSUED.

" CHARIOTS CONFRONTED CHARIOTS...

"...CAVALRY CONTENDED WITH CAVALRY...

"...AND INFANTRYMEN ENGAGED IN HAND-TO-HAND FIGHTING.

"DUHSHASANA'S SHARP ARROWS WOUNDED NAKULA.

" NAKULA IN TURN SHOWERED ARROWS ON HIM AND INJURED HIM.

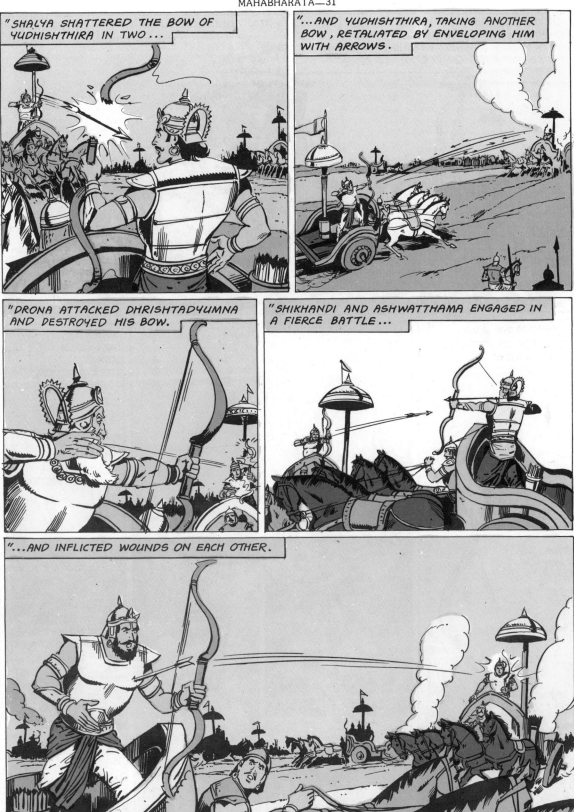

"SHALYA SHATTERED THE BOW OF YUDHISHTHIRA IN TWO...

"...AND YUDHISHTHIRA, TAKING ANOTHER BOW, RETALIATED BY ENVELOPING HIM WITH ARROWS.

"DRONA ATTACKED DHRISHTADYUMNA AND DESTROYED HIS BOW.

"SHIKHANDI AND ASHWATTHAMA ENGAGED IN A FIERCE BATTLE...

"...AND INFLICTED WOUNDS ON EACH OTHER.

amar chitra katha

"IN THE FURY OF WAR, THE WARRIORS VIOLATED MANY RULES SET DOWN FOR DHARMAYUDDHA — A RIGHTEOUS WAR. WARRIORS ON CHARIOTS CLASHED WITH CAVALRYMEN AND THOSE MOUNTED ON ELEPHANTS FOUGHT INFANTRYMEN.

"JAYADRATHA AND DRUPADA CONFRONTED EACH OTHER.

"MANY LAY WOUNDED OR DEAD.

AAAH!

WATER!

"SHALYA SHOT UTTARA THE PRINCE OF THE MATSYA KINGDOM, DEAD.

"THEREUPON, UTTARA'S BROTHER SHWETA CAME UP IN A WILD FURY TO ATTACK THE KAURAVAS.

"THE KAURAVA ARMY BEGAN TO SCATTER BEFORE THE FIERCENESS OF HIS WRATH.

"SEEING THE WHOLE ARMY RETREATING IN FEAR OF SHWETA, THE MIGHTY BHEESHMA RELEASED THE BRAHMASTRA—

"...AND PRINCE SHWETA WAS KILLED.

GLOOM DESCENDED ON THE PANDAVA ARMY AS THEIR HERO FELL.

"THE DISHEARTENED PANDAVAS RETURNED TO THEIR CAMP AT THE END OF THE DAY. YUDHISHTHIRA LAMENTED —

O KRISHNA, BHEESHMA WROUGHT HAVOC UPON OUR ARMY TODAY. IF THIS CONTINUES, WE SHALL CERTAINLY BE ANNIHILATED AT HIS HANDS.

DO NOT WORRY, YUDHISHTHIRA. YOU HAVE VALIANT HEROES IN YOUR ARMY WHO WILL NOT HESITATE TO LAY DOWN THEIR LIVES FOR YOUR SAKE.

"ON THE SECOND DAY OF THE WAR, DHRISHTADYUMNA, THE COMMANDER-IN-CHIEF, INSTILLED HOPE IN THE PANDAVA ARMY.

TODAY I SHALL CONFRONT THE MIGHTY BHEESHMA, KRIPA, DRONA, SHALYA AND JAYADRATHA.

"THE LOUD BLOWING OF CONCH SHELLS SIGNALLED THE BEGINNING OF THE WAR.

"THE TWO ARMIES CHARGED AGAINST EACH OTHER.

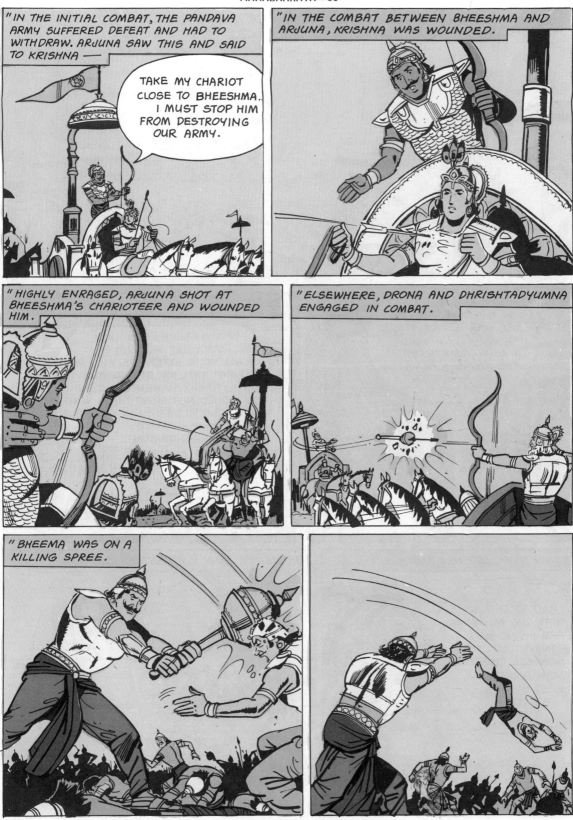

"IN THE INITIAL COMBAT, THE PANDAVA ARMY SUFFERED DEFEAT AND HAD TO WITHDRAW. ARJUNA SAW THIS AND SAID TO KRISHNA —

TAKE MY CHARIOT CLOSE TO BHEESHMA. I MUST STOP HIM FROM DESTROYING OUR ARMY.

"IN THE COMBAT BETWEEN BHEESHMA AND ARJUNA, KRISHNA WAS WOUNDED.

"HIGHLY ENRAGED, ARJUNA SHOT AT BHEESHMA'S CHARIOTEER AND WOUNDED HIM.

"ELSEWHERE, DRONA AND DHRISHTADYUMNA ENGAGED IN COMBAT.

"BHEEMA WAS ON A KILLING SPREE.

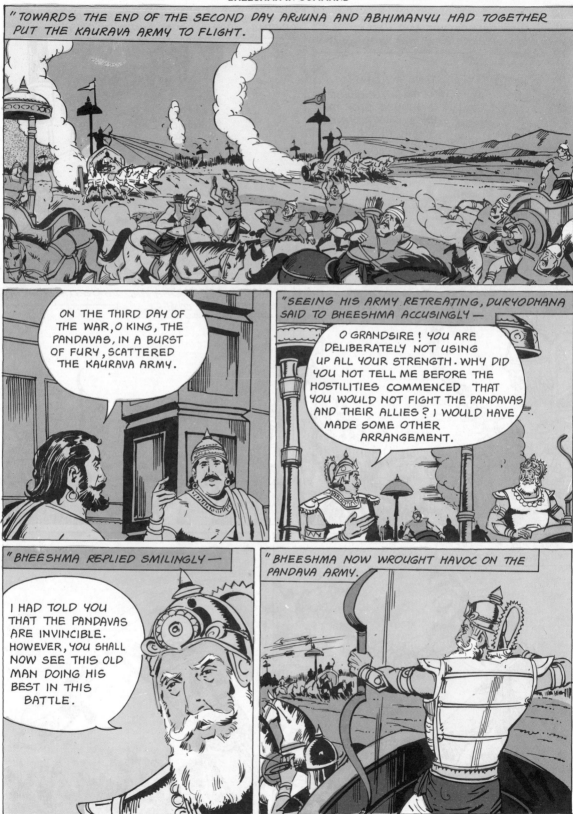

"TOWARDS THE END OF THE SECOND DAY ARJUNA AND ABHIMANYU HAD TOGETHER PUT THE KAURAVA ARMY TO FLIGHT.

ON THE THIRD DAY OF THE WAR, O KING, THE PANDAVAS, IN A BURST OF FURY, SCATTERED THE KAURAVA ARMY.

"SEEING HIS ARMY RETREATING, DURYODHANA SAID TO BHEESHMA ACCUSINGLY —

O GRANDSIRE! YOU ARE DELIBERATELY NOT USING UP ALL YOUR STRENGTH. WHY DID YOU NOT TELL ME BEFORE THE HOSTILITIES COMMENCED THAT YOU WOULD NOT FIGHT THE PANDAVAS AND THEIR ALLIES? I WOULD HAVE MADE SOME OTHER ARRANGEMENT.

"BHEESHMA REPLIED SMILINGLY —

I HAD TOLD YOU THAT THE PANDAVAS ARE INVINCIBLE. HOWEVER, YOU SHALL NOW SEE THIS OLD MAN DOING HIS BEST IN THIS BATTLE.

"BHEESHMA NOW WROUGHT HAVOC ON THE PANDAVA ARMY.

O KRISHNA, BHEESHMA HAS BECOME TERROR INCARNATE TO OUR ARMY. DRIVE THE CHARIOT IN HIS DIRECTION.

"ON CONFRONTING BHEESHMA, ARJUNA SHOT A VOLLEY OF ARROWS AT HIM.

BRAVO ARJUNA! YOU ARE DOING VERY WELL.

"BUT BHEESHMA'S FURY CONTINUED UNABATED.

BHEESHMA WILL SURELY SLAUGHTER THE PANDAVA ARMY IN HIS RAGE. I WILL KILL HIM.

"AS KRISHNA RUSHED AT BHEESHMA WITH HIS SUDARSHANA CHAKRA—

O KRISHNA! I KNOW NOT OF A HIGHER HONOUR THAN THAT OF DYING AT YOUR NOBLE HANDS. I WELCOME YOUR ATTACK, O LORD.

"BUT ARJUNA AND BHEEMA TRIED TO RESTRAIN KRISHNA.

DO NOT TAKE UP ARMS, O KRISHNA! CONTROL YOUR ANGER!

"AND THEN ARJUNA TOOK A VOW.

NEVER AGAIN WILL I BE FOUND WANTING IN MY ZEAL TO FIGHT NOR NEGLIGENT OF MY DUTY AS A KSHATRIYA. I WILL KILL ALL THE KAURAVAS.

"KRISHNA WAS PLEASED AT THIS DECLARATION AND RESUMED HIS SEAT IN THE CHARIOT.

"ARJUNA NOW RELEASED THE DIVINE MAHENDRA WEAPON FROM HIS BOW...

"...THIS WEAPON ALONE CAUSED THE DEATH OF TEN THOUSAND RATHIS (CHARIOT-RIDERS) AND SEVEN HUNDRED ELEPHANTS.

"THE KAURAVA SOLDIERS RETURNED TO THEIR CAMP, EXHAUSTED AND DEMORALISED.

"ON THE FOURTH DAY ARJUNA AND BHEESHMA AGAIN CONFRONTED EACH OTHER.

"DHRISHTADYUMNA FOUGHT WITH SHALYA...

"... WHILE BHEEMA LET LOOSE HIS FURY AGAINST THE ELEPHANTS IN THE ARMY.

"OTHERS TOO JOINED BHEEMA IN KILLING THE ELEPHANTS.

"HIS SON GHATOTKACHA TOO INFLICTED HEAVY CASUALTIES ON THE KAURAVA ARMY.

THUS THE KAURAVAS LOST THE BATTLE ON THE FOURTH DAY TOO.

"ON THE FIFTH DAY, VIRATA FACED BHEESHMA...

"... BHEEMA FACED DURYODHANA...

"...WHILE SINGLE-HANDEDLY ABHIMANYU CONTENDED WITH SEVERAL OF DHRITARASHTRA'S SONS.

"ON THIS DAY ARJUNA KILLED THOUSANDS OF KAURAVAS RIDING IN THEIR CHARIOTS.

"EXHAUSTED, BOTH ARMIES RETURNED TO THEIR RESPECTIVE CAMPS AT SUNDOWN.

"ON THE MORNING OF THE SIXTH DAY —

ALAS, SANJAYA, FATE SEEMS TO FAVOUR PANDAVAS IN THIS WAR AND NOT US.

THIS WAR HAS BEEN OF YOUR OWN MAKING, O KING. HOWEVER, LET ME NARRATE TO YOU HOW THE BATTLE IS FOUGHT.

"THE TWO ARMIES STOOD FACING EACH OTHER AT DAWN.

"BHEEMA SUDDENLY GOT DOWN FROM HIS CHARIOT AND CHARGED HEADLONG AT THE KAURAVA RANKS.

"DHRISHTADYUMNA CAME IN SEARCH OF BHEEMA.

BHEEMA'S CHARIOT IS EMPTY!

"HE ENQUIRED OF THE CHARIOTEER —

WHERE IS DEAR BHEEMA?

O LORD, HE HAS GONE AWAY TOWARDS THE KAURAVA ARMY LEAVING ME ALONE HERE.

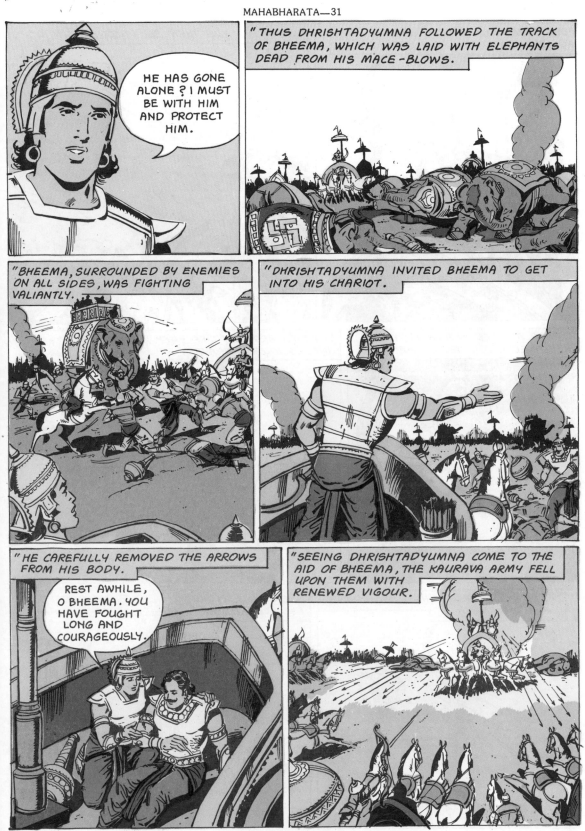

"THUS DHRISHTADYUMNA FOLLOWED THE TRACK OF BHEEMA, WHICH WAS LAID WITH ELEPHANTS DEAD FROM HIS MACE-BLOWS.

HE HAS GONE ALONE? I MUST BE WITH HIM AND PROTECT HIM.

"BHEEMA, SURROUNDED BY ENEMIES ON ALL SIDES, WAS FIGHTING VALIANTLY.

"DHRISHTADYUMNA INVITED BHEEMA TO GET INTO HIS CHARIOT.

"HE CAREFULLY REMOVED THE ARROWS FROM HIS BODY.

REST AWHILE, O BHEEMA. YOU HAVE FOUGHT LONG AND COURAGEOUSLY.

"SEEING DHRISHTADYUMNA COME TO THE AID OF BHEEMA, THE KAURAVA ARMY FELL UPON THEM WITH RENEWED VIGOUR.

"DHRISHTADYUMNA THEN USED A POWERFUL WEAPON AGAINST THEM...

"...WHICH MADE THEM ALL UNCONSCIOUS.

"DRONA ARRIVED IN A CHARIOT AND RELEASED A COUNTER-WEAPON...

"...WHICH BROUGHT LIFE BACK INTO THE UNCONSCIOUS KAURAVAS.

"DRONA THEN TURNED HIS FURY AGAINST DHRISHTADYUMNA...

"...AND KILLED DHRISHTADYUMNA'S HORSES AND CHARIOTEER.

ABHIMANYU! I'M COMING OVER TO YOUR CHARIOT!

"DRONA CONTINUED FIGHTING FIERCELY. THE PANDAVA ARMY TREMBLED BEFORE HIM IN FEAR.

"ELSEWHERE BHEEMA TORMENTED DURYODHANA WITH AN INCESSANT SHOWER OF ARROWS. DURYODHANA WAS WOUNDED ALL OVER HIS BODY.

"KRIPA THEN INVITED DURYODHANA TO CLIMB ON TO HIS CHARIOT.

COME IN HERE, DURYODHANA.

SIT DOWN AND REST FOR A WHILE, DURYODHANA.

"A NUMBER OF KAURAVAS RIDING THEIR CHARIOTS SURROUNDED ABHIMANYU AND ATTACKED HIM...

"...BUT THE YOUNG ABHIMANYU REPULSED THE ATTACK.

"BHEESHMA, OF MATCHLESS VALOUR, SLAUGHTERED SEVERAL BATTALIONS.

"AFTER THIS HE RETIRED FOR THE DAY WITH HIS FORCES.

"ON REACHING THE CAMP DURYODHANA SAID TO BHEESHMA —

I AM AFRAID OF BHEEMA'S RAGE. O GRANDSIRE, UNDER YOUR GUIDANCE I WISH TO KILL THE PANDAVAS.

"BHEESHMA REASSURED HIM.

DO NOT WORRY, O PRINCE. I WILL DO MY BEST TO CARRY OUT YOUR WISH.

"BHEESHMA THEN GAVE DURYODHANA AN OINTMENT TO HEAL HIS WOUNDS.

"THE TWO ARMIES FEELING REFRESHED IN THE MORNING AGAIN FACED EACH OTHER ON THE SEVENTH DAY...

amar chitra katha

"...AND PLUNGED WITH GUSTO IN THIS BATTLE IN WHICH BROTHER KILLED BROTHER.

"DURYODHANA ANNOUNCED—

O HEROES! PROTECT BHEESHMA FOR HE IS DETERMINED TO FIGHT ARJUNA TO THE FINISH.

"VIRATA THEN FORGED AHEAD TO FACE DRONA.

" DRONA DESTROYED VIRATA'S BANNER AND BOW...

"...AND THEN SHOT HIS CHARIOTEER AND HORSES DEAD.

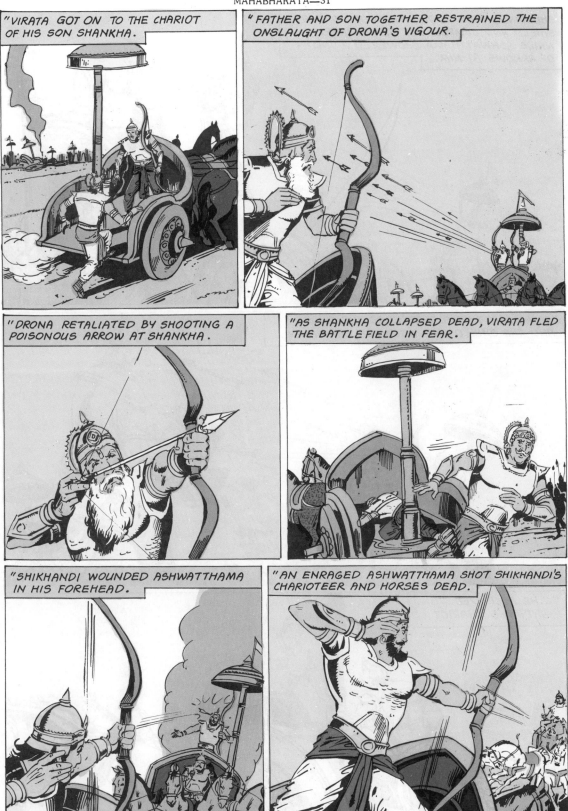

"VIRATA GOT ON TO THE CHARIOT OF HIS SON SHANKHA.

" FATHER AND SON TOGETHER RESTRAINED THE ONSLAUGHT OF DRONA'S VIGOUR.

"DRONA RETALIATED BY SHOOTING A POISONOUS ARROW AT SHANKHA.

"AS SHANKHA COLLAPSED DEAD, VIRATA FLED THE BATTLE FIELD IN FEAR.

"SHIKHANDI WOUNDED ASHWATTHAMA IN HIS FOREHEAD.

"AN ENRAGED ASHWATTHAMA SHOT SHIKHANDI'S CHARIOTEER AND HORSES DEAD.

amar chitra katha

"SHIKHANDI THEN TOOK UP A SWORD AND A SHIELD AND JUMPED OUT OF HIS CHARIOT, WHILE ASHWATTHAMA SHOWERED A VOLLEY OF ARROWS AT HIM.

"AS ASHWATTHAMA SHATTERED THE SWORD AND THE SHIELD AND WOUNDED SHIKHANDI...

"...HE ASCENDED SATYAKI'S CHARIOT.

"AND SATYAKI WAGED A FEARSOME BATTLE AGAINST THE KAURAVA ARMY AND KILLED MANY A BRAVE WARRIOR.

"BY THE SETTING SUN THE WEARY SOLDIERS RETURNED TO THEIR CAMPS.

"THEY DRESSED EACH OTHER'S WOUNDS...

"...AND SLEPT PEACEFULLY.

"ON THE EIGHTH DAY, BHEEMA KILLED AS MANY AS SEVENTEEN OF DHRITARASHTRA'S SONS.

"ARJUNA'S SON IRAVAN * WAS KILLED BY THE KAURAVAS. ARJUNA'S DISTRESS KNEW NO BOUNDS.

ALAS! IRAVAN, MY SON, IS NO MORE!

"BHEEMA AND HIS SON GHATOTKACHA REIGNED SUPREME IN VIOLENT FURY.

* SON OF ULOOPI

"AT DUSK WHEN THE TWO ARMIES RETIRED, DURYODHANA WAS ANGUISHED TO FIND THE FIELD STREWN WITH CORPSES OF SOLDIERS, DEAD ANIMALS, THE WRECKAGE OF CHARIOTS AND WEAPONS.

WHAT A RUIN!

"WHEN BACK AT THE CAMP HE CONSULTED KARNA, WHO HAD NOT YET TAKEN PART IN THE FIGHTING.

O KARNA, WE ARE NOT ABLE TO CAUSE EVEN A DENT IN THE PANDAVA ARMY, WHILE THEY KILL OUR MEN INDISCRIMINATELY. I FEEL DEJECTED AND HELPLESS.

"KARNA REPLIED —

BHEESHMA IS THE CAUSE OF YOUR DEFEAT. HE IS ALWAYS FAVOURING THE PANDAVAS. REMOVE HIM AND PUT ME IN CHARGE. ALL PANDAVAS WILL BE DESTROYED BY ME.

"DURYODHANA THEN APPROACHED BHEESHMA.

O GRANDSIRE! YOUR BRAVERY IS MATCHLESS. BUT IF YOU ARE SHIELDING THE PANDAVAS OUT OF AFFECTION FOR THEM, THEN ALLOW KARNA TO TAKE COMMAND. HE WILL CERTAINLY INFLICT DEFEAT ON THEM.

HE WISHES TO REMOVE ME FROM THE WAR. ALAS! THIS ACCURSED STATE OF MY DEPENDENCE WILL FORCE ME TO FIGHT WITH ARJUNA.

HE HAS RESOLVED TO DO IT.

GO AND SLEEP WELL, DURYODHANA. I SHALL DO YOUR BIDDING TOMORROW. BUT AT NO COST SHALL I FIGHT SHIKHANDI, WHO WAS EARLIER A WOMAN.

"DURYODHANA GOT BACK TO HIS CAMP AND SPOKE TO DUHSHASANA.

BHEESHMA HAS PROMISED TO KILL ALL THE PANDAVAS TOMORROW. THIS IS AN OPPORTUNITY WHICH WE HAVE AWAITED FOR YEARS.

BHEESHMA WILL NOT FIGHT SHIKHANDI. SO CHOOSE THE BEST OF OUR WARRIORS AND LET THEM GIVE THE BEST POSSIBLE PROTECTION TO BHEESHMA FROM SHIKHANDI TOMORROW.

VERY WELL.

"ON THE NINTH DAY AS THE TWO ARMIES STOOD FACING EACH OTHER, ARJUNA SAW BHEESHMA PLACED UNDER THE PROTECTION OF THE MIGHTIEST OF THE KAURAVAS.

"HE THEN TOLD DHRISHTADYUMNA, THE PANDAVA COMMANDER-IN-CHIEF —

PLACE SHIKHANDI AGAINST BHEESHMA TODAY. I WILL PROTECT HIM FROM BHEESHMA.

THE NINTH MORNING OF THE WAR, O KING, THUS SAW THE KAURAVA AND THE PANDAVA ARMIES, FIRMLY RESOLVED TO KILL OR BE KILLED.

"THUS ENDS THE THIRTY-FIRST SESSION OF OUR RENDERING OF VYASA'S IMMORTAL ITIHASA, THE MAHABHARATA."

amar chitra katha

"...EVIL OMENS APPEARED.

" THE SUN SEEMED BLOTTED AND A RAIN OF METEORS FELL FROM THE SKY FOREBODING DISASTER.

" ABHIMANYU LED A FIERCE ATTACK ON THE KAURAVA ARMY.

" CHARIOTS, CAVALRYMEN AND ELEPHANTS FELL TO HIS SURE ARROWS.

amar chitra katha

"THE KAURAVA SOLDIERS FLED IN TERROR. DURYODHANA CRIED TO THE RAKSHASA, ALAMBUSHA —

THIS ABHIMANYU IS AS FEROCIOUS AS HIS FATHER ARJUNA!

ALAMBHUSHA, GO AND KILL ABHIMANYU WHILE I LAUNCH AN ATTACK ON ARJUNA WITH DRONA AND OTHERS.

VERY WELL, DURYODHANA.

" ALAMBUSHA RUSHED AT THE PANDAVA ARMY...

"...AND BROUGHT SLAUGHTER IN ITS RANKS.

" THE FIVE SONS OF DRAUPADI FOUGHT ALAMBUSHA VALOROUSLY, BUT TO NO AVAIL.

"ABHIMANYU THEN CAME TO THE RESCUE OF HIS BROTHERS.

" HE RELEASED POWERFUL WEAPONS ON ALAMBUSHA.

"WHEREUPON THE RAKSHASA, USING HIS MAGICAL POWERS, ENVELOPED THE PANDAVA ARMY IN DARKNESS.

OH! I CAN'T SEE ANYTHING!

WHERE IS ABHIMANYU?

"ABHIMANYU THEN RELEASED THE BHASKARA WEAPON...

"...WHICH DISPELLED THE DARKNESS. NOW LIGHT SHONE FORTH.

"HAVING DESTROYED THE ILLUSION OF DARKNESS CREATED BY ALAMBUSHA, ABHIMANYU TORMENTED HIM WITH ARROWS.

"ALAMBUSHA HAD TO FLEE THE BATTLEFIELD IN MORTAL FEAR OF THE YOUNG ABHIMANYU.

"THE KAURAVAS SET UPON BHEEMA AN ENTIRE BATTALION OF ELEPHANT-WARRIORS.

"DESCENDING FROM HIS CHARIOT BHEEMA ATTACKED THE ELEPHANTS AND THEIR RIDERS.

"HE SLEW MANY OF THEM.

" THE FRIGHTENED ELEPHANTS RETREATED IN FEAR, TRAMPLING MANY OF THE KAURAVA ARMY ITSELF UNDERFOOT.

" SATYAKI CHARGED AT BHEESHMA AND WOUNDED HIM.

" BHEESHMA DISCHARGED A SHARP, SNAKE-LIKE ARROW ON SATYAKI...

"... BUT SATYAKI DODGED IT.

" HIGHLY ENRAGED, BHEESHMA THREW HIMSELF WITH FURY ON THE PANDAVA ARMY.

amar chitra katha

"THE PANDAVAS CAME TO THE RESCUE OF SATYAKI AND SURROUNDED BHEESHMA.

"SEEING THIS, DURYODHANA SAID TO DUHSHASANA —

BHEESHMA IS IN DANGER, WE MUST SEND REINFORCEMENTS FOR HIS PROTECTION.

"DURYODHANA THEN SENT SHAKUNI WITH A TEN-THOUSAND STRONG CAVALRY TO CHECK THE ADVANCE OF THE PANDAVAS.

"BUT YUDHISHTHIRA, NAKULA AND SAHADEVA ROUTED IT COMPLETELY.

"RESOLVED TO CONTAIN THE INDOMITABLE PANDAVAS, BHEESHMA CAME TO THE FORE.

"HE LET LOOSE ALL HIS STRENGTH AGAINST THE PANDAVA ARMY.

" BEFORE SUNSET THE BATTLEFIELD WAS A SCENE OF UTTER RUIN AND DESOLATION.

RUN ! RUN !

" KRISHNA BROUGHT THE CHARIOT TO A HALT AND SAID TO ARJUNA —

THIS IS YOUR CHANCE, O ARJUNA ! ATTACK BHEESHMA NOW !

" A RELUCTANT ARJUNA REPLIED —

AS YOU WISH, KRISHNA. STEER THE CHARIOT TOWARDS BHEESHMA.

amar chitra katha

"AS ARJUNA CONFRONTED BHEESHMA, THE LATTER RAINED ARROWS ON HIM.

?

ARJUNA SEEMS RELUCTANT TO FIGHT. I MUST DO SOMETHING!

"KRISHNA JUMPED OFF THE CHARIOT...

"...AND CHARGED AGAINST BHEESHMA.

KRISHNA IS FURIOUS!

BHEESHMA IS AS GOOD AS DEAD NOW!

"BHEESHMA, HOWEVER, WELCOMED KRISHNA.

COME, O LOTUS-EYED! KILL ME IN THIS GREAT WAR! I CHERISH NOTHING MORE THAN DEATH AT YOUR HANDS!

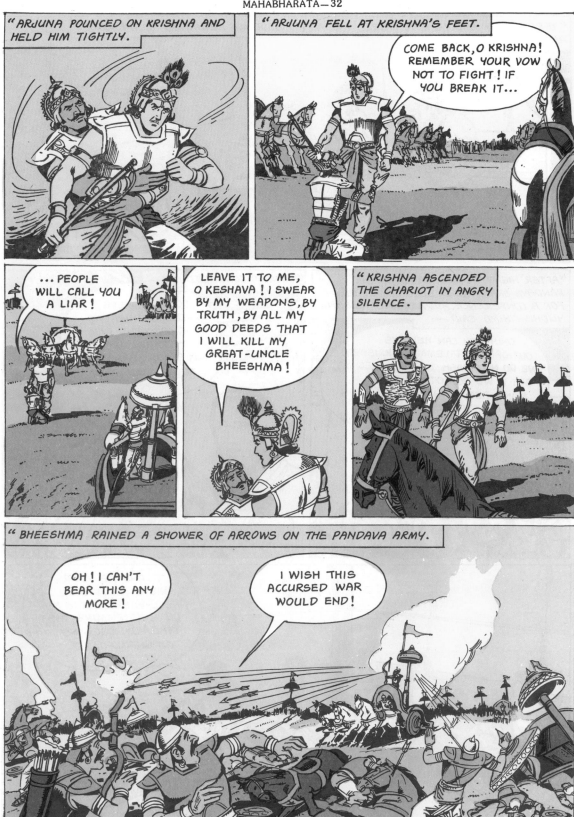

"TERRORISED AND DEMORALISED, THE PANDAVA ARMY RETURNED TO THE CAMP AFTER SUNSET.

"AFTER NIGHTFALL, LEADERS OF THE PANDAVA ARMY ASSEMBLED TOGETHER FOR A CONFERENCE. ADDRESSING KRISHNA YUDHISHTHIRA SAID —

ONLY YOU CAN HELP US OUT OF THIS DILEMMA, O KRISHNA. WE DO NOT WISH TO KILL BHEESHMA, BUT IF WE DO NOT, HE MAY BRING ABOUT THE ANNIHILATION OF OUR ARMY.

"KRISHNA CONSOLED HIM —

DO NOT GRIEVE, O YUDHISHTHIRA. AT YOUR COMMAND, I AM READY TO KILL BHEESHMA. BUT ARJUNA HAS VOWED TO KILL HIM...

...AND AS YOUR FRIEND, ALLY AND WELL-WISHER, IT IS MY DUTY TO ENSURE THAT THE VOW DOES NOT GO UNFULFILLED.

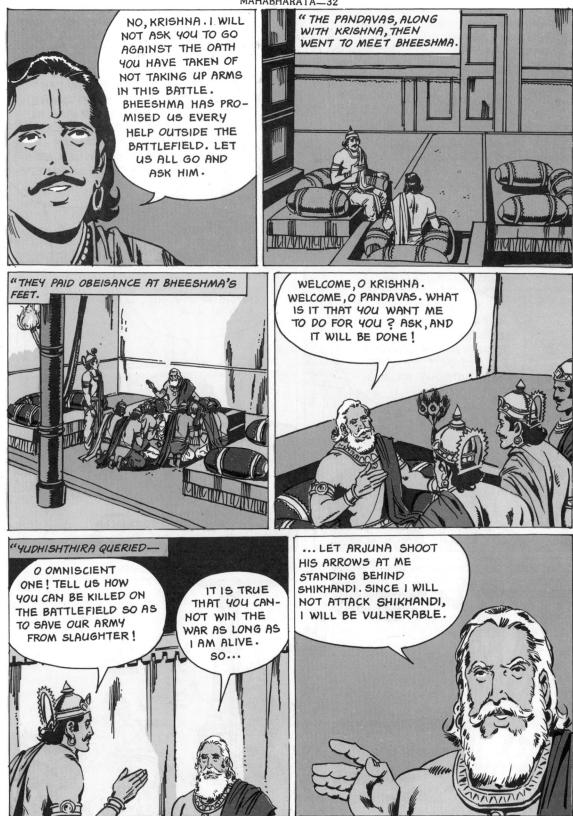

NO, KRISHNA. I WILL NOT ASK YOU TO GO AGAINST THE OATH YOU HAVE TAKEN OF NOT TAKING UP ARMS IN THIS BATTLE. BHEESHMA HAS PROMISED US EVERY HELP OUTSIDE THE BATTLEFIELD. LET US ALL GO AND ASK HIM.

"THE PANDAVAS, ALONG WITH KRISHNA, THEN WENT TO MEET BHEESHMA.

"THEY PAID OBEISANCE AT BHEESHMA'S FEET.

WELCOME, O KRISHNA. WELCOME, O PANDAVAS. WHAT IS IT THAT YOU WANT ME TO DO FOR YOU? ASK, AND IT WILL BE DONE!

"YUDHISHTHIRA QUERIED—

O OMNISCIENT ONE! TELL US HOW YOU CAN BE KILLED ON THE BATTLEFIELD SO AS TO SAVE OUR ARMY FROM SLAUGHTER!

IT IS TRUE THAT YOU CANNOT WIN THE WAR AS LONG AS I AM ALIVE. SO...

... LET ARJUNA SHOOT HIS ARROWS AT ME STANDING BEHIND SHIKHANDI. SINCE I WILL NOT ATTACK SHIKHANDI, I WILL BE VULNERABLE.

amar chitra katha

HEARING THIS, THE PANDAVAS BOWED TO BHEESHMA AND RETURNED TO THEIR CAMP.

"BACK IN THE PANDAVA CAMP, A DEPRESSED AND EMBARRASSED ARJUNA ASKED KRISHNA —

WHAT SHALL I DO, O KRISHNA? HOW CAN I BRING MYSELF TO KILL THIS GRAND OLD MAN IN WHOSE LAP I HAVE PLAYED AS A CHILD? HOW CAN I ATTACK HIM WHEN HE CHOOSES TO BE UNARMED?

"BUT KRISHNA REMAINED FIRM.

REMEMBER YOUR DHARMA AS A KSHATRIYA. REMEMBER, YOU VOWED TO KILL HIM. REMEMBER, YOU CANNOT WIN THE WAR WITHOUT KILLING HIM.

MOREOVER, HE CHOSE TO OPPOSE YOU IN WAR.

"THE NEXT MORNING WHEN THE PANDAVA ARMY SET OUT...

"...SHIKHANDI WAS AT ITS HEAD.

"THE TWO ARMIES CHARGED AGAINST EACH OTHER.

"WHEN BHEESHMA AND SHIKHANDI CAME FACE TO FACE—

I SHALL KILL YOU TODAY, O BHEESHMA.

I SHALL NOT TAKE UP ARMS AGAINST YOU.

"WHEN ARJUNA SAW THIS CONFRONTATION, HE SAID TO SHIKHANDI —

KILL HIM, SHIKHANDI, FOR HE CANNOT HARM YOU. I TOO WILL HELP YOU. SHAME ON US IF WE TWO TOGETHER CANNOT KILL HIM.

THE REDOUBTABLE BHEESHMA WAS, HOWEVER, MORE THAN A MATCH FOR THE PANDAVA ARMY.

"IN THE INTENSE WARFARE THAT ENSUED ...

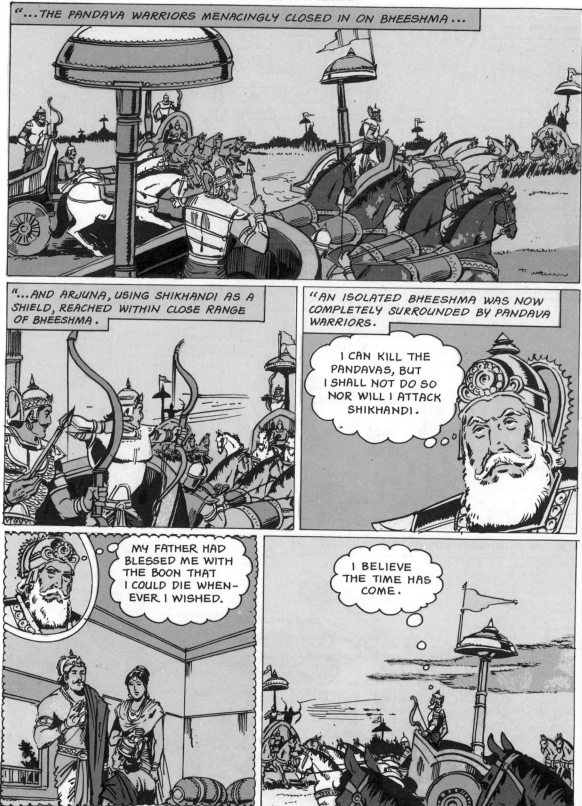

"...THE PANDAVA WARRIORS MENACINGLY CLOSED IN ON BHEESHMA..."

"...AND ARJUNA, USING SHIKHANDI AS A SHIELD, REACHED WITHIN CLOSE RANGE OF BHEESHMA.

"AN ISOLATED BHEESHMA WAS NOW COMPLETELY SURROUNDED BY PANDAVA WARRIORS.

I CAN KILL THE PANDAVAS, BUT I SHALL NOT DO SO NOR WILL I ATTACK SHIKHANDI.

MY FATHER HAD BLESSED ME WITH THE BOON THAT I COULD DIE WHENEVER I WISHED.

I BELIEVE THE TIME HAS COME.

"ARJUNA'S SHARP ARROWS WOUNDED BHEESHMA.

"BHEESHMA SAID TO DUHSHASANA —

THESE SHARP AND MIGHTY ARROWS CANNOT BE THOSE OF SHIKHANDI. I AM CERTAIN THEY ARE ARJUNA'S.

"THE PANDAVAS RAINED AN INCESSANT SHOWER OF ARROWS ON BHEESHMA.

"WITH A FEW HOURS TO GO BEFORE SUNSET, BHEESHMA LOOKED TO THE SKY IN THE EAST ...

"...AND FELL.

"IN HEAVEN THE GODS LAMENTED LOUDLY THE FALL OF THIS MIGHTY HERO.

THE SUN IS YET IN HIS SOUTHERN VOYAGE. I DO NOT WISH TO DIE AT THIS INAUSPICIOUS HOUR.

"HOLY SAGES, LIVING ON THE MANSAROVAR,* TOOK THE FORM OF SWANS AND CAME TO VISIT BHEESHMA. BHEESHMA ASSURED THEM —

I SHALL NOT DIE TILL THE SUN TRAVELS NORTHWARD.

"THE KAURAVA WARRIORS WERE OVERCOME BY GRIEF.

* A MYTHICAL LAKE SAID TO EXIST ON THE HIMALAYAS.

amar chitra katha

"BHEESHMA SPOKE UP—

WELCOME, O VALIANT WARRIORS! I AM PLEASED TO SEE YOU ALL HERE.

THEN—

MY HEAD HANGS LOOSE. ONE OF YOU MUST GIVE ME A HEAD-REST.

"SEVERAL SOFT AND EXCELLENT PILLOWS WERE BROUGHT BUT BHEESHMA REFUSED THEM ALL.

THESE ARE NOT FIT FOR A SOLDIER.

ARJUNA, GIVE ME A HEAD-REST BEFITTING MY BRAVERY AND COURAGE.

"ARJUNA SET THREE ARROWS ON HIS GANDEEVA...

"...AND SHOT THEM INTO THE GROUND UNDER BHEESHMA'S HEAD.

"BHEESHMA WAS PLEASED.

O ARJUNA! YOU HAVE GIVEN ME THE MOST APPROPRIATE HEAD-REST.

"AND THEN—

GIVE UP STRIFE NOW, O KINGS.

"AS PHYSICIANS CAME UP TO REMOVE THE ARROWS FROM BHEESHMA'S BODY, HE CALLED OUT TO DURYODHANA.

SON, SEND THESE PHYSICIANS AWAY WITH DUE HONOUR. I WISH TO BE CREMATED, AS BEFITS A HERO, ALONG WITH THESE ARROWS.

"THE NEXT MORNING A LARGE NUMBER OF PEOPLE, AS WELL AS THE KAURAVA AND PANDAVA WARRIORS, CAME TO PAY THEIR LAST RESPECTS TO BHEESHMA.

amar chitra katha

"FAINT WITH EXHAUSTION AND BREATHING HEAVILY, BHEESHMA UTTERED ONLY ONE WORD —

W-A-T-E-R !

"THE KINGS BROUGHT THE CHOICEST FOOD AND PITCHERS BRIMMING WITH COOL WATER. BUT BHEESHMA WOULD NOT ACCEPT THEM.

I DO NOT DESIRE THESE. I WISH TO SEE ARJUNA.

"AS ARJUNA ARRIVED —

O ARJUNA! YOU ALONE CAN PROVIDE ME WITH THE DIVINE WATER I WISH TO DRINK.

"ARJUNA CLIMBED UP HIS CHARIOT AND SHOT THE PARJANYA* WEAPON INTO THE EARTH.

* LITERALLY, RAIN

amar chitra katha

"PEOPLE WATCHED IN AMAZEMENT AS BHEESHMA QUAFFED THE WATER.

"HIS THIRST QUENCHED, BHEESHMA SAID TO DURYODHANA —

O DURYODHANA, MAKE PEACE WITH THE ALL-POWERFUL ARJUNA. DO NOT DELAY NOW ANY MORE. LET MY DEATH BE THE HARBINGER OF PEACE.

GIVE AWAY HALF THE KINGDOM TO YUDHISHTHIRA, O DURYODHANA. LET THERE BE PEACE AND HAPPINESS AMONG PEOPLE.

"BUT BHEESHMA'S WORDS OF WISDOM DID NOT APPEAL TO DURYODHANA AND HE LEFT SAYING —

NEVER

"KARNA WAS FILLED WITH A NAMELESS FEAR ON HEARING OF THE FALL OF BHEESHMA.

"HE HESITANTLY APPROACHED BHEESHMA. HE WAS IN TEARS.

O BHEESHMA! I AM THE SAME KARNA WHOM YOU ALWAYS DESPISED!

"BHEESHMA OPENED HIS EYES AND WAVED THE GUARDS AWAY.

"BHEESHMA EMBRACED KARNA AFFECTIONATELY.

CHILD ! YOU ARE NOT RADHA'S BUT KUNTI'S SON BY THE GOD SURYA*. AND I DO NOT DESPISE YOU.

I SPOKE TO YOU HARSHLY NOW AND THEN BECAUSE, PROVOKED BY DURYO-DHANA, YOU SPOKE ILL OF THE PANDAVAS...

...AND I WISHED TO DIMINISH YOUR ENERGY AND MORALE ONLY TO PREVENT A SCHISM IN THE FAMILY.

I DO NOT DESPISE YOU, O KARNA. THE PANDAVAS ARE YOUR BROTHERS. JOIN HANDS WITH THEM. THIS IS THE FAVOUR I ASK OF YOU AT THIS HOUR.

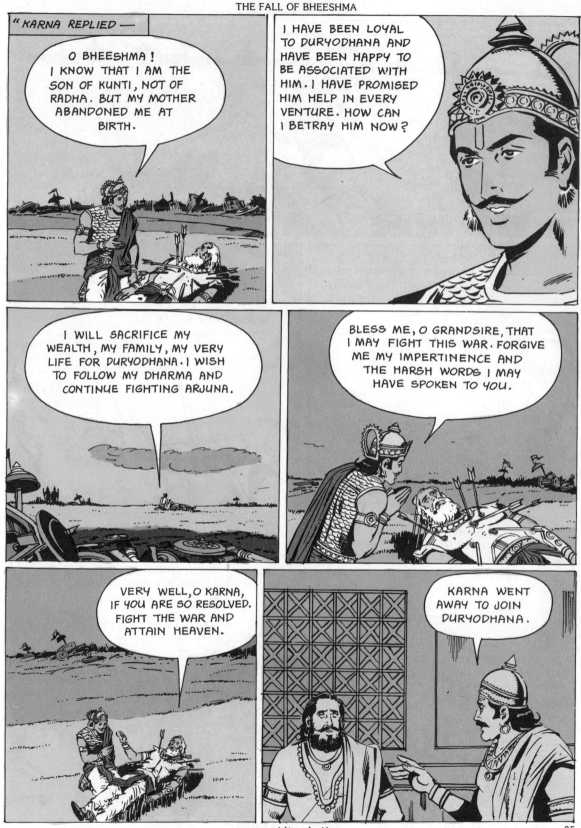

"KARNA THEN RECALLED HIS DREAM IN WHICH HIS FATHER SURYA + APPEARED IN THE FORM OF A LEARNED BRAHMANA.

SON, INDRA IS ABOUT TO COME TO YOU IN THE GUISE OF A BRAHMANA.

HE IS AWARE OF YOUR GENEROSITY. HE WILL ASK YOU FOR THE KAVACHA* AND KUNDALAS,⊕ THAT MAKE YOU INVINCIBLE IN WAR.

+ KARNA WAS BORN TO KUNTI WITH THE BLESSINGS OF SURYA, THE SUN GOD.
* ARMOUR   ⊕ EAR-RINGS.

"KARNA REPLIED —

DO NOT GIVE THEM AWAY TO INDRA, MY SON. HE WISHES TO MAKE YOU VULNERABLE TO HIS SON ARJUNA.

I CANNOT REFUSE A MENDICANT, O SURYA. I VALUE MY REPUTATION MORE THAN MY VERY LIFE. I SHALL GIVE AWAY MY KAVACHA AND KUNDALAS, IF INDRA ASKS FOR THEM.

WELL, IF YOU ARE DETERMINED TO DONATE THEM, ASK INDRA FOR A POWERFUL WEAPON IN RETURN.

"KARNA WOKE UP, THOUGHTFUL.

WAS IT A DREAM? IF NOT, I SHALL CERTAINLY ASK INDRA FOR A MIGHTY WEAPON IN RETURN FOR MY KAVACHA AND KUNDALAS.

" IN THE MORNING AS KARNA STOOD IN THE STREAM OF A RIVER, PAYING HOMAGE TO SURYA, A BRAHMANA APPROACHED HIM.

WELCOME, O BRAHMANA. OF WHAT SERVICE CAN I BE TO YOU?

O HERO! GIVE ME YOUR KAVACHA AND KUNDALAS.

O KING, KARNA RECEIVED FROM INDRA THE HIGHLY POTENT AMOGHA WEAPON. INDRA, HOWEVER, WARNED KARNA NOT TO USE THE WEAPON UNTIL AND UNLESS HIS VERY LIFE WAS THREATENED.

"THUS ENDS THE THIRTY-SECOND SESSION OF OUR RENDERING OF VYASA'S IMMORTAL ITIHASA, THE MAHABHARATA.

amar chitra katha

Mahabharata–33
DRONA'S VOW

O KING, THE FALL OF BHEESHMA PLUNGED THE KAURAVA ARMY IN GRIEF. THE HAPLESS WARRIORS CALLED UPON KARNA TO SAVE THEM FROM THE DOOM THAT SEEMED CERTAIN.

"THE GRIEF-STRICKEN KAURAVAS REMEMBERED KARNA.

THE TIME HAS COME FOR KARNA TO COME TO OUR AID. HE HAD PROMISED TO ABSTAIN FROM THE WAR AS LONG AS BHEESHMA WAS ALIVE.

YES, THIS IS THE OPPORTUNITY FOR HIM TO PROVE HIS VALOUR. LET US SUMMON HIM.

"RISING TO THE OCCASION, KARNA ARRIVED RIDING HIS CHARIOT TO MEET THE GRIEF-STRICKEN DURYO-DHANA."

THE MIGHTY BHEESHMA HAS FALLEN. IT IS AS IF THE SUN ITSELF HAS FALLEN FROM THE SKIES.

THE KAURAVA FORCES HAVE BEEN ORPHANED AND DEMORALISED. I MUST PROTECT THEM AS ABLY AS DID BHEESHMA.

GIVE ME, O WARRIORS, THE BEST OF WEAPONS AND EQUIPMENT, SO THAT I MAY DISCHARGE MY DUTY OF PROTECTING YOU AT THIS HOUR OF DISTRESS.

"KARNA'S CHARIOT WAS THEN FILLED WITH WEAPONS."

"KARNA PREPARED HIMSELF FULLY FOR THE BATTLE AHEAD."

"DURYODHANA THEN SAID —

O KARNA, I REGARD YOU AS THE MAN WHO CAN SAVE US AFTER BHEESHMA. BEHOLD THESE GREAT WARRIORS, AND TELL ME...

...WHO, AMONG THEM IS FIT TO BE OUR NEXT COMMANDER-IN-CHIEF.

"KARNA REPLIED —

O KING, NOT ONLY IS DRONA THE SENIORMOST AMONG US BUT HE HAS BEEN ALSO A TEACHER TO MOST OF US. THERE IS NONE AMONG US WHO WILL NOT FOLLOW A LEADER LIKE DRONA.

HENCE I WOULD ADVISE YOU TO APPOINT THIS VENERABLE WARRIOR OUR NEXT COMMANDER-IN-CHIEF.

"DURYODHANA SAID TO DRONA —

O LION AMONG MEN! I BESEECH YOU TO BE OUR COMMANDER-IN-CHIEF AND TO LEAD US INTO BATTLE.

"DRONA REPLIED —

O KING, I AM WELL VERSED IN ALL THE MARTIAL ARTS. I ACCEPT YOUR OFFER, BUT ON ONE CONDITION.

I SHALL FIGHT UNTO DEATH ALL THE PANDAVA WARRIORS EXCEPT DHRISHTA-DYUMNA FOR HE IS DESTINED TO KILL ME.

"DURYODHANA THEN PERFORMED THE INVESTITURE CEREMONY OF DRONA AS THE COMMANDER-IN-CHIEF OF THE KAURAVA FORCES.

" DRONA THEN ARRAYED THE KAURAVA FORCES AND PROCEEDED TO THE BATTLEFIELD.

"WITH THE MIGHTY KAURAVA WARRIORS BY HIS SIDE, DRONA LAUNCHED A FIERCE ATTACK ON THE PANDAVA ARMY.

"THE PANDAVA FORCES WERE SCATTERED BEFORE THE ONSLAUGHT.

"YUDHISHTHIRA SAID TO ARJUNA AND DHRISHTADYUMNA —

WE MUST STOP DRONA.

amar chitra katha

"DRONA SAID TO DURYODHANA —

O KING! BY GIVING ME THE COMMAND OF THE FORCES, YOU HAVE BESTOWED AN HONOUR ON ME. TELL ME, WHAT MAY I DO TO PLEASE YOU?

"DURYODHANA SAID —

O REVERED ONE! IF YOU WISH TO PLEASE ME, SEIZE YUDHISHTHIRA AND BRING HIM BEFORE ME.

" DRONA ASKED —

O KING! YOU WANT ME ONLY TO CAPTURE HIM? YOU DON'T WANT HIM TO BE KILLED?

"DURYODHANA REPLIED —

BECAUSE, O VENERABLE ONE, YUDHISHTHIRA'S DEATH WILL SPELL NOT MY VICTORY, BUT MY DOOM.

IF YUDHISHTHIRA IS KILLED, THE REST OF THE PANDAVAS WILL NEVER SPARE OUR LIVES.

INSTEAD, IF YUDHISHTHIRA IS CAPTURED AND AGAIN PERSUADED TO PLAY DICE WITH ME HE WILL LOSE IN THE GAME. THE PANDAVAS WILL ONCE AGAIN BE BANISHED INTO THE FOREST.

"DRONA WAS THOUGHTFUL—

I SHOULD HAVE SUSPECTED HIS WICKED MOTIVE.

"HE THEN LAID DOWN A CONDITION.

SO LONG AS YUDHISHTHIRA IS UNDER THE PROTECTION OF ARJUNA, I CANNOT CAPTURE HIM. SO YOU MUST SEPARATE ARJUNA FROM YUDHISHTHIRA.

O KING, DURYODHANA KNEW THAT DRONA HAD A SOFT CORNER FOR THE PANDAVAS. HE THEREFORE MADE A PUBLIC ANNOUNCEMENT OF DRONA'S PROMISE SO THAT HE COULD NOT GO BACK ON HIS WORDS.

"WHEN YUDHISHTHIRA GOT TO KNOW OF DRONA'S RESOLVE, HE SPOKE TO ARJUNA.

O ARJUNA, YOU ARE AWARE OF DRONA'S INTENT AS WELL AS THE CONDITION LAID DOWN BY HIM.

THINK OF A STRATEGY THAT WILL ENSURE THAT I WILL BE UNDER YOUR IMMEDIATE PROTECTION.

"ARJUNA REPLIED —

O KING, IT IS AS REPREHENSIBLE FOR ME TO KILL MY TEACHER AS IT IS TO ABANDON YOU. HENCE I SHALL NOT LET EITHER HAPPEN.

THE SKY MAY FALL TO PIECES AND THE EARTH MAY SPLIT ASUNDER, BUT DRONA WILL NOT TAKE YOU CAPTIVE AS LONG AS I AM ALIVE.

"AFTER THIS BRIEF CONFERENCE AMONG THE PANDAVAS, THE WAR WAS RESUMED BY THE BELLIGERENT ARMIES.

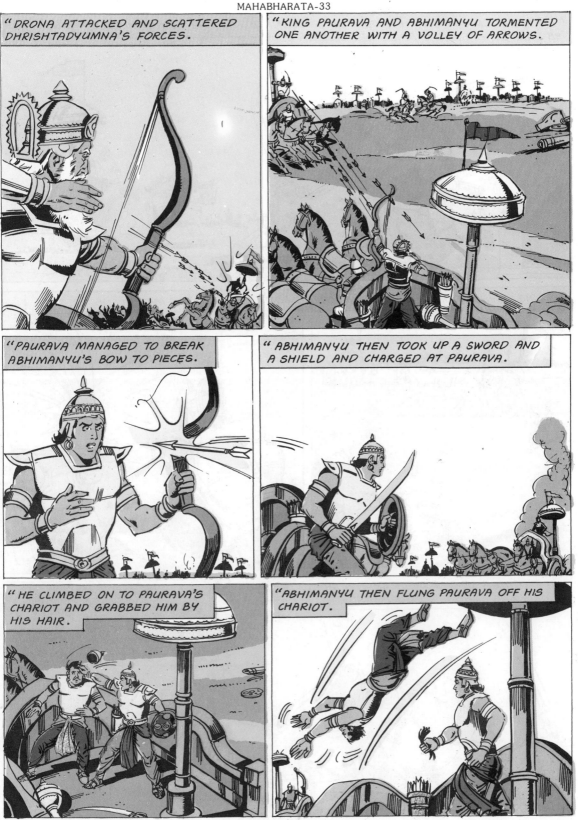

"DRONA ATTACKED AND SCATTERED DHRISHTADYUMNA'S FORCES.

"KING PAURAVA AND ABHIMANYU TORMENTED ONE ANOTHER WITH A VOLLEY OF ARROWS.

"PAURAVA MANAGED TO BREAK ABHIMANYU'S BOW TO PIECES.

"ABHIMANYU THEN TOOK UP A SWORD AND A SHIELD AND CHARGED AT PAURAVA.

"HE CLIMBED ON TO PAURAVA'S CHARIOT AND GRABBED HIM BY HIS HAIR.

"ABHIMANYU THEN FLUNG PAURAVA OFF HIS CHARIOT.

amar chitra katha

"AN ENRAGED JAYADRATHA COULD NOT TOLERATE PAURAVA BEING HUMBLED THUS. HE JUMPED OFF HIS CHARIOT IN A FURY.

"SEEING JAYADRATHA COMING, ABHIMANYU RUSHED AT HIM.

"BOTH FOUGHT WITH MATCHLESS VALOUR.

"JAYADRATHA STRUCK ABHIMANYU'S SHIELD BUT HIS SWORD WAS SMASHED INTO PIECES.

"JAYADRATHA RUSHED BACK TO HIS CHARIOT.

"ABHIMANYU TOO RETURNED TO HIS CHARIOT AND WAS SOON SURROUNDED BY SEVERAL KAURAVA WARRIORS.

"ABHIMANYU FOUGHT THEM BRAVELY.

"SHALYA RELEASED A POWERFUL WEAPON ON ABHIMANYU.

" BUT ABHIMANYU GRABBED IT BY HAND...

"...AND SENT IT BACK TO SHALYA.

"THE WEAPON KILLED THE CHARIOTEER AND FLUNG SHALYA OFF THE CHARIOT. THE PANDAVAS CHEERED ABHIMANYU.

VICTORY TO ABHIMANYU!

HAIL ABHIMANYU!

"HIGHLY ENRAGED, SHALYA RUSHED AT ABHIMANYU WITH A MACE.

" ABHIMANYU TOO TOOK UP A MACE BUT BHEEMA INTERVENED.

LET ME DEAL WITH HIM, ABHIMANYU.

" BHEEMA AND SHALYA HAD A TERRIBLE FIGHT WITH MACES.

"...AND BHEEMA KNOCKED SHALYA UNCONSCIOUS.

"NARRATING THE WAR TO THE BLIND DHRITARASHTRA, SANJAYA SAID.

O KING, THE KAURAVAS TOOK THE HEAVILY WOUNDED SHALYA AWAY FROM THE BATTLEFIELD.

"DRONA TOLD HIS CHARIOTEER—

TAKE MY CHARIOT CLOSE TO YUDHISHTHIRA.

"THE PANDAVA WARRIORS TRIED THEIR BEST TO CONTAIN DRONA'S ADVANCE.

"BUT DRONA SOON REACHED CLOSE TO YUDHISHTHIRA. THE PANDAVA SOLDIERS WERE PANIC-STRICKEN.

ALAS!

YUDHISHTHIRA IS KILLED!

"BUT ARJUNA CHARGED UP TO THE DEFENCE OF YUDHISHTHIRA.

"UNABLE TO WITHSTAND ARJUNA'S ONSLAUGHT, DRONA WAS FORCED TO RETREAT.

AT SUNDOWN, THE TIRED ARMIES RETURNED TO THEIR CAMPS.

amar chitra katha

"AN EMBARRASSED DRONA SAID TO DURYODHANA —

I HAD TOLD YOU, O KING, THAT YUDHISHTHIRA IS INACCESSIBLE TO ME AS LONG AS ARJUNA IS SHIELDING HIM.

BUT IF SOMEBODY CHALLENGES ARJUNA TO A BATTLE AND LURES HIM AWAY, I SHALL BE ABLE TO TAKE YUDHISHTHIRA CAPTIVE.

"SUSHARMA, THE KING OF TRIGARTAS, SAID —

GIVE US THIS ASSIGNMENT, O KING. ARJUNA HAS TIME AND AGAIN INSULTED US AND WE ARE BURNING WITH THE DESIRE FOR REVENGE. WE WANT TO KILL HIM.

"THE KAURAVA WARRIORS EVOLVED A STRATEGY FOR THE NEXT DAY'S WAR.

"THE KAURAVAS NOW BROUGHT THE PREVIOUS NIGHT'S PLAN INTO OPERATION THE NEXT MORNING.

ARJUNA WILL BE LURED AWAY BY THE SAMSHAPTAKAS.*

NOW MY GOAL IS CLOSE AT HAND.

THE VALIANT BHAGADATTA CAN DEAL WITH THE REMAINING PANDAVA ARMY.

"BHAGADATTA ATTACKED BHEEMA IN HIS CHARIOT.

BHAGADATTA'S ELEPHANT TRAMPLED THE CHARIOT UNDERFOOT.

"BUT BHEEMA KNEW HOW TO BRING A RAGING ELEPHANT UNDER CONTROL. HE QUICKLY DUCKED UNDER THE ELEPHANT'S BELLY.

"AS HE STROKED THE ELEPHANT ON THE BELLY, THE BEAST QUIETENED DOWN.

I MUST WAIT FOR ANOTHER ELEPHANT TO COME THIS WAY.

* MERCENARIES WHO HAVE VOWED TO FIGHT THE BATTLE TO DEATH.

"UNABLE TO SEE BHEEMA ANYWHERE, THE PANDAVA ARMY PANICKED.

ALAS! BHEEMA HAS BEEN KILLED BY THIS ELEPHANT.

"BHEEMA THEN ESCAPED QUIETLY FROM UNDERNEATH THE ELEPHANT.

"YUDHISHTHIRA AND HIS FORCES ATTACKED BHAGADATTA'S ELEPHANT, WHO WAS NOW ON THE RAMPAGE AGAIN AFTER BHEEMA'S ESCAPE.

"THE ELEPHANT GATHERED UP SATYAKI'S CHARIOT IN HIS TRUNK AND HURLED IT FAR.

"ARJUNA WAS ALARMED BY THE WILD FURY OF THE ELEPHANT.

O KRISHNA, BHAGADATTA'S ELEPHANT IS PLAYING HAVOC WITH OUR ARMY. TAKE THE CHARIOT TO HIM. I SHALL...

"SUDDENLY A CALL AROSE FROM THE NORTHERN QUARTER.

ARJUNA! ARJUNA!

COME HITHER! FIGHT WITH US!

"ARJUNA WAS NOW ON THE HORNS OF A DILEMMA.

THE SAMSHAPTAKAS ARE DARING ME TO FIGHT. SHOULD I ACCEPT THEIR CHALLENGE OR BRING BHAGDATTA'S ELEPHANT TO HEEL?

I CANNOT LET A CHALLENGE FOR BATTLE GO UNANSWERED.

"TURNING TO THE SAMSHAPTAKAS, ARJUNA LAUNCHED A MERCILESS ATTACK ON THEM.

"THE SAMSHAPTAKAS WERE WELL MATCHED AGAINST ARJUNA. THEY HARASSED HIM AND HIS CHARIOTEER KRISHNA GREATLY.

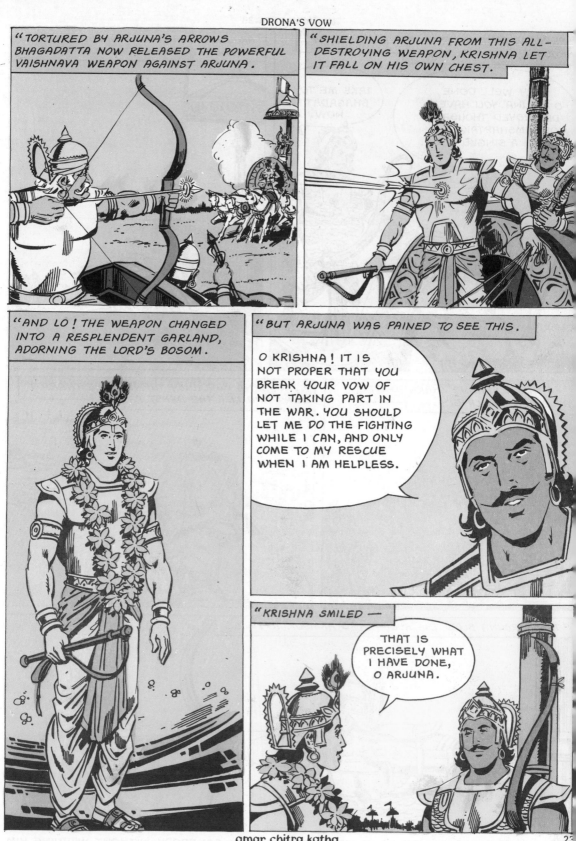

"TORTURED BY ARJUNA'S ARROWS BHAGADATTA NOW RELEASED THE POWERFUL VAISHNAVA WEAPON AGAINST ARJUNA.

"SHIELDING ARJUNA FROM THIS ALL-DESTROYING WEAPON, KRISHNA LET IT FALL ON HIS OWN CHEST.

"AND LO! THE WEAPON CHANGED INTO A RESPLENDENT GARLAND, ADORNING THE LORD'S BOSOM.

"BUT ARJUNA WAS PAINED TO SEE THIS.

O KRISHNA! IT IS NOT PROPER THAT YOU BREAK YOUR VOW OF NOT TAKING PART IN THE WAR. YOU SHOULD LET ME DO THE FIGHTING WHILE I CAN, AND ONLY COME TO MY RESCUE WHEN I AM HELPLESS.

"KRISHNA SMILED —

THAT IS PRECISELY WHAT I HAVE DONE, O ARJUNA.

"MANY YEARS AGO PRITHVI, THE GODDESS EARTH APPROACHED ME WHEN I WAS IN THE FORM OF VISHNU.

O LORD! GIVE MY SON NARAKASURA THE MOST POWERFUL WEAPON.

SO BE IT.

O ARJUNA, I GAVE THIS ALL-DESTROYING UNCONQUERABLE WEAPON TO NARAKASURA.

AND BHAGADATTA OBTAINED IT FROM HIM. WHO CAN ENDURE THE TERRIBLE IMPACT OF SUCH A WEAPON BUT ME?

O ARJUNA, I HAVE PROTECTED YOU BY DEPRIVING HIM OF THE WEAPON. PROCEED NOW TO KILL HIM.

"IN ONE SHOT ARJUNA SENT BHAGADATTA'S ELEPHANT TO ITS DEATH.

"AND THEN —

O ARJUNA! LOOK CAREFULLY AT BHAGDATTA. HE IS A VERY OLD MAN BUT VERY VALOROUS. HIS EYELIDS ARE KEPT OPEN BY A PIECE OF CLOTH AROUND HIS FOREHEAD.

"ARJUNA'S NEXT AIMED HIS ARROW AT THE CLOTHBAND AND TORE IT AWAY.

"WITH ANOTHER ARROW HE PUT AN END TO THE LIFE OF BHAGDATTA.

"ARJUNA THEN SWIFTLY TURNED TO CONFRONT THE TWO SONS OF SHAKUNI WHO WERE RAINING ARROWS ON HIM.

"HE KILLED BOTH OF THEM.

"THIS ENRAGED SHAKUNI WHO BROUGHT FORTH HIS ILLUSORY POWERS TO CONFOUND ARJUNA.

"FIERCE BEASTS ROSE TO THREATEN ARJUNA ON ALL SIDES.

"ARJUNA DESTROYED THEM AND DISPELLED THE DARKNESS BY THE WEAPON OF LIGHT.*

"SEEING THE ILLUSION DESTROYED, SHAKUNI FLED ON HIS SWIFT HORSE.

* JYOTI-ASTRA

amar chitra katha

"TORMENTED BY ARJUNA'S FURY, THE KAURAVA FORCES RAN HELTER-SKELTER.

"IN THEIR EXTREME BEWILDERMENT AND FEAR, THEY EVEN ATTACKED EACH OTHER.

"THE FLEEING, HELPLESS KAURAVAS CALLED OUT —

KARNA! O KARNA!

SAVE US, O KARNA!

FEAR NOT, MY MEN, I'M HERE TO PROTECT YOU.

"KARNA DID TRY TO CONFRONT ARJUNA...

"...BUT COULD NOT BEAR ARJUNA'S WRATH FOR LONG AND FLED THE FIELD.

"THE FRIGHTENED KAURAVAS FOLLOWED SUIT.

"THE SETTING SUN SIGNALLED THE END OF THE HOSTILITIES FOR THE DAY, MUCH TO THE RELIEF OF BOTH ARMIES.

"DURYODHANA WAS DISHEARTENED SINCE HIS PLAN TO CAPTURE YUDHISHTHIRA HAD FAILED.

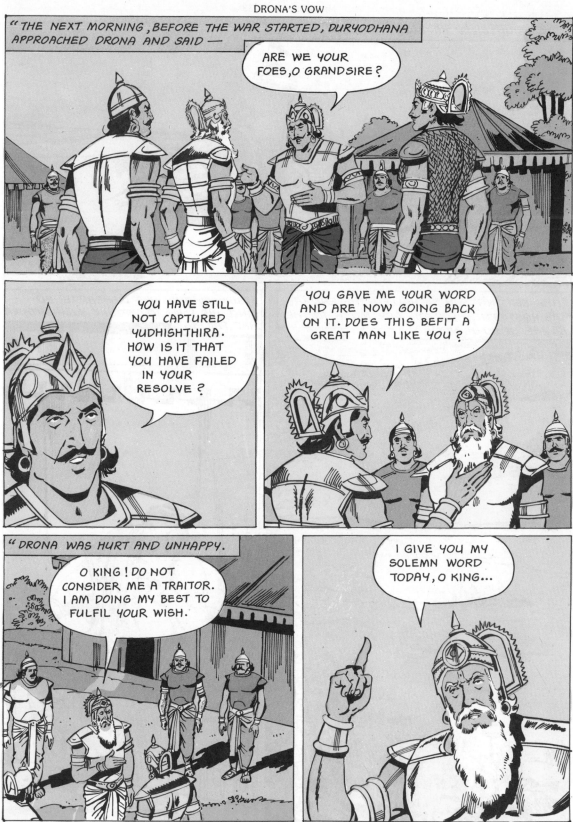

"THE NEXT MORNING, BEFORE THE WAR STARTED, DURYODHANA APPROACHED DRONA AND SAID —

ARE WE YOUR FOES, O GRANDSIRE?

YOU HAVE STILL NOT CAPTURED YUDHISHTHIRA. HOW IS IT THAT YOU HAVE FAILED IN YOUR RESOLVE?

YOU GAVE ME YOUR WORD AND ARE NOW GOING BACK ON IT. DOES THIS BEFIT A GREAT MAN LIKE YOU?

"DRONA WAS HURT AND UNHAPPY.

O KING! DO NOT CONSIDER ME A TRAITOR. I AM DOING MY BEST TO FULFIL YOUR WISH.

I GIVE YOU MY SOLEMN WORD TODAY, O KING...

...THAT I WILL CERTAINLY SLAY ONE OF THE GREAT MAHARATHIS OF THE PANDAVA ARMY BEFORE SUNDOWN.

THE THIRTEENTH DAY OF THE WAR DAWNED, O KING, SPELLING DISASTER FOR THE PANDAVAS.

THUS ENDS THE THIRTY-THIRD SESSION OF OUR RENDERING OF VYASA'S IMMORTAL ITIHASA — THE MAHABHARATA.

Mahabharata – 34
The Slaying Of Abhimanyu

O KING, ON THE THIRTEENTH DAY OF THE WAR, DRONA RESOLVED TO KILL AT LEAST ONE GREAT PANDAVA MAHARATHI* IN THE COURSE OF THE DAY'S BATTLE. HE ARRAYED HIS FORCES IN A CHAKRAVYUHA⊕

"JAYADRATHA STOOD FIRM LIKE MOUNT MERU BESIDE DRONA AT THE ENTRANCE TO THE CHAKRAVYUHA. BEHIND HIM WERE ASHWATTHAMA AND OTHER WARRIORS.

IT IS A FORMATION, THAT IS ALMOST IMPREGNABLE CHALLENGING THE SKILL OF THE MIGHTIEST OF WARRIORS. ARJUNA OF COURSE IS AN EXCEPTION.

* THE HIGHEST HONOUR BESTOWED ON A WARRIOR. ⊕ WHEEL FORMATION.

THERE IS SCARCELY ANYTHING ABOUT WARFARE THAT ARJUNA DOESN'T KNOW. YOU MUST SOMEHOW DISTRACT HIS ATTENTION FROM THE CHAKRAVYUHA.

"TO THE FAR SOUTH OF THE BATTLEFIELD AWAY FROM THE CHAKRAVYUHA, THE SAMSHAPTAKAS* HAILED ARJUNA.

ARJUNA! YOU HAVE STILL NOT VANQUISHED US!

THE SAMSHAPTAKAS ARE AGAIN CHALLENGING ME!

"ARJUNA RESPONDED TO THEIR CHALLENGE AGAIN, LEAVING THE PANDAVA ARMY TO STRUGGLE AGAINST DRONA'S DIFFICULT CHAKRA FORMATION. ALL THE GREAT PANDAVA WARRIORS DHRISTRADYUMNA, SHIKHANDI, NAKULA, SAHADEVA...

* MERCENARIES WHO VOW NOT TO LEAVE THE BATTLEFIELD, WITHOUT WINNING.

"...GHATOTKACHA, DRUPADA, VIRATA AND OTHERS TRIED TO PENETRATE THE FORMATION BUT IN VAIN.

"A SHOWER OF ARROWS FROM DRONA HELD THEM IN CHECK.

"THE PANCHALAS WERE COMPLETELY ROUTED BY DRONA.

"YUDHISHTHIRA WAS EXASPERATED.

IS THERE NONE IN OUR ARMY WHO CAN FACE DRONA'S WRATH?

"HE TURNED TO ABHIMANYU, THE YOUNG SON OF ARJUNA —

DO SOMETHING TO SAVE US THE EMBARRASSMENT WHEN ARJUNA RETURNS FROM FIGHTING THE SAMSHAPTAKAS.

NONE OF US KNOW HOW TO GET ACROSS THIS CHAKRAVYUHA.

BESIDES KRISHNA, ARJUNA AND PRADYUMNA, ONLY YOU KNOW HOW TO BREAK THROUGH THE CHAKRAVYUHA.

ABHIMANYU, USE YOUR VALOUR AND SKILL AT THIS CRUCIAL HOUR AND DESTROY DRONA'S FORCES!

amar chitra katha

"ABHIMANYU REPLIED —

O GREAT KING! FOR THE GLORY OF MY RACE I SHALL CERTAINLY FORCE MY WAY THROUGH THIS FORMIDABLE FORMATION BUT...

...I KNOW ONLY HOW TO PENETRATE THE CHAKRAVYUHA.

IF I AM TRAPPED INSIDE, I WON'T KNOW HOW TO FIND MY WAY OUT.

O ABHIMANYU! MAKE AN INROAD INTO THIS IMPENETRABLE FORMATION. WE WILL ALL FOLLOW YOU INSIDE AND PROTECT YOU THEREAFTER.

"BHEEMA SAID —

SON, I WILL COME WITH YOU. BESIDES DHRISTRADYUMNA, WITH HIS VALIANT PANCHALAS, WILL FOLLOW YOU.

AT EVERY POINT WHERE YOU BREAK THROUGH THE FORMATION, WE WILL KILL THE MIGHTY WARRIORS OF THE KAURAVAS AND CONTINUE TO SHATTER THE CHAKRA.

"THE VALOROUS ABHIMANYU DECLARED —

SUCH A FEAT WILL I PERFORM TODAY THAT MY PARENTS AND MY UNCLE KRISHNA WILL BE PROUD OF ME.

COME, CHARIOTEER, LEAD ME ON TO DRONA.

"THE CHARIOTEER REPLIED —

THIS IS A TREMENDOUS TASK ASSIGNED TO YOU BY YOUR ELDERS. PAUSE AND PONDER AWHILE BEFORE YOU SET FORTH.

"ABHIMANYU LAUGHED ALOUD.

I CAN VANQUISH DRONA'S FORCES WITH EASE. LET US PROCEED WITHOUT DELAY.

amar chitra katha

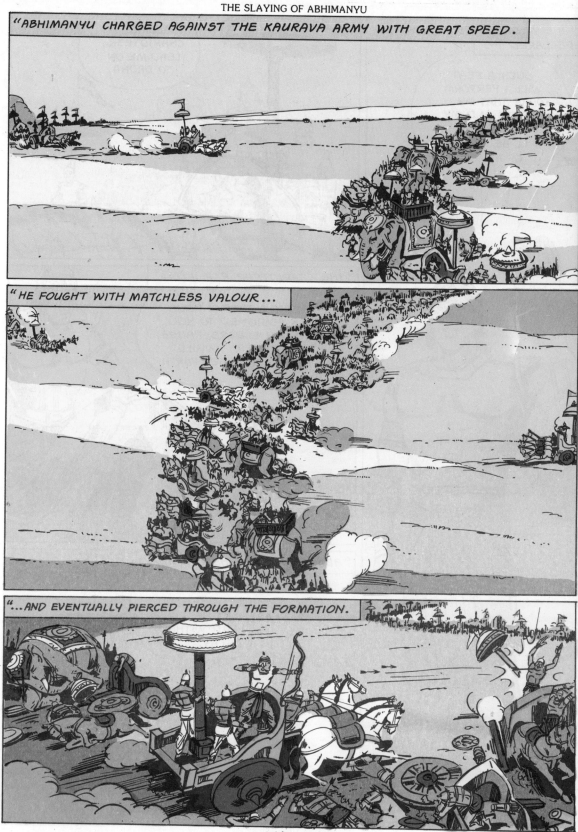

"ABHIMANYU CHARGED AGAINST THE KAURAVA ARMY WITH GREAT SPEED.

"HE FOUGHT WITH MATCHLESS VALOUR...

"...AND EVENTUALLY PIERCED THROUGH THE FORMATION.

"DRONA ENTREATED THE FLEEING KAURAVAS —

HALT, O MIGHTY WARRIORS! PROTECT DURYODHANA FOR HIS VERY LIFE IS IN DANGER.

"EXHORTED BY DRONA, SOME OF THE MIGHTY WARRIORS RETURNED TO THE SCENE AND SURROUNDED DURYODHANA TO PROTECT HIM.

"DURING THE FIERCE BATTLE THAT ENSUED, ABHIMANYU SHATTERED KARNA'S ARMOUR.

AAH!

"ONE OF HIS ARROWS MADE SHALYA UNCONSCIOUS.

amar chitra katha

"EXCEEDINGLY PLEASED WITH ABHIMANYU'S VALOUR, DRONA SAID TO KRIPA —

THERE IS NONE AS VALIANT IN BATTLE AS YOUNG ABHIMANYU AND YET HE APPEARS TO BE FIGHTING WITH RESTRAIN-

"THIS MADE DURYODHANA VERY ANGRY. HE DECLARED —

DRONA IS DELIBERATELY SPARING THE LIFE OF ABHIMANYU, SON OF HIS FAVOURITE PUPIL ARJUNA.

SAFE UNDER DRONA'S PROTECTION, ABHIMANYU IS ACTING BRAVE AND MIGHTY. VANQUISH HIM! KILL HIM!

"DUHSHASANA SAID —

I SWEAR I WILL KILL THIS SON OF ARJUNA!

"AS DUHSHASANA APPROACHED, ABHIMANYU SHATTERED HIS BOW WITH AN ARROW.

"HE THEN SHOT ARROW AFTER DEADLY ARROW WHICH WOUNDED DUHSHASANA AND KNOCKED HIM UNCON-SCIOUS.

amar chitra katha

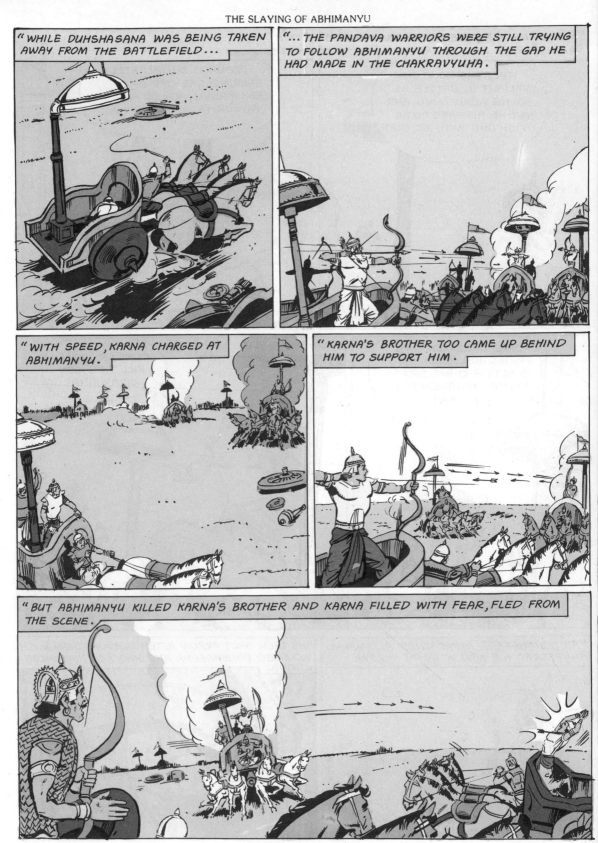

"WHILE DUHSHASANA WAS BEING TAKEN AWAY FROM THE BATTLEFIELD...

"...THE PANDAVA WARRIORS WERE STILL TRYING TO FOLLOW ABHIMANYU THROUGH THE GAP HE HAD MADE IN THE CHAKRAVYUHA.

"WITH SPEED, KARNA CHARGED AT ABHIMANYU.

"KARNA'S BROTHER TOO CAME UP BEHIND HIM TO SUPPORT HIM.

"BUT ABHIMANYU KILLED KARNA'S BROTHER AND KARNA FILLED WITH FEAR, FLED FROM THE SCENE.

"ABHIMANYU GREATLY TORMENTED THE KAURAVA ARMY.

"MEANWHILE, THE OTHER PANDAVAS WERE TRYING TO BREAK INTO THE CHAKRAVYUHA IN A BID TO REACH ABHIMANYU.

"SEEING THIS, JAYADRATHA RUSHED TO THE SPOT...

"...AND RESTRAINED THE PANDAVAS WHILE BRAVELY WITHSTANDING THEIR ONSLAUGHT.

"THE KAURAVAS HAILED JAYADRATHA'S VALOUR AND RUSHED TO HIS SUPPORT.

BRAVO, JAYADRATHA!

WELL DONE, JAYADRATHA!

SANJAYA, I'M SURPRISED AT THE VALOUR AND STRENGTH OF JAYADRATHA. HOW DID HE ACCOMPLISH THIS REMARKABLE FEAT SINGLE-HANDED?

O KING, WHEN THE PANDAVAS WERE LIVING IN THE FOREST, JAYADRATHA HAD ABDUCTED DRAUPADI. HOWEVER, THE PANDAVAS CHASED HIM, FOUGHT WITH HIM AND FREED DRAUPADI.

"A HUMILIATED JAYADRATHA THEN PERFORMED SEVERE AUSTERITES. SHIVA THEN BLESSED HIM —

FOR A BOON, HE ASKED SHIVA THE POWER TO OPPOSE THE PANDAVAS IN WARFARE. HENCE ON THE THIRTEENTH DAY, HE WAS ABLE TO CONTAIN THEIR ADVANCE.

amar chitra katha

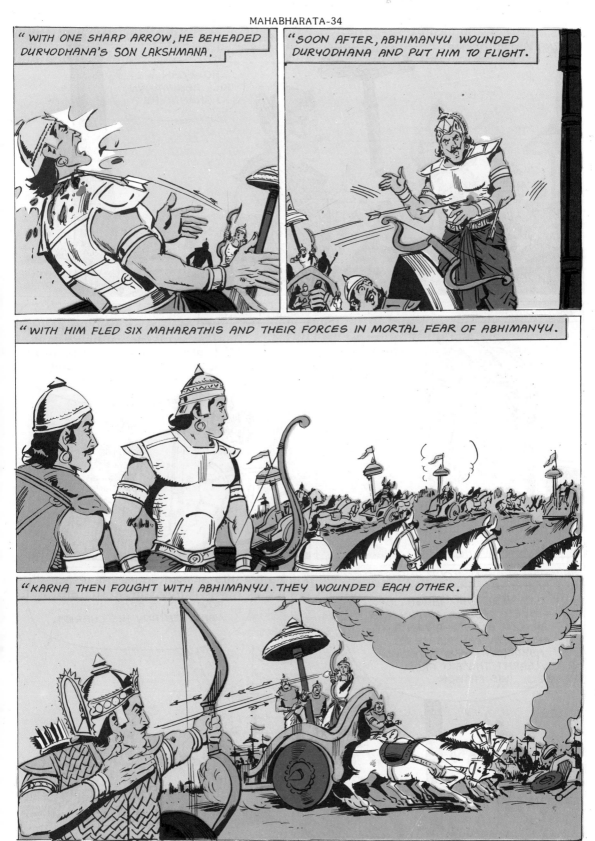

"WITH ONE SHARP ARROW, HE BEHEADED DURYODHANA'S SON LAKSHMANA.

"SOON AFTER, ABHIMANYU WOUNDED DURYODHANA AND PUT HIM TO FLIGHT.

"WITH HIM FLED SIX MAHARATHIS AND THEIR FORCES IN MORTAL FEAR OF ABHIMANYU.

"KARNA THEN FOUGHT WITH ABHIMANYU. THEY WOUNDED EACH OTHER.

"SEEING ALL THE KAURAVAS TORMENTED BY ABHIMANYU, KARNA ASKED DRONA —

HOW CAN WE KILL ABHIMANYU, O GRANDSIRE?

"DRONA ANSWERED —

HURT AS I AM BY HIS ARROWS, I CANNOT HELP BUT ADMIRE HIS SPEED AND SKILL.

"KARNA SAID —

OH! THE PAIN HE IS CAUSING ME WITH HIS ARROWS IS TOO MUCH FOR ME TO BEAR. BUT FOR THE CALL OF DUTY AS A WARRIOR I WOULD HAVE FLED THE FIELD.

"DRONA LAUGHED ALOUD AND SAID TO KARNA—

IT WAS I WHO TAUGHT HIS FATHER, ARJUNA, TO DON THE ARMOUR IN SUCH A WAY THAT NO ARROW CAN PIERCE IT. ABHIMANYU HAS OBVIOUSLY LEARNT THE ART FROM HIS FATHER.

HIS ARMOUR IS IMPENETRABLE. TRY, IF YOU CAN, TO CUT HIS BOW STRING FROM BEHIND, AND DESTROY HIS CHARIOT.

"EAGERLY FOLLOWING DRONA'S ADVICE, KARNA SHOT ABHIMANYU'S BOW TO PIECES.

"KRITAVARMA KILLED ABHIMANYU'S HORSES.

"AND KRIPA SHOT DEAD BOTH THE REAR ATTENDANTS OF ABHIMANYU.

"AND THEN SIX MAHARATHIS SHOWERED ARROWS ON THE YOUNG WARRIOR WHO HAD BEEN DEPRIVED OF HIS CHARIOT.

"UNDAUNTED, ABHIMANYU PICKED UP A SWORD AND SHIELD AND JUMPED INTO THE FRAY.

"DRONA CUT THE SWORD AT THE HILT WITH SHARP ARROWS.

"ABHIMANYU'S SHIELD WAS SHATTERED BY KARNA.

"THE YOUNG WARRIOR THEN PICKED UP A WHEEL OF HIS CART AND RUSHED AT DRONA.

"BUT THE KAURAVA WARRIORS BROKE THE WHEEL INTO PIECES.

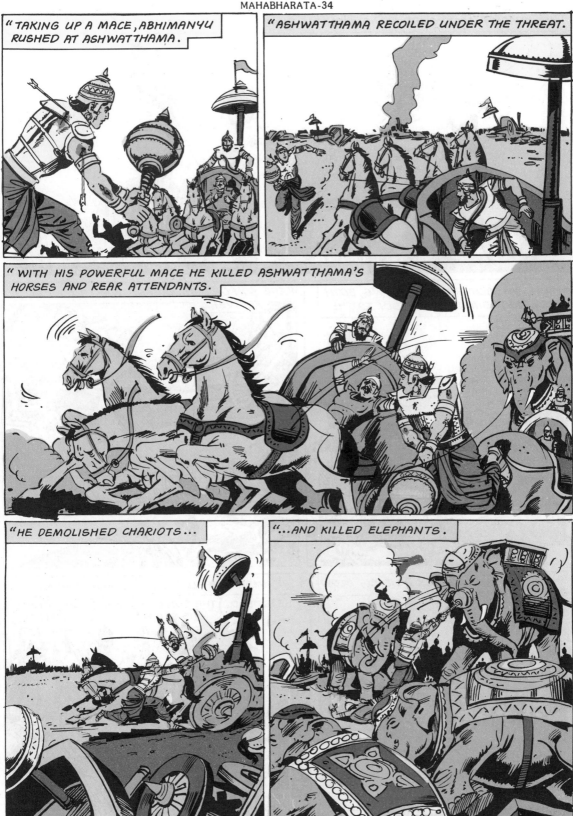

"TAKING UP A MACE, ABHIMANYU RUSHED AT ASHWATTHAMA.

"ASHWATTHAMA RECOILED UNDER THE THREAT.

"WITH HIS POWERFUL MACE HE KILLED ASHWATTHAMA'S HORSES AND REAR ATTENDANTS.

"HE DEMOLISHED CHARIOTS...

"...AND KILLED ELEPHANTS.

"THE SOLDIERS OF THE PANDAVA ARMY WERE TERRIFIED TO HEAR THE NEWS. THEY BEGAN TO FLEE THE BATTLEFIELD.

RUN!

ABHIMANYU IS DEAD!

ABHIMANYU KILLED!

RUN!

"YUDHISHTHIRA TRIED TO STOP HIS MEN FROM RUNNING AWAY.

COME BACK! ABHIMANYU HAS SURELY ATTAINED HEAVEN BY THE VALOUR SHOWN ON THE BATTLEFIELD. HAVE PATIENCE, WE WILL OVERCOME THE ENEMIES.

"BUT THE DEMORALISED PANDAVA ARMY RETURNED TO THE CAMP IN DEEP SORROW.

"INCONSOLABLE, YUDHISHTHIRA LAMENTED.

ALAS! KRISHNA'S BELOVED NEPHEW, THE VALIANT ABHIMANYU, IS DEAD.

HOW WILL I FACE ARJUNA NOW? HOW WILL I FACE THE BEREAVED MOTHER SUBHADRA?

HOW WILL WE RELATE THIS TRAGEDY TO KRISHNA AND ARJUNA?

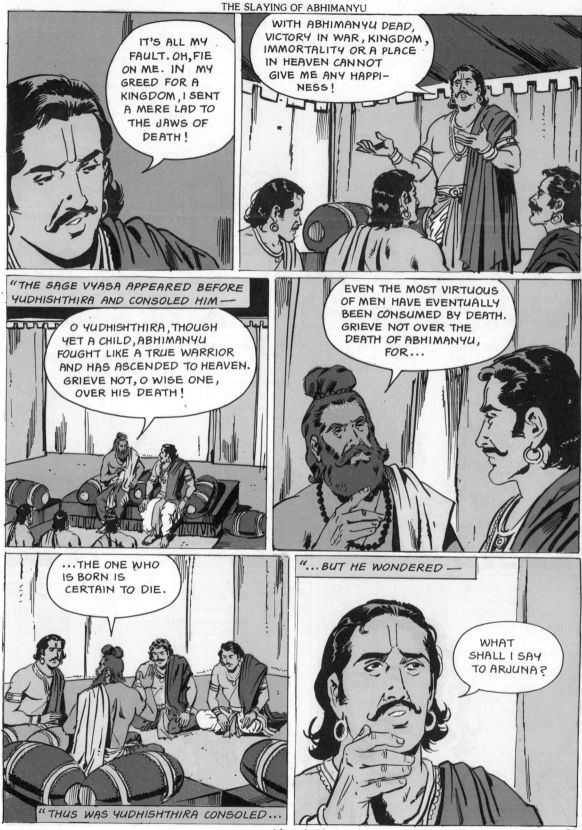

IT'S ALL MY FAULT. OH, FIE ON ME. IN MY GREED FOR A KINGDOM, I SENT A MERE LAD TO THE JAWS OF DEATH!

WITH ABHIMANYU DEAD, VICTORY IN WAR, KINGDOM, IMMORTALITY OR A PLACE IN HEAVEN CANNOT GIVE ME ANY HAPPINESS!

"THE SAGE VYASA APPEARED BEFORE YUDHISHTHIRA AND CONSOLED HIM—

O YUDHISHTHIRA, THOUGH YET A CHILD, ABHIMANYU FOUGHT LIKE A TRUE WARRIOR AND HAS ASCENDED TO HEAVEN. GRIEVE NOT, O WISE ONE, OVER HIS DEATH!

EVEN THE MOST VIRTUOUS OF MEN HAVE EVENTUALLY BEEN CONSUMED BY DEATH. GRIEVE NOT OVER THE DEATH OF ABHIMANYU, FOR...

...THE ONE WHO IS BORN IS CERTAIN TO DIE.

"...BUT HE WONDERED—

WHAT SHALL I SAY TO ARJUNA?

"THUS WAS YUDHISHTHIRA CONSOLED...

"MEANWHILE, ARJUNA ON HIS WAY BACK FROM HIS WAR WITH THE SAMSHAPTAKAS SAID TO KRISHNA ...

O KRISHNA! I SEE ILL OMENS. MY HEART BEATS FASTER, MY VOICE QUAVERS AND MY BODY GOES LIMP, I WONDER ...

A NAMELESS ANXIETY GRIPS ME, O KESHAVA. I HOPE MY BROTHER, KING YUDHISHTHIRA, IS WELL.

"KRISHNA CONSOLED ARJUNA AND STEERED THE CHARIOT TOWARDS THE CAMP.

"AS THEY ENTERED THE CAMP, ARJUNA WAS SHOCKED BY THE SILENCE THAT GREETED HIM. HE ASKED KRISHNA —

WHY ARE THE INSTRUMENTS NOT PLAYING AUSPICIOUS MUSIC TODAY? WHY DO MY SOLDIERS TURN THEIR FACES AWAY?

WHY DOES NOT MY SON ABHIMANYU COME RUNNING TO GREET ME?

"WHEN HE SAW HIS BROTHERS IMMERSED IN A DEEP GLOOM...

"...HE GUESSED THE TRUTH.

ALAS! MY SON IS NO MORE!

I HEARD THAT DRONA HAD ARRAYED HIS FORCES IN CHAKRAVYUHA FORMATION. AMONG YOU ONLY ABHIMANYU KNEW HOW TO PENETRATE THAT.

I HAD NOT YET TAUGHT ABHIMANYU HOW TO COME OUT OF THE CHAKRA FORMATION. COULD IT BE THAT...

...YOU SENT THE CHILD INTO THE DEADLY FORMATION?

"HIS WORDS MET WITH SILENCE ALL AROUND.

TELL ME HOW MY BRAVE SON WAS KILLED IN BATTLE.

FOR WHOSE SAKE WILL I LIVE NOW THAT MY DEAR SON IS NO MORE? WHENCE WILL MY HEART FIND PEACE.

THE BELOVED OF ALL, ABHIMANYU LIES FORLORN AMID BEASTS AND BIRDS OF PREY.

HOW UNFORTUNATE I AM TO BE BEREFT OF YOU, MY SON!

"TURNING TO YUDHISHTHIRA HE SAID—

DID MY SON DIE FIGHTING THE MIGHTY MAHARATHIS?

SURELY THEY MUST HAVE POUNCED ON HIM WHEN HE WAS ISOLATED. AND HE MUST HAVE REMEMBERED ME WHILE DYING.

HOW WILL I FACE DRAUPADI AND SUBHADRA?

"SEEING ARJUNA IN UTTER SORROW, KRISHNA CONSOLED HIM.

DO NOT DESPAIR SO, FRIEND. TAKE COURAGE.

ALL GREAT WARRIORS CRAVE FOR DEATH IN THE BATTLEFIELD AND ABHIMANYU WAS FORTUNATE TO DIE SO BRAVELY.

YOUR SORROW IS CASTING A GLOOM OVER ALL YOUR BROTHERS AND FRIENDS HERE. REASSURE THEM, O HERO!

"ARJUNA LOOKED UP AT HIS BROTHERS AND SAID—

TELL ME HOW EXACTLY ABHIMANYU WAS KILLED. TOMORROW I WILL BE THE DEATH OF ALL THOSE WHO KILLED HIM.

"AND THEN HE ASKED—

HOW COULD ABHIMANYU BE KILLED WHEN ALL OF YOU, FULLY ARMED, WERE PROTECTING HIM? HAD I KNOWN THAT THE PANDAVAS AND PANCHALAS WERE TOGETHER INCAPABLE OF PROTECTING MY SON...

...I WOULD MYSELF HAVE LOOKED AFTER HIM.

I SHOULD BLAME MYSELF FOR LEAVING HIM WITH COWARDS LIKE YOU, WHO COULD NOT DEFEND A MERE LAD AND WHO CAN ONLY TALK BIG.

"NO ONE WAS ABLE TO FACE THE AGONIZED ARJUNA OR TO SPEAK A WORD TO HIM...

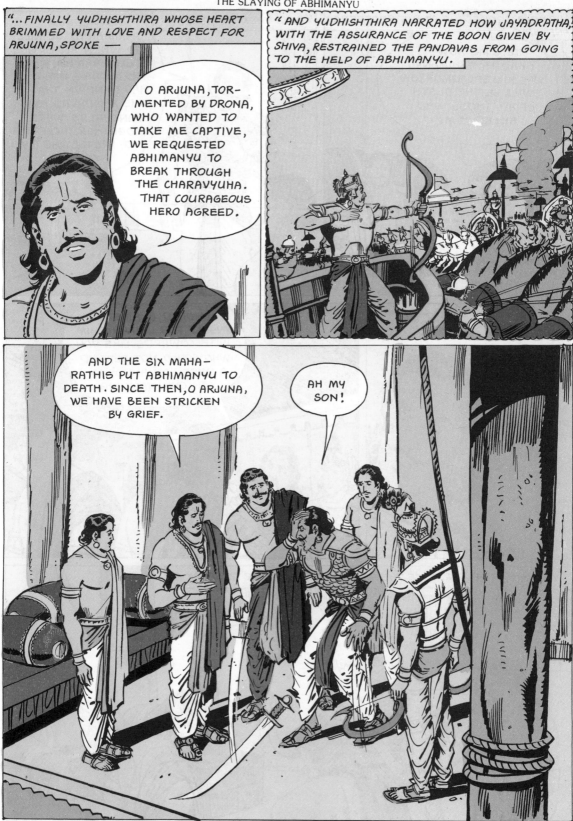

"...FINALLY YUDHISHTHIRA WHOSE HEART BRIMMED WITH LOVE AND RESPECT FOR ARJUNA, SPOKE —

O ARJUNA, TORMENTED BY DRONA, WHO WANTED TO TAKE ME CAPTIVE, WE REQUESTED ABHIMANYU TO BREAK THROUGH THE CHARAVYUHA. THAT COURAGEOUS HERO AGREED.

"AND YUDHISHTHIRA NARRATED HOW JAYADRATHA, WITH THE ASSURANCE OF THE BOON GIVEN BY SHIVA, RESTRAINED THE PANDAVAS FROM GOING TO THE HELP OF ABHIMANYU.

AND THE SIX MAHA-RATHIS PUT ABHIMANYU TO DEATH. SINCE THEN, O ARJUNA, WE HAVE BEEN STRICKEN BY GRIEF.

AH MY SON!

"SOON HE RECOVERED. TREMBLING IN INDIGNATION, HE ANNOUNCED.

I WILL KILL JAYADRATHA TOMORROW.

ANYONE WHO DARES TO PROTECT JAYADRATHA SHALL DIE AT MY HANDS.

"AND THEN—

IF I FAIL TO KILL JAYADRATHA BY SUNDOWN TOMORROW, I WILL CONSIGN MYSELF TO FLAMES.

O KING, ANGERED BY THE DEATH OF HIS SON, ARJUNA THUS TOOK THE VOW TO KILL JAYADRATHA BEFORE SUNDOWN NEXT DAY.

"THUS ENDS THE THIRTY-FOURTH SESSION OF OUR RENDERING OF VYASA'S IMMORTAL ITIHASA MAHABHARATA.

amar chitra katha

YOU, THE BRAVEST OF KSHATRIYAS, CAN MATCH ARJUNA IN WARFARE. DURYODHANA, ONLY YOU CAN PROTECT ME FROM ARJUNA'S VOW.

"IN HIS CONFUSION, JAYADRATHA WAVERED BETWEEN SEEKING HELP AND JUST RUNNING AWAY.

AH! BUT WHO CAN CHANGE ARJUNA'S OATH. I SHALL JUST DISAPPEAR FROM HERE.

FEAR NOT. WHO CAN DARE TO KILL YOU WHILE YOU ARE AMIDST BRAVE KSHATRIYAS?

"RECITING THE NAMES OF KAURAVA WARRIORS, DURYODHANA SAID:

I WILL GUARD YOU. BESIDES, THERE ARE HEROES LIKE KARNA, CHITRASENA, DUHSHASANA, AND SEVERAL OTHERS WHO, ALONG WITH THEIR ARMIES, WILL PROTECT YOU. SO, CASTE OFF THIS FEAR!

YOU ARE YOURSELF A GREAT WARRIOR AND MY ELEVEN AKSHAUHINIS* WILL STRIVE HARD TO PROTECT YOU.

"THEN BOTH OF THEM WENT TO DRONA.

TELL ME, GURUDEV, HOW DO I COMPARE WITH ARJUNA IN MY AIM, RANGE, SPEED AND NIMBLENESS IN SHOOTING AN ARROW?

I HAVE TAUGHT YOU BOTH EQUALLY WELL, BUT THE POSSESSION OF CELESTIAL WEAPONS, CONSTANT PRACTICE AND HIS ENDURANCE GIVES ARJUNA AN EDGE OVER YOU.

YET THERE IS NO CAUSE FOR YOU TO FEAR ARJUNA WHILE I PROTECT YOU. SUCH A FORMIDABLE VYUHA** SHALL I BUILD THAT EVEN ARJUNA WILL NOT BE ABLE TO BREAK THROUGH.

✳ A COMPLETE DIVISION CONSISTING OF 21870 ELEPHANTS, 21870 CHARIOTS, 65610 CAVALRY AND 109350 INFANTRY.   ✳✳ ARMY FORMATION

2

PREPARE TO FIGHT WITH ALL YOUR MIGHT, UNDAUNTED BY THE FEAR OF DEATH, WHICH IS INEVITABLE FOR MORTALS LIKE US.

BECALMED BY DRONA'S WORDS, JAYAD-RATHA RESOLVED TO FIGHT. THE KAURAVA CAMP TOO RESOUNDED WITH REJOICING.

"MEANWHILE KRISHNA TOOK ARJUNA ASIDE.

THIS VOW YOU HAVE TAKEN WITHOUT CONSULTING ANY OF US, IS A LITTLE FOOLHARDY.

YOU'VE TAKEN ON THIS ENORMOUS TASK WITH-OUT MY ADVICE. WE ARE OPEN TO RIDICULE NOW.

"KRISHNA THEN RELATED THE NEWS HE HAD RECEIVED FROM HIS SPIES.

IN TOMORROW'S BATTLE, KARNA, BHOORI-SHRAVA, ASHVATTHAMA, VRISHASENA, KRIPA AND SHALYA WILL BE IN FRONT OF JAYADRATHA.

DURYODHANA HAS DESIGNED A VYUHA THAT WILL RESEMBLE A CART FROM THE FRONT AND WILL BE LOTUS SHAPED BEHIND. IN THE CORE OF THE LOTUS, BEHIND A NEEDLE FORMATION, WILL BE JAYADRATHA, PROTECTED BY MIGHTY WARRIORS.

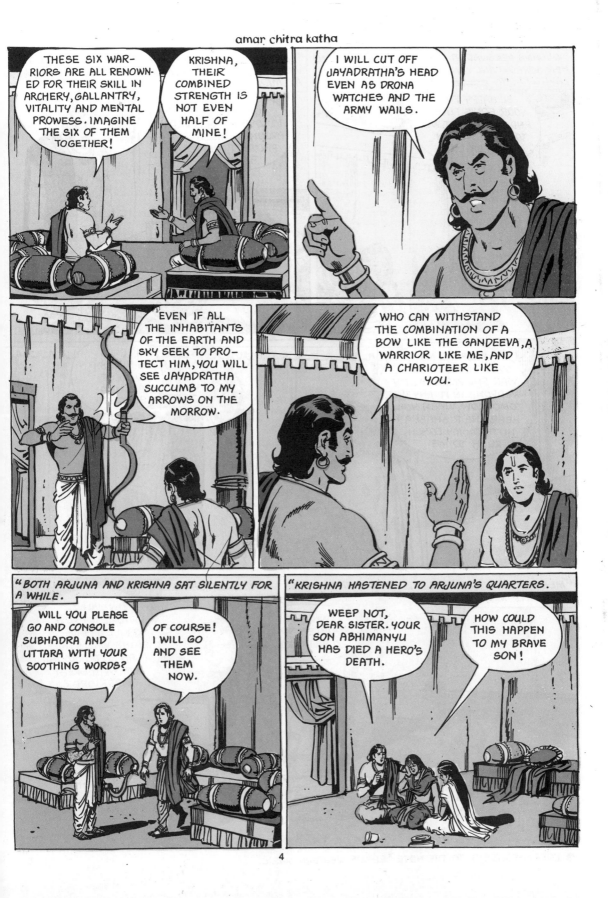

THESE SIX WAR-RIORS ARE ALL RENOWN-ED FOR THEIR SKILL IN ARCHERY, GALLANTRY, VITALITY AND MENTAL PROWESS. IMAGINE THE SIX OF THEM TOGETHER!

KRISHNA, THEIR COMBINED STRENGTH IS NOT EVEN HALF OF MINE!

I WILL CUT OFF JAYADRATHA'S HEAD EVEN AS DRONA WATCHES AND THE ARMY WAILS.

EVEN IF ALL THE INHABITANTS OF THE EARTH AND SKY SEEK TO PRO-TECT HIM, YOU WILL SEE JAYADRATHA SUCCUMB TO MY ARROWS ON THE MORROW.

WHO CAN WITHSTAND THE COMBINATION OF A BOW LIKE THE GANDEEVA, A WARRIOR LIKE ME, AND A CHARIOTEER LIKE YOU.

"BOTH ARJUNA AND KRISHNA SAT SILENTLY FOR A WHILE.

WILL YOU PLEASE GO AND CONSOLE SUBHADRA AND UTTARA WITH YOUR SOOTHING WORDS?

OF COURSE! I WILL GO AND SEE THEM NOW.

"KRISHNA HASTENED TO ARJUNA'S QUARTERS.

WEEP NOT, DEAR SISTER. YOUR SON ABHIMANYU HAS DIED A HERO'S DEATH.

HOW COULD THIS HAPPEN TO MY BRAVE SON!

4

6

"AS THEY SPED PAST LIKE ARROWS RELEASED FROM A BOW, THEY BEHELD A GLOWING MOUNTAIN, RADIANT LIKE THE SUN. ON THE PEAK WAS SEATED LORD SHIVA.

"AFTER BOWING TO THE LORD, ARJUNA AND KRISHNA BEGAN TO PRAY TO HIM.

I WILL GRANT YOUR DESIRE. GO FETCH THE BOW AND ARROW FROM THE CELESTIAL LAKE YONDER.

AS SUGGESTED BY LORD SHIVA, ARJUNA AND KRISHNA RESCUED THE BOW AND ARROW WHICH WERE DISGUISED AS FEROCIOUS SERPENTS. ARJUNA THEN LEARNT THE MANTRA* FOR USING THE PASHUPATA FROM THE LORD HIMSELF.

"THUS ARMED AND WITH GREAT ELATION IN THEIR HEARTS, ARJUNA AND KRISHNA RETURNED TO THEIR CAMP.

"THE DAWN OF THE FOURTEENTH DAY OF THE WAR FOUND THE PANDAVAS IN A HAPPY MOOD. ARJUNA SAID TO SATYAKI:

WHILE I MUST KILL JAYADRATHA TODAY, I AM DUTY BOUND TO PROTECT YUDHISHTHIRA. TODAY, I ENTRUST YOU WITH THIS ONEROUS TASK.

AS YOU WISH, ARJUNA.

* CHANT

7

"MEANWHILE AT DAYBREAK, DRONA ARRAYED HIS TROOPS IN A COMPLEX FORMATION."

ALONG WITH SIX MIGHTY WARRIORS, ONE LAKH CAVALRY, SIXTY THOUSAND CHARIOTS, FOURTEEN THOUSAND ELEPHANTS AND TWENTY-ONE THOUSAND INFANTRY, POSITION YOURSELF AT A DISTANCE OF SIX KOSA** FROM ME, O, JAYADRATHA!

"THE TRIPLE FORMATION WAS QUITE FORMIDABLE WITH DRONA GUARDING THE LOTUS FORMATION AND DURMAR-SHANA STATIONED IN FRONT OF THE SHAKATAVYUHA* JUST THEN ARJUNA ARRIVED ON THE SCENE.

LEAD ME, O KRISHNA TO DURMARSHANA.

"LIKE A STRONG GALE SCATTERING CLOUDS, ARJUNA'S ARROWS DESTROYED DURMARSHANA'S FORCES. AN ENRAGED DUHSHASANA THEN CONFRONTED ARJUNA.

"SUCH WAS ARJUNA'S SPEED THAT NO ONE COULD MAKE OUT WHEN HE PLACED HIS ARROW, WHEN HE PULLED THE BOWSTRING AND WHEN HE RELEASED THE ARROW. THUS TORTURED, DUHSHASANA RAN FOR PROTECTION TO DRONA.

* CART-FORMATION   ** ABOUT 2 MILES (3.2 KM.)

9

ARJUNA HAS MANAGED TO CRUSH OUR FORCES AND PIERCE THROUGH THE COMPLEX FORMATION. WHY! HE EVEN PASSED YOU BY. SURELY THE WARRIORS PROTECTING JAYADRATHA WILL LOSE HEART NOW...

"EXTREME DISTRESS AT THE STATE OF HIS ARMY MADE DURYODHANA RECKLESS IN HIS SPEECH.

...WE DO OUR BEST TO KEEP YOU HAPPY. YET YOU ARE BENT ON PLEASING THE PANDAVAS. HAD I KNOWN THAT YOU ARE LIKE A KNIFE CONCEALED IN A HONEYPOT, I WOULD HAVE LET JAYADRATHA GO HOME. DO SOMETHING NOW TO SAVE HIM.

I FORGIVE YOUR OUTBURST, LIKE A FATHER FORGIVES HIS SON. BUT THE TRUTH IS ARJUNA IS TOO FAST FOR ME NOW THAT I AM GETTING OLD.

BESIDES, THIS IS AN EXCELLENT OPPORTUNITY FOR ME TO FULFIL MY VOW OF KILLING YUDHISHTHIRA, UNPROTECTED AS HE IS WITHOUT ARJUNA. GO FORTH AND CONFRONT ARJUNA.

YOU EXPECT ME TO CONQUER ARJUNA, WHO GOT PAST AN ACE WARRIOR LIKE YOU?

I WILL TIE A GOLDEN ARMOUR ON YOU WHICH WILL BE IMPENETRABLE TO ALL WEAPONS. WITH IT, YOU WILL BE ABLE TO CONFRONT EVEN ARJUNA.

"MEANWHILE THE PANDAVA ARMY LAUNCHED AN ATTACK ON DRONA'S TROOPS. A FEARSOME BATTLE TOOK PLACE BETWEEN DRONA AND DHRISHTADYUMNA, WHO HAD JUMPED FROM HIS CHARIOT ONTO DRONA'S HORSES.

"KRISHNA, WHO WAS SOOTHING THE HORSES AND REMOVING THE ARROWS FROM THEIR BODIES, SAID TO ARJUNA:

ARJUNA! THERE IS NO WATER HERE FOR THE HORSES TO DRINK.

HERE IS THE WATER!

"AS SOON AS HIS ARROW STRUCK THE GROUND, THERE APPEARED A PLACID POOL, WITH BEAUTIFUL LOTUSES AND WATERBIRDS ENHANCING THE VIEW. BESIDES IT, WAS A COTTAGE MADE ENTIRELY OF ARROWS TO WHICH KRISHNA LED THE HORSES. SAFE IN ITS CONFINES, HE REMOVED THEIR ARROWS, MASSAGED THEM AND QUENCHED THEIR THIRST.

"KRISHNA THEN YOKED THE HORSES BACK TO THE CHARIOT AND RUSHED TO FULFIL THEIR MISSION.

"DURYODHANA CHASED THEM, IN THE HOPE OF SAVING JAYAD-RATHA, AND SOON OVERTOOK THEM.

LEAD ME TO HIM!

IT IS SHEER GOOD LUCK THAT DURYODHANA IS HERE, FACING YOU. KILL HIM! REMEMBER HOW HE CHEATED YOU OUT OF YOUR KINGDOM!

"HEARING KRISHNA AND ARJUNA ROAR WITH JOY, THE HEARTS OF KAURAVA SOLDIERS WERE FILLED WITH FOREBODING.

OUR KING IS DEAD.

DURYODHANA IS KILLED!

"DURYODHANA QUICKLY REASSURED HIS MEN AND CLAIMED THAT HE WOULD IN FACT KILL HIS ADVERSARIES.

COME, PARTHA!* TRY ALL YOUR CELESTIAL AND EARTHLY WEAPONS ON ME.

"EVEN AS HE CHALLENGED ARJUNA, DURYODHANA HURLED TEN ARROWS AT KRISHNA'S CHEST AND SEVERAL OTHERS AT ARJUNA. ARJUNA THEN AIMED HIS POWERFUL ARROWS AT DURYODHANA, BUT...

THIS IS STRANGE INDEED, ARJUNA, YOUR ARROWS ARE JUST SLIDING OFF FROM HIS BODY INSTEAD OF PIERCING IT.

I BELIEVE DRONA HAS TIED ON AN IMPENETRABLE ARMOUR ON DURYODHANA. IT WILL RESIST ALL WEAPONS. NEVERTHELESS, TODAY YOU SHALL SEE ME DEFEAT DURYODHANA.

"...WITH HIS WELL-AIMED ARROWS, ARJUNA SYSTEMATICALLY DESTROYED DURYODHANA'S HORSES, THEN HIS CHARIOTEER AND FINALLY THE CHARIOT ITSELF.

"CLEVERLY, HE AIMED HIS ARROWS UNDER DURYODHANA'S NAILS. UNABLE TO BEAR THE PAIN, DURYODHANA TOOK TO HIS HEELS.

"BUT SOON HE RETURNED, ACCOMPANIED BY EIGHT MIGHTY WARRIORS, AND SURROUNDED ARJUNA IN ORDER TO PROTECT JAYADRATHA.

"BUT ARJUNA PROVED MORE THAN A MATCH FOR THEM, AND DISPELLED THEIR FORCES.

"MEANWHILE, YUDHISHTHIRA BECAME APPREHENSIVE AT HEARING THE SOUND FROM THE KAURAVA ARMY. HE SAID TO SATYAKI —

ARJUNA, YOUR GURU AND TEACHER APPEARS TO BE IN TROUBLE. YOU MUST GO TO HIS AID.

BUT I CANNOT! ARJUNA HAS ENTRUSTED ME TO GUARD OVER YOU TODAY.

HE HAS LEFT YOU IN MY CARE. I CANNOT LEAVE YOU UNLESS I AM ASSURED OF YOUR PROTECTION.

GO TO ARJUNA. BHEEMA AND THE OTHER BROTHERS WILL UNDOUBTEDLY PROTECT ME.

"YUDHISHTHIRA ARRANGED FOR SATYAKI'S CHARIOT TO BE LOADED WITH WEAPONS AND IMPLEMENTS, AND SENT HIM AWAY.

"SATYAKI THEN FORCED HIS WAY THROUGH THE KAURAVA FORMATION, TRYING TO FOLLOW ARJUNA. BUT DRONA STOPPED HIM...

YOUR MENTOR RAN AWAY LIKE A COWARD. UNLESS YOU TOO DECIDE TO FOLLOW HIS EXAMPLE, YOU WILL NOT ESCAPE ALIVE TODAY.

BUT A DISCIPLE MUST ALWAYS FOLLOW HIS GURU!

"REALISING THAT DRONA WOULD FOLLOW HIM, SATYAKI DEFTLY GUIDED HIS CHARIOTEER TO MAKE A WAY THROUGH THE VARIOUS ARMIES, CONSTITUTING THE KAURAVA FORCE.

"WHOEVER CAME IN HIS PATH, WAS RUTHLESSLY ATTACKED.

"MEANWHILE, YUDHISHTHIRA'S ANXIETY GREW.

I SENT SATYAKI TO LOOK FOR ARJUNA. NOW I'M WORRIED ABOUT BOTH OF THEM.

"NEARLY FAINT WITH WORRY, HE APPROACHED BHEEMA.

WHAT IS WRONG? NEVER BEFORE HAVE I SEEN YOU SO ANXIOUS. I'LL DO ANYTHING TO REMOVE YOUR ANXIETY.

I HEAR KRISHNA BLOWING HIS CONCH IN ANGER. SURELY ARJUNA HAS BEEN KILLED IN BATTLE.

GO AND SEEK OUT ARJUNA AND SATYAKI. I COMMAND YOU TO DO SO. SIGNAL ME, WHEN YOU DO FIND THEM SAFE, WITH YOUR LION ROAR.

DISCARD YOUR WORRY AND SORROW. I WILL DO AS YOU BID.

"BHEEMA TOO LEFT, LEAVING YUDHISHTHIRA IN DHRISHTADYUMNA'S CARE —

YOU KNOW THAT DRONA WILL TRY ANYTHING TO CAPTURE YUDHISHTHIRA. PROTECTING HIM IS NOW YOUR TASK FOR THE DAY.

I WILL DO AS YOU WISH.

O KING! ON HIS WAY, BHEEMA WAS ACCOSTED BY YOUR SONS, BUT HE CROSSED THEIR PATH AND FELL UPON DRONA'S ARMY.

"EXPECTING BHEEMA TO PAY HIS RESPECTS BEFORE PROCEEDING, DRONA SAID —

WITH MY CONSENT, YOUR BROTHER, ARJUNA PENETRATED THE FORMATION. YOU MAY ALSO DO SO.

ARJUNA DOESN'T NEED YOUR CONSENT THOUGH HE MAY HAVE INDEED SHOWN DUE RESPECT TO YOU.

BUT I AM NOT LIKE THE KIND-HEARTED ARJUNA. I AM BHEEMASENA —YOUR ENEMY!

"BHEEMA LIFTED HIS MACE AND TWIRLED IT AT DRONA, WHO DEFTLY JUMPED OUT OF HIS CHARIOT.

"SEVERAL WARRIOR KINGS THEN RUSHED TO SURROUND BHEEMA, BUT HE BORE THEIR ATTACK LIKE A MIGHTY MOUNTAIN.

"MEANWHILE, CLIMBING ONTO ANOTHER CHARIOT, DRONA AGAIN JOINED THE FRAY. BUT BHEEMA WAS READY.

"JUST AS A MIGHTY GALE TEARS TREES ASUNDER, BHEEMA CRUSHED THE KAURAVAS AND FORGED HIS WAY AHEAD.

"AS SOON AS HE SIGHTED ARJUNA, BHEEMA ROARED LIKE A THUNDERCLOUD...

"...WHICH WAS ECHOED BY ARJUNA AND KRISHNA. THESE FEROCIOUS SOUNDS REACHED YUDHISHTHIRA AND GLADDENED HIS HEART.

"KARNA ATTACKED BHEEMA AND THE BATTLE THAT ENSUED MADE MIGHTY WARRIORS TREMBLE WITH FEAR.

"ALTHOUGH HE EASILY DESTROYED ALL THOSE WHO CAME TO KARNA'S AID, BHEEMA REFRAINED FROM KILLING KARNA AS HE RECALLED THAT ARJUNA HAD VOWED TO DO SO.

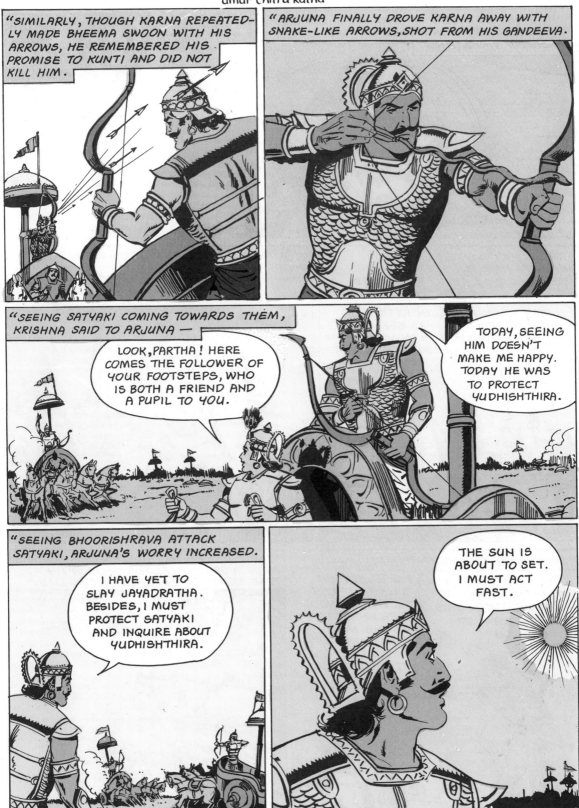

"SIMILARLY, THOUGH KARNA REPEATEDLY MADE BHEEMA SWOON WITH HIS ARROWS, HE REMEMBERED HIS PROMISE TO KUNTI AND DID NOT KILL HIM.

"ARJUNA FINALLY DROVE KARNA AWAY WITH SNAKE-LIKE ARROWS, SHOT FROM HIS GANDEEVA."

"SEEING SATYAKI COMING TOWARDS THEM, KRISHNA SAID TO ARJUNA —

LOOK, PARTHA! HERE COMES THE FOLLOWER OF YOUR FOOTSTEPS, WHO IS BOTH A FRIEND AND A PUPIL TO YOU.

TODAY, SEEING HIM DOESN'T MAKE ME HAPPY. TODAY HE WAS TO PROTECT YUDHISHTHIRA.

"SEEING BHOORISHRAVA ATTACK SATYAKI, ARJUNA'S WORRY INCREASED.

I HAVE YET TO SLAY JAYADRATHA. BESIDES, I MUST PROTECT SATYAKI AND INQUIRE ABOUT YUDHISHTHIRA.

THE SUN IS ABOUT TO SET. I MUST ACT FAST.

"THE FIGHT BETWEEN SATYAKI AND BHOORISHRAVA PROGRESSED FROM AN ARMED COMBAT TO BAREHAND WRESTLING.

"WHEN BHOORISHRAVA YANKED SATYAKI'S HAIR, PUT HIS FOOT ON HIS CHEST AND WAS ABOUT TO CUT HIS HEAD OFF, KRISHNA BESEECHED ARJUNA—

SURELY YOU MUST SAVE HIM NOW. HE IS HERE FOR YOUR SAKE.

MY ATTENTION HAS BEEN ENTIRELY ON JAYADRATHA. BUT NOW I MUST HELP SATYAKI.

"WITH A SHARP ARROW ARJUNA AIMED AT BHOORISHRAVA'S RIGHT ARM.

"BHOORISHRAVA WAS ENRAGED.

HOW COULD YOU ATTACK ME WHILE I WAS NOT LOOKING? DOES THIS BEFIT A WARRIOR LIKE YOU?

DID YOU FOLLOW THE CODE OF CONDUCT WHEN YOU WERE ABOUT TO STAB THE WEARY, HELPLESS SATYAKI? IT WAS MY DUTY TO INTERFERE THEN.

"REALISING HIS MISTAKE, BHOORISHRAVA MADE A SEAT OF ARROWS, TOOK UP A YOGIC POSE, AND PLANNED TO GIVE UP HIS LIFE.

"MEANWHILE SATYAKI GAINED CONSCIOUSNESS AND ATTACKED BHOORISHRAVA.

"HIS ACTION MET WITH A SALVO OF CRITICISM FROM ALL SIDES.

THOSE OF YOU WHO FEEL I HAVE ACTED WRONGLY, HOW DO YOU JUDGE THE KILLING OF ABHIMANYU? I FEEL I DID RIGHT.

"AFTER BHOORISHRAVA WAS KILLED, ARJUNA SAID TO KRISHNA —

LEAD THE CHARIOT ONTO JAYADRATHA. BEHOLD HOW FAST THE SUN IS SETTING!

"SEEING THE PACE AT WHICH ARJUNA WAS APPROACHING JAYADRATHA, SEVERAL KAURAVA WARRIORS GOT READY TO REPEL HIM.

"DURYODHANA SAID TO KARNA —

THE DECISIVE HOUR IS NEAR, KARNA! IF HE CANNOT KILL JAYADRATHA BY SUN-DOWN, ARJUNA MUST HIMSELF DIE.

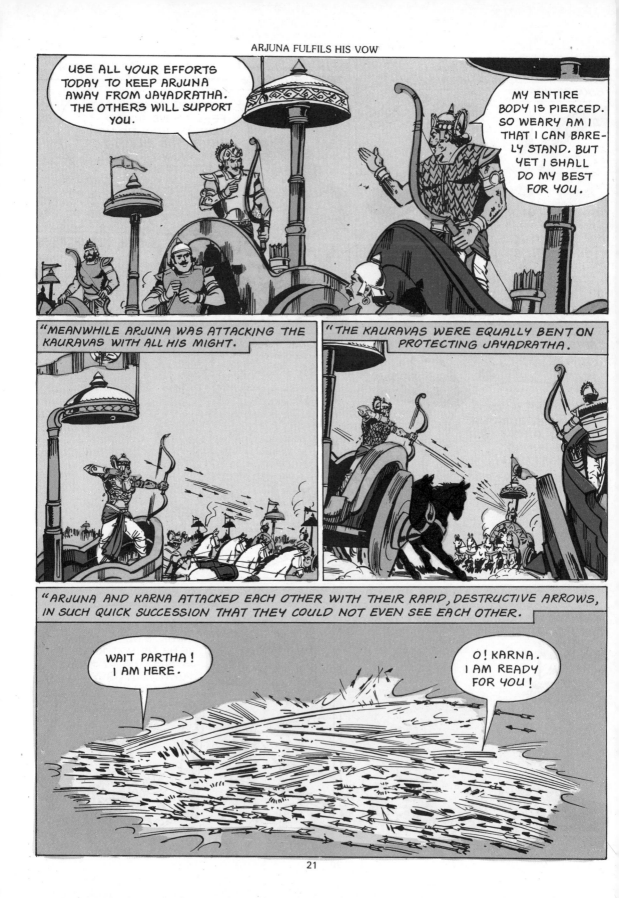

"THE BATTLEFIELD LAY STREWN WITH DEAD, HEADLESS, FALLEN ELEPHANTS, WRECKED CHARIOTS AND THOUSANDS OF WOUNDED SOLDIERS TREMBLING WITH PAIN. MAKING HIS WAY THROUGH ALL THIS, ARJUNA SPED TOWARDS JAYADRATHA. HIS ARROWS CAME IN SUCH QUICK SUCCESSION THAT THEY LOOKED LIKE A HUGE FLOCK OF SWANS FLYING THROUGH THE AIR.

"AS SOON AS HE REACHED WHERE JAYADRATHA WAS, HE SHOT 64 ARROWS AT HIM AND WOUNDED HIM.

"INFURIATED, JAYADRATHA WOUNDED BOTH KRISHNA AND ARJUNA WITH HIS ARROWS AND ONE OF HIS ARROWS PIERCED THROUGH ARJUNA'S BANNER.

"ARJUNA BEHEADED JAYADRATHA'S CHARIOTEER AND WITH ANOTHER ARROW BROUGHT DOWN JAYADRATHA'S BANNER AS WELL AS THE POST.

"SEEING THE COURSE OF THE SUN IN THE WEST, KRISHNA TOLD ARJUNA —

JAYADRATHA IS PROTECTED BY SIX WARRIORS YOU MUST KILL THEM FIRST.

USING MY YOGIC POWERS, I WILL CREATE AN ILLUSION SO THAT JAYADRATHA ALONE WILL SEE THE SUN SETTING.

CONSIDERING HIMSELF SAFE AFTER SUNSET, HE WILL EXPOSE HIMSELF.

AT THAT OPPORTUNE MOMENT, ATTACK AND KILL HIM. DON'T BE DISMAYED IF THE SUN APPEARS TO HAVE SET.

AS YOU WISH, OH LORD!

WITH HIS IMMENSE YOGIC POWERS, THE GREAT KRISHNA CREATED AN ILLUSION OF DARKNESS AND MADE THE SUN DISAPPEAR.

THE KAURAVA ARMY REJOICED AT THE APPARENT SUNSET.

OH KING. SO ENGROSSED WERE THEY IN CELEBRATING THE END OF THE DAY, NONE OF YOUR SOLDIERS CARED TO LOOK AT THE SUN. BUT JAYADRATHA DID SO.

KRISHNA SAID TO ARJUNA.

LOOK ARJUNA! HOW THE RELIEVED JAYADRATHA RAISES HIS HEAD TOWARDS THE SUN!...

24

DON'T MISS THIS MOMENT! CUT HIS HEAD OFF AND FULFIL YOUR PLEDGE.

"WISHING TO OVERCOME THE RESISTANCE OF THE GREAT WARRIORS PROTECTING JAYADRATHA, IN QUICK SUCCESSION, ARJUNA SHOT IN ALL 90 ARROWS AT KRIPACHARYA, KARNA, SHALYA, DURYODHANA AND VRISHASENA ...

...THE MIGHTY WARRIORS FLED FROM THERE.

"ARJUNA SHOT 60 ARROWS AT JAYADRATHA.

"THEN AS ARJUNA SET A FIERY ARROW ON HIS GANDEEVA, KRISHNA CAUTIONED HIM.

HEAR ME WELL, OH ARJUNA! JAYADRATHA'S FATHER HAS BLESSED HIS SON THUS.

IN BATTLE, WHO-EVER CAUSES THE HEAD OF MY ONLY SON TO FALL ON EARTH, HIS HEAD WILL IMMEDIATELY SHATTER INTO HUNDREDS OF FRAGMENTS.

"WITH A NUMBER OF SUCCESSIVE ARROWS, ARJUNA SENT THE HEAD HIGHER AND HIGHER...

"...WHILE SIMULTANEOUSLY FIGHTING SIX MIGHTY WARRIORS.

"THE ARROWS CARRIED THE HEAD TO THE OUTSKIRTS OF THE BATTLEFIELD...

"...WHERE JAYADRATHA'S FATHER SAT. IN PENANCE.

"HE WAS OFFERING HIS EVENING PRAYERS TO THE SUN, WHEN THE HEAD OF HIS SON FELL ON HIS LAP.

"UNAWARE OF ITS PRESENCE, WHEN HE GOT UP AFTER COMPLETING HIS PRAYER, THE HEAD FELL FROM HIS LAP ONTO THE GROUND...

...AND THAT VERY MOMENT HIS OWN HEAD SPLIT INTO A HUNDRED PIECES.

"SURPRISED AT THIS TURN OF EVENTS, THE SOLDIERS BEGAN TO PRAISE ARJUNA AND KRISHNA.

THEREUPON, O KING, AFTER JAYAD-RATHA WAS THUS SLAIN, KRISHNA DISPELLED THE ILLUSION OF DARKNESS.

"IT WAS THEN THAT THE KAURAVAS REALISED THAT THEY HAD BEEN TAKEN IN BY THE ILLUSION OF DARKNESS CREATED BY KRISHNA.

IT WAS THUS THAT THE MIGHTY ARJUNA, DECIMATED EIGHT AKSHAUHINIS OF THE KAURAVA ARMY, KILLED JAYADRATHA AND FULFILLED HIS VOW.

"THUS ENDS THE 35TH SESSION OF OUR RENDERING OF VAISHAMPAYANA'S RECITAL OF VYASA'S IMMORTAL ITIHASA, THE MAHABHARATA.

Mahabharata – 36
THE BATTLE AT MIDNIGHT

AFTER FULFILLING HIS VOW TO KILL JAYADRATHA BEFORE SUNDOWN, ARJUNA BEGAN TO ATTACK THE KAURAVA FORCES WITH RENEWED VIGOUR.

"ANXIOUS TO LEARN THE DETAILS OF THE BATTLE, THE BLIND PATRIARCH DHRITARASHTRA ASKED SANJAYA –

HOW DID MY SONS REACT TO THE SLAYING OF JAYADRATHA?

THEY COULD NOT CONTAIN THEIR ANGER...

"...INFURIATED BY THE KILLING OF JAYADRATHA, KRIPACHARYA AND ASHWATTHAMA ATTACKED ARJUNA...

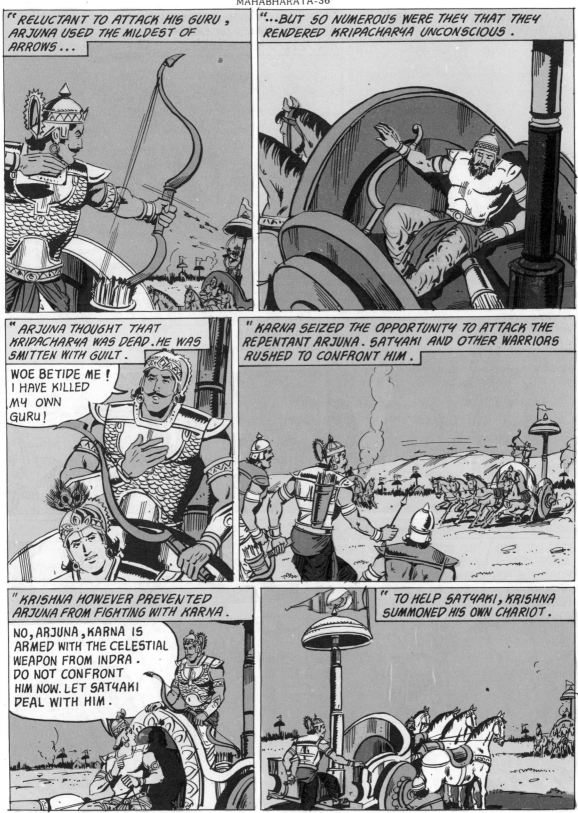

"RELUCTANT TO ATTACK HIS GURU, ARJUNA USED THE MILDEST OF ARROWS...

"...BUT SO NUMEROUS WERE THEY THAT THEY RENDERED KRIPACHARYA UNCONSCIOUS.

"ARJUNA THOUGHT THAT KRIPACHARYA WAS DEAD. HE WAS SMITTEN WITH GUILT.

WOE BETIDE ME! I HAVE KILLED MY OWN GURU!

"KARNA SEIZED THE OPPORTUNITY TO ATTACK THE REPENTANT ARJUNA. SATYAKI AND OTHER WARRIORS RUSHED TO CONFRONT HIM.

"KRISHNA HOWEVER PREVENTED ARJUNA FROM FIGHTING WITH KARNA.

NO, ARJUNA, KARNA IS ARMED WITH THE CELESTIAL WEAPON FROM INDRA. DO NOT CONFRONT HIM NOW. LET SATYAKI DEAL WITH HIM.

"TO HELP SATYAKI, KRISHNA SUMMONED HIS OWN CHARIOT.

"A FEARFUL BATTLE ENSUED BETWEEN SATYAKI AND KARNA.

"WITH SHARP IRON ARROWS SATYAKI INFLICTED SEVERE INJURIES ON KARNA AND FELLED HIS CHARIOT.

THEN HE REMEMBERED ARJUNA'S VOW TO KILL KARNA. HE THEREFORE SPARED KARNA'S LIFE.

"AS THE SUN BEGAN TO SET, KRISHNA AND ARJUNA PROCEEDED TO MEET YUDHISHTHIRA.

ARJUNA HAS FULFILLED HIS VOW. JAYADRATHA IS DEAD!

YOUR WORDS FILL MY HEART WITH JOY.

YUDHISHTHIRA SAID TO KRISHNA —

IT IS YOU WHO MADE IT POSSIBLE FOR ARJUNA TO FULFIL HIS VOW, O LORD OF THE UNIVERSE!

NO YUDHISHTHIRA, YOUR AUSTERITIES AND RIGHTEOUS CONDUCT AND ARJUNA'S SKILL AS A MATCHLESS WARRIOR ARE RESPONSIBLE FOR THIS VICTORY.

"JAYADRATHA'S DEATH HAD BROKEN DURYODHANA'S SPIRIT.

I AM NOW CONVINCED THAT NONE CAN EQUAL ARJUNA'S PROWESS.

"HE THEN WENT TO DRONA —

HOW MANY KINGS HAVE GIVEN UP THEIR LIVES FOR ME ! EVEN THE INVINCIBLE BHEESHMA IS LYING SUPINE IN THE BATTLE-FIELD. SEVEN DIVISIONS OF OUR ARMY ARE DESTROYED.

I HAVE ALWAYS TOLD YOU THAT ARJUNA IS INVINCIBLE. HE COULD KILL JAYADRATHA IN SPITE OF SO MANY OF YOU STRIVING HARD TO PROTECT HIM. YET, I ASSURE YOU, YOU WILL NOT FIND ME WANTING IN MY EFFORTS. TILL I KILL ALL THE PANDAVAS, I WILL NOT TAKE OFF MY ARMOUR.

I WILL PENETRATE THE ENEMY FORCES. MEANWHILE PROTECT YOUR MEN, FOR TODAY THE BATTLE MAY CONTINUE INTO THE NIGHT.

" AS THEY WALKED TOWARDS THE BATTLEFIELD, DURYODHANA CONFIDED IN KARNA —

DRONA HAD PROMISED TO PROTECT JAYADRATHA, BUT HE ALLOWED ARJUNA TO GO PAST HIM. AFTER ALL, ARJUNA HAS ALWAYS BEEN HIS FAVOURITE PUPIL.

amar chitra katha

THAT IS NOT FAIR! THE ACHARYA DID TRY HIS BEST. BUT ARJUNA MANAGED TO GET PAST HIM. I FEEL DRONACHARYA IS NOT TO BE BLAMED.

COME, LET US NOT TRY TO OPPOSE DESTINY, BUT LET US DO OUR BEST IN BATTLE.

"WHILE TALKING, THEY SAW THE ARMIES ON THE BATTLEFIELD.

"BECAUSE OF THE FADING LIGHT, THEY COULD NOT SEE CLEARLY THE THOUSANDS OF ARROWS DISCHARGED BY THE WARRIORS.

"IGNORING THE PROTESTS OF KARNA, KRIPA AND DRONA, DURYODHANA MADE HIS WAY THROUGH THE PANDAVA FORCES.

" AS THE MORNING SUN DISPELS THE DARKNESS , DURYODHANA DESTROYED MANY PANDAVA SOLDIERS .

" JUST THEN YUDHISHTHIRA CHARGED TOWARDS HIM.

" AND THE TWO WERE LOCKED IN COMBAT .

" WITH HIS POWERFUL ARROWS , DURYODHANA INFLICTED INJURIES ON YUDHISHTHIRA , HIS CHARIOTEER AND ALL THE FOUR HORSES .

" DURYODHANA WAS ALSO SERIOUSLY INJURED BY YUDHISHTHIRA'S BARRAGE OF ARROWS AND HE SAT DOWN IN THE CHARIOT.

SOON THE DUEL TURNED INTO A GENERAL FIGHT.

amar chitra katha

"AS THE MIGHTY WARRIORS LIKE NAKULA, SAHADEVA AND VIRATA ATTACKED DRONA WITH THEIR ARMIES...

"THE NIGHT TURNED DARK AND OMINOUS ENOUGH TO PUT FEAR IN THE HEARTS OF THE BRAVEST OF WARRIORS.

THE SILENCE OF THE NIGHT WAS BROKEN BY THE PIERCING SOUND FROM BUGLES, THE TRUMPETING OF ELEPHANTS, THE NEIGHING OF HORSES AND THE HOWLING OF JACKALS.

"BHEEMA WENT ABOUT ATTACKING DHRITARASHTRA'S SONS WITH SLAPS AND BLOWS USING HIS BARE HANDS.

MEANWHILE SOMADATTA ATTACKED SATYAKI TO AVENGE THE DEATH OF HIS SON, BHOORISHRAVA.

"HE SAID TO SATYAKI—
HOW COULD YOU ATTACK MY SON WHEN HE WAS UNARMED?

SO WHAT! AND NOW I WILL KILL YOU TOO.

" SOMADATTA FAINTED AS A RESULT OF SATYAKI'S ATTACK AND HAD TO BE CARRIED AWAY .

" SEEING THIS , AN ENRAGED DRONA RUSHED TOWARDS SATYAKI .

" SO FURIOUS WAS HE THAT ANYONE WHO COME IN HIS WAY WAS INSTANTLY KILLED .

"ARJUNA THEN SAID TO KRISHNA —

PLEASE DRIVE ME TOWARDS DRONA .

" BHEEMA TOO FOLLOWED .

" JUST THEN GHATOTKACHA , BHEEMA'S SON , APPEARED ON THE SCENE .

"HE WAS ACCOMPANIED BY HIS ARMY OF RAKSHASAS.* HIS ROAR MADE EVEN THE ELEPHANTS TREMBLE WITH FEAR.

"HIS VERY SIGHT FRIGHTENED THE ENEMY FORCES. HIS ARMY STARTED RAINING BOULDERS ON THE KAURAVAS.

FLEE! THE RAKSHASAS BECOME MORE POWERFUL AT NIGHT!

"GHATOTKACHA WITH HIS MAGICAL POWERS CREATED AN AWESOME ILLUSION. WHILE OTHERS FLED IN FEAR, ASHWATTHAMA ALONE WAS UNDAUNTED...

...AND HE DESTROYED THE ILLUSION. THE ENRAGED GHATOTKACHA, SMITTEN BY THE THE ARROWS OF ASHWATTHAMA...

...TOOK UP A CHAKRA** AND HURLED IT AT ASHWATTHAMA.

* DEMONS.

** DISC.

9

"WITH HIS WELL-AIMED ARROWS, ASHWATTHAMA NIMBLY CAST IT ASUNDER.

"GHATOTKACHA'S SON NOW JOINED THE FIGHT, ALSO USING MAGIC.

"BUT HE SOON SUCCUMBED TO ASHWATTHAMA'S ARROWS. GHATOTKACHA WAS FURIOUS.

ASHWATTHAMA, JUST WAIT! YOU CANNOT ESCAPE ALIVE TODAY!

OH! GO AND FIGHT WITH SOMEONE ELSE. DO NOT IRRITATE ME OR ELSE ...

"GHATOTKACHA TRIED VARIOUS TRICKS AND CREATED ILLUSION AFTER ILLUSION TO SCARE ASHWATTHAMA.

"A CALM AND COLLECTED ASHWATTHAMA ASSURED THE WORRIED DURYODHANA.

LEAVE THIS TO ME, O KING! GO AND REASSURE YOUR SOLDIERS.

WITH AN ARROW THAT RESEMBLED THE MACE OF YAMA* ASHWATTHAMA WOUNDED GHATOTKACHA, WHO FELL TO THE GROUND.

* GOD OF DEATH

"MANY KINGS IN THE PANDAVA ARMY FELT THAT GHATOTKACHA HAD BEEN KILLED, AND LOST THE WILL TO FIGHT. BHEEMA THEN ATTACKED THE KAURAVA ARMY WITH RENEWED VIGOUR.

"SANJAYA NARRATED THE GRUESOME DETAILS.

TEN OF YOUR BRAVE SONS ATTACKED BHEEMA BUT HE KILLED ALL OF THEM.

"MEANWHILE DRONA RAINED VARIOUS CELESTIAL WEAPONS ON YUDHISHTHIRA, INCLUDING TH BRAHMASTRA*.

"BUT HIS EFFORTS WERE FUTILE SINCE YUDHISHTHIRA MATCHED HIM WEAPON FOR WEAPON, AND FENDED OFF HIS ATTACK.

"DRONA NOW TURNED AWAY AND ATTACKED DRUPADA'S ARMY ONLY TO FIND ARJUNA AND BHEEMA CONFRONTING HIM.

"KAURAVA SOLDIERS ENFEEBLED BY LACK OF SLEEP AND TERRIFIED BY THE DARK NIGHT, RAN AMOK UNDER ARJUNA'S ONSLAUGHT.

* A WEAPON INVOKING THE POWER OF BRAHMA.

"ADDRESSING KARNA, DURYODHANA SAID—

KARNA, MY FRIEND, THE TIME HAS COME FOR YOU TO PROVE YOUR FRIENDSHIP. COME TO THE RESCUE OF MY MEN.

REST ASSURED, I SWEAR I WILL KILL THE PANDAVAS AND PANCHALAS AND LAY THE EARTH AT YOUR FEET TO RULE OVER.

"KRIPACHARYA INTERVENED WITH A MOCKING SMILE—

IF WORDS WERE ENOUGH, THEN INDEED YOU ARE THE MAN DURYODHANA NEEDS NOW.

YOU MAY BRAG ABOUT YOUR PROWESS TILL YOU FACE ARJUNA'S ARROWS.

JUST AS BRAHMANAS ARE RENOWNED FOR THEIR SERMONS, KSHATRIYAS FOR THEIR VALOUR, YOUR PROWESS IS IN BUILDING CASTLES IN THE AIR.

YOU WILL SEE ME KILL ARJUNA WITH THE HELP OF THE SHAKTI GIVEN BY INDRA.

"WHEN KRIPACHARYA CONTINUED HIS TAUNTS, KARNA FLARED UP.

ONE MORE WORD FROM YOU AND I WILL CUT OFF YOUR TONGUE.

ENRAGED BY KARNA'S VERBAL DUEL WITH HIS UNCLE KRIPA, ASHWATTHAMA RUSHED TOWARDS KARNA WITH HIS DRAWN SWORD RAISED UP. BUT DURYODHANA SAID —

SHED THIS ANGER. WE HAVE A GREAT TASK BEFORE US.

WE WILL FORGIVE KARNA NOW. BUT SOON ARJUNA WILL SHATTER HIS EGO.

"KRIPA CONFIDED IN ASHWATTHAMA.

IN HIS RAGE, DURYODHANA WANTS TO CONFRONT ARJUNA. STOP HIM BEFORE HE GETS KILLED.

"ASHWATTHAMA AT ONCE WENT TO DURYODHANA.

DO NOT INSULT ME BY RUSHING TO FIGHT ARJUNA WHEN I AM ALIVE. LEAVE THAT TO ME.

AH! BUT BOTH YOU AND YOUR FATHER ARE BESOTTED WITH YOUR LOVE FOR THE PANDAVAS. ELSE YOU WOULD HAVE ROUTED THEIR ARMY WITH EASE.

"ASHWATTHAMA REALISED THAT DURYODHANA WAS SPEAKING IN ANGER.

OF COURSE WE DO LOVE THE PANDAVAS. BUT IN THE BATTLEFIELD WE FIGHT THEM WITH ALL OUR MIGHT. JUST WATCH MY PROWESS TODAY.

"TRUE TO HIS WORD, ASHWATTHAMA CHALLENGED THE ENEMY FORCES.

COME, RAIN YOUR ARROWS ON ME!

"SEEING THE PANDAVA SOLDIERS FLEEING UNDER ASHWATTHAMA'S ATTACK, DHRISHTADYUMNA CHALLENGED HIM—

COME FIGHT WITH ME IF YOU ARE A TRUE WARRIOR.

STAND STILL FOR JUST TWO MINUTES AND I WILL SEND YOU TO THE ABODE OF YAMA*

"THE DUEL OF WORDS BETWEEN ASHWATTHAMA AND DHRISHTADYUMNA WAS AS FIERCE AS THE ONE WITH ARROWS.

WAIT! WAIT! I WILL PIERCE YOUR BODY WITH ARROWS!

* GOD OF DEATH

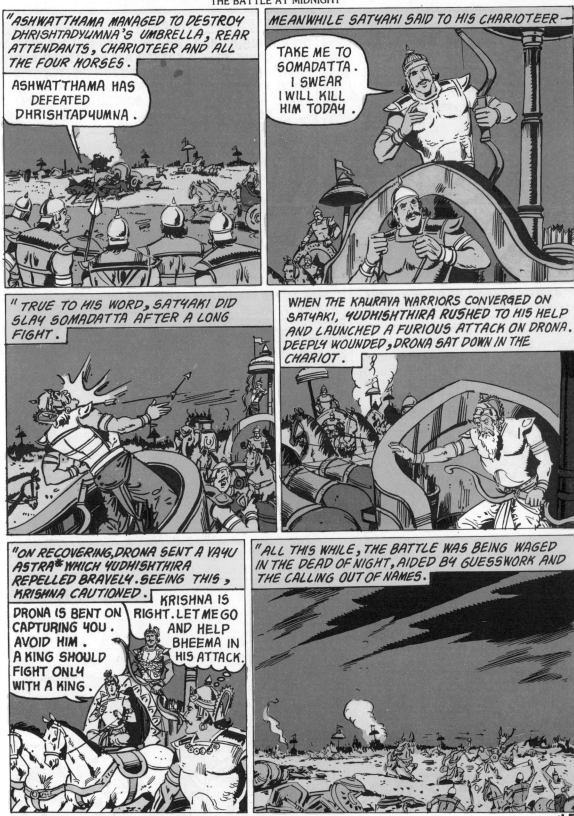

"ASHWATTHAMA MANAGED TO DESTROY DHRISHTADYUMNA'S UMBRELLA, REAR ATTENDANTS, CHARIOTEER AND ALL THE FOUR HORSES.

ASHWATTHAMA HAS DEFEATED DHRISHTADYUMNA.

MEANWHILE SATYAKI SAID TO HIS CHARIOTEER—

TAKE ME TO SOMADATTA. I SWEAR I WILL KILL HIM TODAY.

"TRUE TO HIS WORD, SATYAKI DID SLAY SOMADATTA AFTER A LONG FIGHT.

WHEN THE KAURAVA WARRIORS CONVERGED ON SATYAKI, YUDHISHTHIRA RUSHED TO HIS HELP AND LAUNCHED A FURIOUS ATTACK ON DRONA. DEEPLY WOUNDED, DRONA SAT DOWN IN THE CHARIOT.

"ON RECOVERING, DRONA SENT A VAYU ASTRA* WHICH YUDHISHTHIRA REPELLED BRAVELY. SEEING THIS, KRISHNA CAUTIONED.

DRONA IS BENT ON CAPTURING YOU. AVOID HIM. A KING SHOULD FIGHT ONLY WITH A KING.

KRISHNA IS RIGHT. LET ME GO AND HELP BHEEMA IN HIS ATTACK.

"ALL THIS WHILE, THE BATTLE WAS BEING WAGED IN THE DEAD OF NIGHT, AIDED BY GUESSWORK AND THE CALLING OUT OF NAMES.

* ARROW INVOKING THE POWER OF THE WIND GOD.

15

"DURYODHANA COMMANDED THE SOLDIERS ON FOOT.

PUT DOWN YOUR WEAPONS! I COMMAND ALL OF YOU TO CARRY TORCHES.

"THE PANDAVA SOLDIERS DID LIKEWISE AND SOON —

THE WHOLE BATTLEFIELD WAS LIT UP.

"MINDFUL OF DRONA'S INTENT TO FIGHT WITH ALL HIS MIGHT, DURYODHANA EXHORTED HIS KINSMEN —

PROTECT DRONACHARYA ON ALL SIDES. KRITAVARMA, YOU FLANK HIS RIGHT SIDE. SHALYA, YOU BE ON HIS LEFT.

NO ONE BUT DHRISHTADYUMNA CAN CONFRONT DRONA. YOUR DUTY IS NOW TO PROTECT DRONACHARYA FROM HIM.

"IN THE BATTLE THAT ENSUED, SEVERAL DUELS WERE FOUGHT.

ASHWATTHAMA ABLY AVERTED GHATOTKACHA'S ADVANCES.

BHEEMA DEFEATED DURYODHANA.

KARNA AND SAHADEVA MET IN A DUEL.

"SAHADEVA JUMPED DOWN FROM HIS CHARIOT AND PICKED UP THE WHEEL OF THE CHARIOT TO FLING AT KARNA.

DEAR CHILD! DO NOT TRY THE IMPOSSIBLE! WHY TRY TO FIGHT YOUR SUPERIORS?

KARNA SHATTERED THE WHEEL WITH HIS ARROWS BUT SPARED SAHADEVA'S LIFE. LIGHTLY TOUCHING HIM WITH THE TIP OF HIS BOW HE SAID —

GO AND JOIN YOUR BROTHER ARJUNA, OR IF YOU WISH, RETURN TO YOUR HOME.

"MEANWHILE, VIRATA WAS DEFEATED BY SHALYA AND SHIKHANDI WAS VANQUISHED BY KRIPA. HOWEVER, NAKULA SCORED A VICTORY OVER SHAKUNI.

"THE BATTLE THAT RAGED BETWEEN KARNA AND SATYAKI WAS A TERRIBLE ONE.

"KARNA'S FURY WAS CREATING HAVOC AMONG THE PANDAVA FORCES. ARJUNA SAID —

O KRISHNA! TAKE ME TOWARDS KARNA. I MUST KILL HIM OR BE KILLED TODAY.

"AWARE OF THE MIGHTY SHAKTI IN KARNA'S POSSESSION, KRISHNA DEMURRED —

BESIDES YOU, GHATOTKACHA ALONE IS CAPABLE OF FACING KARNA. LET HIM DO SO, WHILE YOU PROTECT YUDHISHTHIRA.

" THEY SUMMONED GHATOTKACHA.

FIGHT KARNA WITH ALL YOUR ASTRAS AND KILL HIM. WE ARE DEPENDING ON YOU.

SATYAKI WILL BE WITH YOU. TOGETHER YOU CAN WORK WONDERS.

I WILL GO AT ONCE. SUCH A BATTLE WILL I WAGE TODAY THAT IT WILL BE REMEMBERED FOR EVER.

" IN THE MIDST OF THAT DREADFUL NIGHT, KARNA AND GHATOTKACHA FACED EACH OTHER.

"JUST AS DURYODHANA WAS ABOUT TO SEND DUHSHASANA TO KARNA'S AID, ALAMBUSHA APPROACHED HIM.

MY FATHER, JATASURA, THE LEADER OF RAKSHASAS, WAS KILLED BY THE PANDAVAS. GIVE ME A CHANCE TO AVENGE HIS DEATH. LET ME FIGHT THE PANDAVAS.

"DURYODHANA WAS GLAD TO OBLIGE.

YOU ARE WELCOME. GO AND FIGHT GHATOTKACHA.

"THE TWO RAKSHASAS FOUGHT WITH VARIOUS WEAPONS AND FINALLY WITH BARE HANDS.

SUDDENLY, GHATOTKACHA JUMPED UP AND SWOOPED DOWN WITH A SWORD.

"WITH A DREADFUL CRY, GHATOTKACHA CUT OFF HIS OPPONENT'S HEAD.

"APPROACHING DURYODHANA, HE THREW ALAMBUSHA'S HEAD TOWARDS HIM.

IT IS SAID ONE SHOULD NOT VISIT A KING WITHOUT A GIFT. WAIT AWHILE AND I WILL BRING YOU A HEAD WHICH IS MORE DEAR TO YOU—KARNA'S!

SO FIERCE WAS THE BATTLE BETWEEN KARNA AND GHATOTKACHA THAT IT MADE MIGHTY WARRIORS TREMBLE. GHATOTKACHA WAS IN THE SKY IN A MINUTE...

... SO THAT WHEN THE SHAKTI PIERCED AND FELLED HIM, A VAST NUMBER OF KAURAVA SOLDIERS WERE CRUSHED UNDER HIS WEIGHT.

" BHEEMA AND OTHER PANDAVAS WERE SHOCKED AT HIS DEATH.

KRISHNA CONSOLED THEM AND SAID TO ARJUNA.

KARNA HAS USED HIS SHAKTI ONCE AND IT HAS RETURNED TO INDRA. OH! HOW I HAD WORRIED ABOUT HIS USING IT AGAINST YOU. NOW BEREFT OF THE SHAKTI, KARNA IS LIKE A FANGLESS SERPENT.

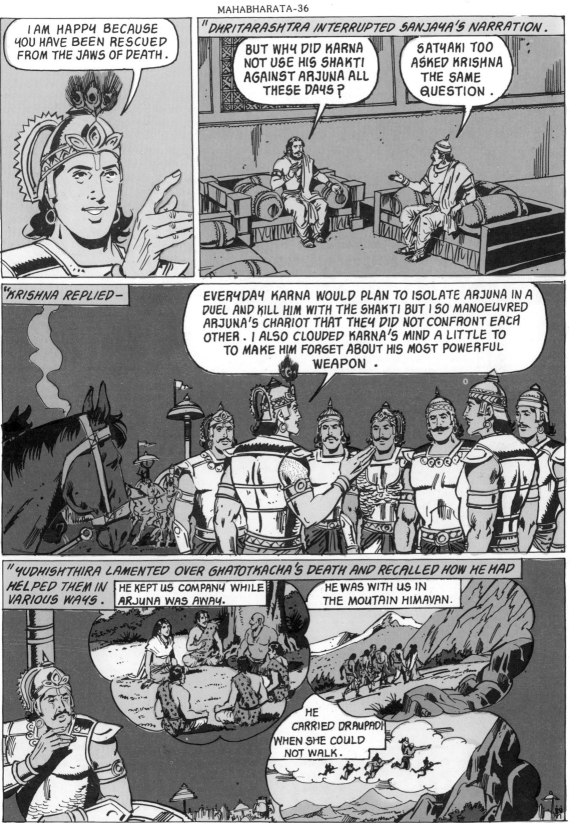

I AM HAPPY BECAUSE YOU HAVE BEEN RESCUED FROM THE JAWS OF DEATH.

"DHRITARASHTRA INTERRUPTED SANJAYA'S NARRATION.

BUT WHY DID KARNA NOT USE HIS SHAKTI AGAINST ARJUNA ALL THESE DAYS?

SATYAKI TOO ASKED KRISHNA THE SAME QUESTION.

"KRISHNA REPLIED—

EVERYDAY KARNA WOULD PLAN TO ISOLATE ARJUNA IN A DUEL AND KILL HIM WITH THE SHAKTI BUT I SO MANOEUVRED ARJUNA'S CHARIOT THAT THEY DID NOT CONFRONT EACH OTHER. I ALSO CLOUDED KARNA'S MIND A LITTLE TO TO MAKE HIM FORGET ABOUT HIS MOST POWERFUL WEAPON.

"YUDHISHTHIRA LAMENTED OVER GHATOTKACHA'S DEATH AND RECALLED HOW HE HAD HELPED THEM IN VARIOUS WAYS.

HE KEPT US COMPANY WHILE ARJUNA WAS AWAY.

HE WAS WITH US IN THE MOUTAIN HIMAVAN.

HE CARRIED DRAUPADI WHEN SHE COULD NOT WALK.

I LOVED HIM AS DEARLY AS I LOVE SAHADEVA. YET HE WAS KILLED IN OUR VERY PRESENCE.

YUDHISHTHIRA WAS ABOUT TO ATTACK KARNA WHEN VYASA APPEARED AND CONSOLED HIM, SAYING THAT GHATOTKACHA'S DEATH HAD BEEN ORDAINED. HE ALSO ASSURED HIM OF VICTORY IN FIVE DAYS.

"IT WAS WELL PAST MIDNIGHT. THE SOLDIERS OF BOTH ARMIES WERE WEARY. RAISING HIS VOICE, ARJUNA ANNOUNCED —

EVERYONE IS TIRED AND EXHAUSTED. THE DARKNESS IS DENSE. IF YOU, KAURAVAS, AGREE, I SUGGEST WE ALL REST IN THE BATTLEFIELD AWHILE.

WE AGREE! WE WILL RESUME FIGHTING LATER.

"AS ARJUNA'S SUGGESTION WAS UNANIMOUSLY ACCEPTED, THE SOLIDERS GRATEFULLY LAY DOWN TO SLEEP.

ONLY ARJUNA COULD BE SO THOUGHTFUL! BLESS HIM.

"THE BATTLEFIELD WHICH HAD RESOUNDED WITH WAR CRIES WAS NOW ENVELOPED IN SILENCE. THE HUGE ARMIES LAY STILL LIKE A PAINTING DRAWN BY A GIFTED ARTIST...

"...TILL THE MOON CAME UP. ONE BY ONE THE MEN BEGAN TO STIR. THE BATTLE WAS RESUMED IN THE BRIGHT LIGHT OF THE MOON.

DURYODHANA SAID TO DRONA —

WITH YOUR RENOWNED PROWESS AND CELESTIAL WEAPONS, YOU COULD EASILY DEFEAT THE PANDAVAS. BUT ALAS! YOU CONTINUE TO FAVOUR THEM.

"THE OFT-REPEATED SARCASM AND ACCUSATION WERE BEGINNING TO IRRITATE DRONA.

SO FAR I HAVE FOUGHT WITH FAIR AND JUST MEANS AND REFRAINED FROM USING DIVINE WEAPONS ON ORDINARY SOLDIERS. NOW IF YOU SO WISH, I WILL USE UNFAIR MEANS AS WELL, TO FIGHT. BUT BELIEVE ME, WHEN I SAY, ARJUNA IS INVINCIBLE.

"DURYODHANA WAS TOUCHED TO THE QUICK BY THIS PRAISE OF HIS ARCH ENEMY. HE SAID—

WE WILL NOW DIVIDE THE ARMY INTO TWO. WITH ONE HALF I WILL ATTACK YOUR FAVOURITE ARJUNA.

I WISH YOU WELL. YOU HAVE LIVED A FULL LIFE; GO AND DO YOUR DUTY NOW. GO, FIGHT ARJUNA.

"ONE HALF OF THE ARMY WITH DURYODHANA, DUHSHASANA, SHAKUNI AND KARNA, SET OUT TO CONFRONT ARJUNA. BUT THEY WERE ROUTED IN NO TIME.

"DRONA LED THE REST OF THE ARMY AND KILLED THREE GRANDSONS OF DRUPADA.

"WITH TWO SHARP JAVELINS, HE KILLED VIRATA AND DRUPADA. DHRISHTADYUMNA WAS STUNNED WITH GRIEF.

THIS MAN HAS KILLED MY FATHER AS WELL AS MY SONS. I WILL NOT LEAVE HIM TODAY.

"SWEARING REVENGE, DHRISHTADYUMNA ATTACKED DRONA AND THE KAURAVAS.

amar chitra katha

"DURYODHANA CAME TO HELP DRONA WITH THE REST OF THE ARMY.

"TRY AS HE MIGHT, DHRISHTADYUMNA COULD NOT REACH DRONA. BHEEMA TAUNTED HIM...

DRONA HAS KILLED YOUR FATHER AND SON. YOU HAVE SWORN TO KILL HIM. HOW CAN YOU SEE HIM ALIVE?

... AND PENETRATING THE KAURAVA ARMY, ENGAGED IN A FIERCE BATTLE WITH KARNA.

"MEANWHILE THE SUN ROSE IN THE EAST.* THE WARRIORS NOW FOUGHT WITH RENEWED VIGOUR. KARNA WAS ENGAGED IN A COMBAT BY BHEEMA.

"BUT THE SPECTACULAR SIGHT WAS THE CONFRONTATION BETWEEN DRONA AND ARJUNA.

"AFTER A PROLONGED FIGHT WITH EARTHLY AND CELESTIAL WEAPONS, DRONA SENT THE BRAHMASTRA TOWARDS ARJUNA WHO COUNTERED IT WITH THE SAME ASTRA.

NOW DRONA TURNED AWAY FROM ARJUNA AND FOUGHT THE PANCHALA ARMY.

* THE FIFTEENTH DAY OF THE BATTLE. 26

"DURYODHANA AND SATYAKI WERE ENGAGED IN A STRANGE ENCOUNTER.

"WHILE THEY RAINED ARROWS AT EACH OTHER, THEY RECALLED WITH NOSTALGIA THEIR EARLIER DAYS.

WHAT HAPPY TIMES WE HAD TOGETHER, DEAR SATYAKI. NOW BECAUSE OF MY GREED, WE MEET AS ENEMIES.

MY DEAR DURYODHANA, THIS IS NEITHER OUR GURU'S HOUSE NOR AN ASSEMBLY. LET US FIGHT LIKE TRUE KSHATRIYAS.

"MEANWHILE DRONA WAS FIGHTING AS IF POSSESSED BY A DEMON. THE PANDAVAS WATCHED AGHAST.

THIS IS NOT LIKE THE ACHARYA AT ALL.

HE DOES NOT LOOK HUMAN.

"THE PANIC AMONG THE SOLDIERS SET KRISHNA THINKING.

DRONA IS USING UNFAIR MEANS. HE IS EVEN USING DIVINE WEAPONS AGAINST ORDINARY SOLDIERS.

"HE SAID TO YUDHISHTHIRA—

IF DRONA KEEPS FIGHTING THUS, YOU WILL HAVE NO ARMY LEFT. WE WILL HAVE TO MAKE HIM LAY DOWN HIS WEAPONS.

YES, BUT HOW?

KRISHNA THOUGHTFULLY SAID—

I AM SURE IF HE HEARS THAT HIS SON ASHWATTHAMA IS NO MORE, HE WILL STOP FIGHTING.

"ARJUNA DID NOT APPROVE OF THIS SUGGESTION. YUDHISHTHIRA AGREED AFTER MUCH PERSUASION. MEANWHILE, BHEEMA KILLED AN ELEPHANT CALLED ASHWATTHAMA. GOING NEAR DRONA HE ANNOUNCED—

ASHWATTHAMA IS DEAD!

DRONA ALMOST FAINTED WITH SHOCK.

BUT SOON RECOVERED.

NO, IT CANNOT BE! NONE CAN KILL MY ASHWATTHAMA.

"DRONA RESUMED FIGHTING WITH ALL WEAPONS AT HIS DISPOSAL, SLAUGHTERING THE PANDAVA FORCES.

"SEEING HIS UNFAIR AND INHUMAN APPROACH, THE RISHIS FROM HEAVEN, LED BY AGNI, CAME TO MEET DRONA.

THIS UNRIGHTEOUSNESS DOES NOT BECOME YOU. LAY DOWN YOUR ARMS AND PREPARE FOR THE END.

"DEEPLY MOVED BY THEIR COUNSEL AND BHEEMA'S EARLIER ANNOUNCEMENT, DRONA LOOKED AT YUDHISHTHIRA AND SAID —

IS IT TRUE THAT MY SON IS DEAD?

YUDHISHTHIRA HAD NEVER SPOKEN AN UNTRUTH IN HIS LIFE. BUT KRISHNA HAD ANTICIPATED THIS SITUATION AND TOLD HIM.

YOU MAY HAVE TO LIE TODAY TO SAVE YOUR ARMY. BUT THE SIN WILL NOT CLING TO YOU.

"SO NOW, HE REPLIED —

ASHWATTHAMA IS DEAD.

ADDING IN AN INAUDIBLE ASIDE —

ASHWATTHAMA THE ELEPHANT.

AS SOON AS THE LIE WAS UTTERED YUDHISHTHIRA'S CHARIOT TOUCHED THE GROUND.*

"HEARING THE NEWS FROM YUDHISHTHIRA, DRONA FAINTED. DHRISHTADYUMNA RUSHED TOWARDS HIM.

"WHEN DRONA GAINED CONSCIOUSNESS, HE COULD NOT GAIN HIS EARLIER STRENGTH. YET HE KILLED DHRISHTADYUMNA'S HORSES.

* BECAUSE OF HIS RIGHTEOUS CONDUCT YUDHISHTHIRA'S CHARIOT WAS ALWAYS FOUR FINGERS' BREADTH ABOVE THE GROUND.

"NOW DRONA SHOT SPECIAL SHORT-RANGE ARROWS, AT DHRISHTADYUMNA.

"SATYAKI INTERVENED IN TIME WITH A VOLLEY OF ARROWS TO DEFEND DHRISHTADYUMNA.

BHEEMA CONFRONTED DRONA AND SAID SARCASTICALLY—

YOU TEACH DHARMA TO OTHERS YET YOU ABANDON YOUR OWN DUTY AS A BRAHMANA, EVEN WITH YOUR SON DEAD, YOU CONTINUE TO FIGHT.

THROWING HIS WEAPONS AWAY, DRONA EXCLAIMED—

O KARNA, O KRIPA, DURYODHANA! FIGHT WITH ALL YOUR MIGHT. I HEREBY LAY DOWN MY ARMS.

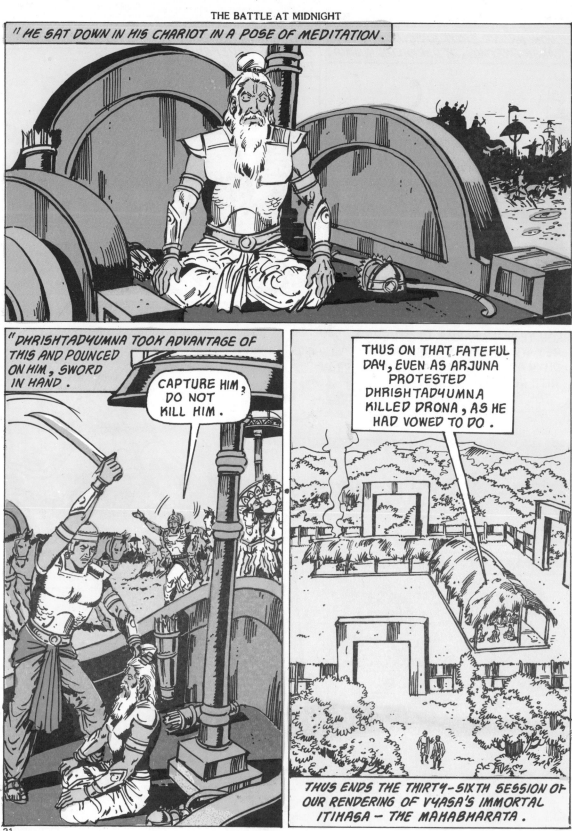

" HE SAT DOWN IN HIS CHARIOT IN A POSE OF MEDITATION.

" DHRISHTADYUMNA TOOK ADVANTAGE OF THIS AND POUNCED ON HIM, SWORD IN HAND.

CAPTURE HIM, DO NOT KILL HIM.

THUS ON THAT FATEFUL DAY, EVEN AS ARJUNA PROTESTED DHRISHTADYUMNA KILLED DRONA, AS HE HAD VOWED TO DO.

THUS ENDS THE THIRTY-SIXTH SESSION OF OUR RENDERING OF VYASA'S IMMORTAL ITIHASA — THE MAHABHARATA.

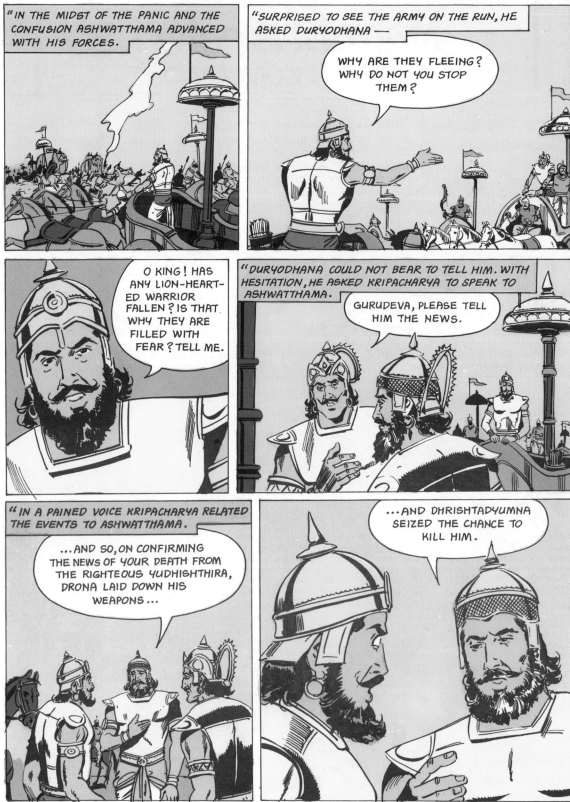

"IN THE MIDST OF THE PANIC AND THE CONFUSION ASHWATTHAMA ADVANCED WITH HIS FORCES.

"SURPRISED TO SEE THE ARMY ON THE RUN, HE ASKED DURYODHANA —

WHY ARE THEY FLEEING? WHY DO NOT YOU STOP THEM?

O KING! HAS ANY LION-HEARTED WARRIOR FALLEN? IS THAT WHY THEY ARE FILLED WITH FEAR? TELL ME.

"DURYODHANA COULD NOT BEAR TO TELL HIM. WITH HESITATION, HE ASKED KRIPACHARYA TO SPEAK TO ASHWATTHAMA.

GURUDEVA, PLEASE TELL HIM THE NEWS.

"IN A PAINED VOICE KRIPACHARYA RELATED THE EVENTS TO ASHWATTHAMA.

...AND SO, ON CONFIRMING THE NEWS OF YOUR DEATH FROM THE RIGHTEOUS YUDHISHTHIRA, DRONA LAID DOWN HIS WEAPONS...

...AND DHRISHTADYUMNA SEIZED THE CHANCE TO KILL HIM.

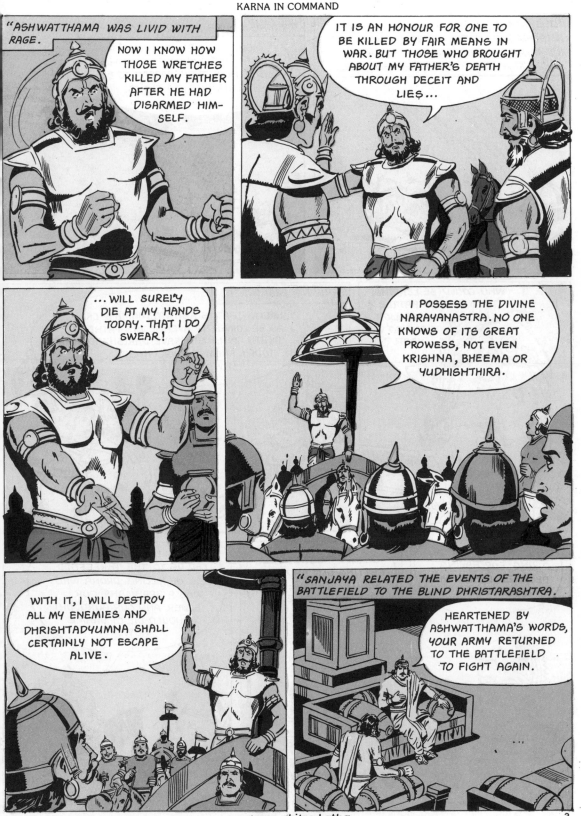

"ASHWATTHAMA WAS LIVID WITH RAGE.

NOW I KNOW HOW THOSE WRETCHES KILLED MY FATHER AFTER HE HAD DISARMED HIMSELF.

IT IS AN HONOUR FOR ONE TO BE KILLED BY FAIR MEANS IN WAR. BUT THOSE WHO BROUGHT ABOUT MY FATHER'S DEATH THROUGH DECEIT AND LIES...

...WILL SURELY DIE AT MY HANDS TODAY. THAT I DO SWEAR!

I POSSESS THE DIVINE NARAYANASTRA. NO ONE KNOWS OF ITS GREAT PROWESS, NOT EVEN KRISHNA, BHEEMA OR YUDHISHTHIRA.

WITH IT, I WILL DESTROY ALL MY ENEMIES AND DHRISHTADYUMNA SHALL CERTAINLY NOT ESCAPE ALIVE.

"SANJAYA RELATED THE EVENTS OF THE BATTLEFIELD TO THE BLIND DHRISTARASHTRA.

HEARTENED BY ASHWATTHAMA'S WORDS, YOUR ARMY RETURNED TO THE BATTLEFIELD TO FIGHT AGAIN.

"THE TUMULT OF CONCH SHELLS AND TRUMPETS HERALDING THE APPROACH OF THE KAURAVAS, INFUSED WITH ENTHUSIASM AGAIN, TOOK THE PANDAVAS BY SURPRISE.

"YUDHISHTHIRA ASKED ARJUNA —

DISHEARTENED BY DRONA'S DEATH, THE KAURAVAS HAD FLED. BUT NOW THEY APPEAR TO BE RETURNING TO FIGHT.

WHO COULD BE LEADING THEM BACK TO BATTLE? WHOSE LION ROAR DO WE HEAR?

"ARJUNA RESPONDED.

SURELY THAT IS ASHWATTHAMA'S CRY AS HE COMES TO AVENGE HIS FATHER'S DEATH. WHO CAN SAVE DHRISHTADYUMNA TODAY FROM THE VALOROUS ASHWATTHAMA?

YOU TOO ARE GUILTY, O KING, FOR HAVING DECEIVED DRONA WITH YOUR ONE LIE.

OH! WE MUST BE ALL GETTING OLD AND SENILE TO HAVE BEHAVED AS WE DID.

OUR GREED FOR A KINGDOM LED US TO THE THREEFOLD SIN OF KILLING DRONA WHO WAS A BRAHMANA, OUR ELDER AND OUR GURU. OH! I SHOULD DIE OF SHAME NOW.

"ALL THE PANDAVAS WERE DUMBSTRUCK AT ARJUNA'S OUTBURST. THEN BHEEMA SPOKE UP.

AH! MY RIGHTEOUS BROTHER! YOU SOUND LIKE A BRAHMANA GIVING A DISCOURSE. BUT AS A TRUE-BLOODED KSHATRIYA, THESE WORDS ILL BECOME YOU.

"ANGER WAS EVIDENT IN WHAT BHEEMA SAID.

WAS NOT OUR KINGDOM SEIZED BY UNFAIR MEANS? WAS IT JUSTICE TO BANISH US TO THE FOREST FOR THIRTEEN LONG YEARS? IT WAS YOU WHO SAID WE MUST WAGE WAR WITH THE KAURAVAS.

ALL THESE YEARS, WE HELD OUR ANGER IN CHECK BECAUSE YUDHISHTHIRA INSISTED THAT WE WAIT TILL OUR EXILE WAS OVER. THE VERY SAME YUDHISHTHIRA, WHOM YOU NOW CHOOSE TO FIND FAULT WITH.

AND TO TOP IT ALL, A WARRIOR OF YOUR STATURE PRAISES ASHWATTHAMA THUS! WHY, ARMED WITH MY MACE, I CAN DEAL WITH HIM ALL BY MYSELF.

"DHRISHTADYUMNA SAID —

ARJUNA, YOU ARE FULL OF PRAISE FOR DRONA NOW. BUT YOU FORGET DRONA HAD FORSAKEN HIS DHARMA AS A BRAHMANA. HE PERFORMED NONE OF THE DUTIES* EXPECTED OF A BRAHMANA.

WAS IT FAIR ON HIS PART TO USE DIVINE WEAPONS ON HELPLESS SOLDIERS?

* ASSISTING IN SACRIFICES, PERFORMING SACRIFICES, GIVING AWAY GIFTS, RECEIVING GIFTS, TEACHING AND STUDYING.

5

HOW CAN YOU BLAME ME FOR KILLING DRONA? YOU KNOW THAT I WAS BORN TO DO SO.

"DHRITARASHTRA, EAGERLY FOLLOWING THE NARRATION OF SANJAYA, INTERVENED.

"WHEN THAT LOWLY DHRISHTADYUMNA CRITICIZED THE GREAT DRONA, DID NO ONE OBJECT?

AT FIRST, THEY WERE ALL SILENT. THEN SATYAKI RETALIATED IN ANGER.

"BRISTLING WITH RAGE, SATYAKI REBUKED DHRISHTADYUMNA.

HOW DARE YOU CRITICIZE OUR GURU AFTER YOUR DASTARDLY ACT? ONE MORE WORD FROM YOU AND I WILL CRUSH YOUR HEAD WITH MY MACE.

"DISMISSING SATYAKI'S THREAT WITH A LAUGH, DHRISHTADYUMNA SAID —

DID YOU NOT COMMIT A SIN WHEN YOU CUT OFF THE HEAD OF BHOORISHRAVA? HOW ARE YOU QUALIFIED TO SPEAK ABOUT WHAT IS RIGHT AND WHAT IS WRONG? PREPARE TO FIGHT THE KAURAVAS. DO NOT INVITE DEATH BY ARGUING WITH ME.

"SATYAKI POUNCED ON DHRISHTADYUMNA.

NO MORE WORDS NOW! I WILL JUST KILL YOU.

"ON KRISHNA'S BIDDING, BHEEMA INTERVENED.

"SAHADEVA ADDRESSED THE TWO HEROES —

COME! SHED YOUR ANGER AND FORGIVE EACH OTHER.

"KRISHNA AND YUDHISHTHIRA FINALLY MANAGED TO PACIFY THE TWO AND THE PANDAVAS PREPARED TO CONFRONT THE ENEMY AGAIN.

"LIKE TWO COLOSSAL MOUNTAINS IN COLLISION, THE TWO ARMIES CHARGED TOWARDS EACH OTHER.

"JUST THEN ASHWATTHAMA INVOKED THE NARAYANASTRA.

"THOUSANDS OF ARROWS SPRANG FORTH FROM THE WEAPON AND CLOUDED THE SKY.

"EVEN AS THE ARROWS FELL ON THE PANDAVAS LIKE GLOWING SERPENTS, MANY A RADIANT DISC APPEARED IN THE SKY.

"STRANGE AND OMINOUS-LOOKING WEAPONS FOLLOWED. THE MORE THE PANDAVA FORCES OPPOSED IT, THE MORE POWERFUL THE ASTRA BECAME.

"SEEING HIS TROOPS BEING DECIMATED BY THE NARAYANASTRA, YUDHISHTHIRA SAID—

DHRISHTADYUMNA! TAKE THE PANCHALA ARMY AND FLEE! SATYAKI, YOU TOO GO HOME.

"ADDRESSING THE SOLDIERS, HE SAID—

DESIST FROM FIGHTING, I TOO WILL ENTER THE FIRE AND END MY LIFE.

"JUST THEN, KRISHNA SIGNALLED TO THE PANDAVA FORCES.

BRAVE WARRIORS, ALIGHT FROM YOUR VEHICLES AND THROW YOUR WEAPONS DOWN! THE ONLY WAY TO ESCAPE THE FURY OF THIS CELESTIAL WEAPON IS TO STAND UNARMED ON THE GROUND.

"AS THE WARRIORS DISMOUNTED, KRISHNA EXPLAINED—

THE MORE YOU OPPOSE IT, THE MORE POWERFUL THE ASTRA WILL BECOME. YOU MUST INSTEAD BOW BEFORE ITS MIGHT.

" THUS DIRECTED BY KRISHNA, THE PANDAVA WARRIORS GOT READY TO RENOUNCE THE WEAPONS AND EVEN THE VERY THOUGHT OF THEM.

" BHEEMA ALONE WAS DEFIANT.

LIKE THE SUN, I STAND UNEQUALLED. I WILL OPPOSE THE NARAYANASTRA EVEN IF NO ONE HAS DONE SO BEFORE.

"AS HE SET FORTH ON HIS CHARIOT TOWARDS ASHWATTHAMA, THE KAURAVAS PELTED HIM WITH ARROWS.

" WITH A LAUGH, ASHWATTHAMA RAINED FIRETIPPED ARROWS ON BHEEMA.

" BHEEMA RESEMBLED A MIGHTY MOUNTAIN COVERED WITH FIRE-FLIES. WHEN HE TRIED TO COUNTER ASHWATTHAMA'S ATTACK WITH HIS OWN ARROWS, THE SPARKLES TURNED TO A FLAMING FIRE. AT THIS THE FRIGHTENED PANDAVA SOLDIERS QUICKLY PROSTRATED THEMSELVES ON THE GROUND.

" WHEN THEY BECAME INACTIVE, THE BRUNT OF THE NARAYANASTRA FELL ON BHEEMA.

" NOW HIS CHARIOT, CHARIOTEER AND HORSES WERE ALL ENVELOPED IN FLAMES. EVEN ARJUNA'S VARUNASTRA* WAS INEFFECTIVE IN QUENCHING THE FIRE.

* CELESTIAL WEAPON OF VARUNA, LORD OF THE SEA.

10

"KRISHNA AND ARJUNA JUMPED DOWN FROM THEIR CHARIOT AND RUSHED TOWARDS BHEEMA LEAVING THEIR ARMS BEHIND.

"THEY WRENCHED OFF HIS WEAPONS AND PULLED HIM DOWN.

"BUT BHEEMA WAS STUBBORN. HE LET OUT A LION ROAR WHICH AGAIN AUGMENTED THE EFFECT OF THE ASTRA. KRISHNA REBUKED HIM.

WHY DO YOU NOT LISTEN, BHEEMA! STOP FIGHTING NOW.

"BOTH KRISHNA AND ARJUNA HELD BHEEMA DOWN TILL THE ASTRA PASSED OVER THEIR HEADS.

"THE AIR COOLED DOWN AND THE SOLDIERS AND ANIMALS REVIVED.

"AS THE PANDAVA FORCES PREPARED TO RESUME THE FIGHT, DURYODHANA TOLD ASHWATTHAMA —

COME ON! SEND THAT WEAPON AGAIN. HURRY!

"ASHWATTHAMA REPLIED WITH A DEEP SIGH —

ALAS! NEITHER DOES THIS WEAPON RETURN NOR CAN IT BE INVOKED AGAIN. IF I TRY TO RECALL IT, IT WILL CERTAINLY DESTROY US.

HAD KRISHNA NOT DISCLOSED THE SECRET OF QUELLING THE NARAYANASTRA, WE WOULD HAVE DESTROYED ALL OUR ENEMIES TODAY.

THEN USE THE OTHER CELESTIAL WEAPONS AT YOUR DISPOSAL.

"ASHWATTHAMA SET OUT TO ATTACK DHRISHTA-DYUMNA.

" WITH TWENTY-FIVE PIERCING ARROWS, HE WOUNDED DHRISHTADYUMNA.

"ON RECOVERING, DHRISHTADYUMNA RAINED COUNTLESS ARROWS IN RETURN.

"BUT NOT FOR LONG. SOON ASHWATTHAMA KILLED HIS HORSES AND CHARIOTEER.

"SATYAKI THEN CAME TO DHRISHTADYUMNA'S RESCUE.

"WITH WELL AIMED ARROWS, SATYAKI KILLED ASHWATTHAMA'S CHARIOTEER AND DESTROYED HIS CHARIOT.

"WHEN DURYODHANA, KRIPA AND KARNA CAME TO HIM, ASHWATTHAMA ASCENDED ANOTHER CHARIOT.

"THE MIGHTY HERO THAT HE WAS, SATYAKI CONTINUED THE FIGHT UNRUFFLED. HE ONCE AGAIN DESTROYED THE CHARIOT OF ASHWATTHAMA.

"LAUGHING ASHWATTHAMA WARNED SATYAKI —

I KNOW YOU HAVE A SOFT CORNER FOR DHRISHTADYUMNA. BUT TODAY NEITHER OF YOU WILL ESCAPE ME.

" SEEING SATYAKI BEING THUS TORMENTED, FIVE MIGHTY PANDAVA WARRIORS CAME TO HIS AID.

" BHEEMA AND ASHWATTHAMA WERE SOON ENGAGED IN WELL-MATCHED BATTLE.

"ASHWATTHAMA INJURED BHEEMA'S CHARIOTEER. RELEASED FROM THE REINS, HIS HORSES TOOK BHEEMA AWAY.

" ARJUNA HAILED ASHWATTHAMA —

LET ME SEE YOUR VALOUR, YOUR STRENGTH, YOUR PROWESS. COME! DISPLAY YOUR LOVE OF THE KAURAVAS AND YOUR HATRED FOR US. TODAY, I WILL CRUSH YOUR PRIDE.

"DHRITARASHTRA WAS SURPRISED TO HEAR THIS. HE INTERRUPTED SANJAYA'S NARRATION.

BUT ARJUNA AND ASHWATTHAMA HAD ALWAYS BEEN FRIENDS. WHY WAS ARJUNA SO RUDE TO HIM?

HE WAS DEEPLY HURT BY THE CRITICISM HURLED AT HIM, THE DEFEAT OF BHEEMA, SATYAKI AND DHRISHTADYUMNA HAD ALSO MADE HIM UNHAPPY.

"ASHWATTHAMA TOOK UP ARJUNA'S CHALLENGE.

"IMPATIENT TO KILL ARJUNA, HE INVOKED THE AGNEYASTRA.*

"NO SOONER HAD THE CELESTIAL WEAPON BEEN RELEASED THAN THE SKY RAINED DOWN ARROWS AND METEORS AND FLAMES OF FIRE ONTO THE BATTLEFIELD WHICH WAS SUDDENLY PLUNGED IN DARKNESS.

"ARJUNA THEN USED THE BRAHMASTRA WHICH SUBDUES THE MOST POWERFUL WEAPONS.

* CELESTIAL WEAPON BELONGING TO AGNI, LORD OF FIRE.

"COUNTERED BY THE BRAHMASTRA, THE DARKNESS LIFTED AND THE AIR COOLED DOWN. THE DEVASTATING EFFECT OF THE AGNEYASTRA ON THE PANDAVA FORCES NOW BECAME VISIBLE.

"BUT ARJUNA AND KRISHNA ESCAPED UNSCATHED. THIS PLUNGED ASHWATTHAMA IN A GLOOM OF DESPAIR.

"THROWING AWAY HIS BOW HE JUMPED OFF HIS CHARIOT.

SHAME ON ME! ALL MY EFFORTS ARE FUTILE.

"AS HE WAS RUNNING OFF THE BATTLEFIELD FULL OF DESPAIR, HE CAME ACROSS SAGE VYASA.

OH, WISE ONE! WHERE DID I GO WRONG? WHY DID THE WEAPON FAIL ME?

"POURING OUT HIS WOE, HE CONTINUED—

HOW COULD SUCH A POWERFUL WEAPON BE QUELLED? HOW COME ARJUNA AND KRISHNA ALWAYS MANAGE TO ESCAPE?

BECAUSE MY SON, YOU USED THE WEAPON AGAINST KRISHNA WHO IS AN INCARNATION OF VISHNU.*

"ON HEARING THIS, ASHWATTHAMA BADE HIS ARMY TO GO BACK TO THE CAMP.

"DURYODHANA, ASHWATTHAMA, KARNA AND OTHERS SPENT THE NIGHT IN DISCUSSING THE STRATEGY TO BE ADOPTED THE NEXT DAY.

WHAT IN YOUR ESTEEMED OPINION SHOULD WE DO NOW?

"ASHWATTHAMA SAID —

THOUGH MANY OF OUR ABLE WARRIORS HAVE BEEN KILLED, WE SHOULD NOT LOSE HEART. WITH KARNA IN COMMAND WE CAN STILL VANQUISH THE ENEMY.

"HIS WORDS WERE ENCOURAGING TO DURYODHANA, ADDRESSING KARNA, HE SAID —

BHEESHMA AND DRONA, OUR TWO VENERABLE COMMANDERS, ARE NO MORE. THEY WERE BRAVE BUT THEY WERE INCLINED TO BE PARTIAL TO THE PANDAVAS.

YOU ARE SURELY THE BEST MAN TO LEAD OUR FORCES NOW. YOU HAVE ALWAYS BEEN CONCERNED ABOUT OUR WELFARE. COME! TAKE CHARGE OF THE ARMY.

I WILL BE GLAD TO DO SO. CONSIDER THE PANDAVAS ALREADY DEFEATED.

"KARNA WAS FORMALLY INSTALLED AS THE THIRD COMMANDER OF THE KAURAVAS.

"ON THE MORNING OF THE SIXTEENTH DAY, THE KAURAVA CAMP RESOUNDED WITH THE VOICE OF KARNA. HE ARRANGED THE FORCES IN THE MAKARA VYUHA.*

COME ON, MY BRAVES! GET READY TO FIGHT.

"THE INSTRUCTIONS HE GAVE WERE VERY CLEAR.

I SHALL BE AT THE MOUTH OF THE VYUHA, SHAKUNI AND ULOOKA WILL BE THE EYES. ASHWATTHAMA, YOU BE AT THE HEAD. DURYODHANA SHOULD BE PLACED IN THE CENTRE SURROUNDED BY HIS ARMY.

"YUDHISHTHIRA REMARKED TO ARJUNA —

ARJUNA, BEHOLD THE KAURAVAS BEREFT OF THEIR MIGHTY WARRIORS. KARNA IS THE ONLY HERO LEFT.

TODAY IT MUST BE YOUR AIM TO KILL HIM. ARRANGE OUR FORCES ACCORDINGLY.

I WILL ARRANGE OUR MEN IN THE SHAPE OF A CRESCENT.

* ARMY ARRAYED IN THE SHAPE OF CROCODILE.

"ARJUNA ARRAYED THE FORCES TO RESEMBLE A HALF MOON WITH BHEEMA ON THE LEFT AND DHRISHTADYUMNA ON THE RIGHT.

"AND SOON THE BATTLE WAS FOUGHT IN REAL EARNEST.

"FIERCE WAS THE DUEL BETWEEN ASHWATTHAMA AND BHEEMA.

WHAT A FIGHT! BHEEMA'S MIGHT IS WELL MATCHED BY ASHWATTHAMA'S SKILL.

"AFTER A VIGOROUS EXCHANGE OF ARROWS, THEY MADE EACH OTHER FAINT.

"ARJUNA WAS MEANWHILE WRECKING DESTRUCTION AMONG THE SAMSHAPTAKAS WHO HAD CHALLENGED HIM ONCE AGAIN.

"EVEN AS HE KEPT REDUCING THEIR NUMBERS, ASHWATTHAMA CALLED OUT TO HIM FROM ANOTHER DIRECTION.

COME, ARJUNA. TREAT ME LIKE YOUR GUEST. ENTERTAIN ME WITH ALL YOUR WEAPONS.

"ARJUNA CONSULTED KRISHNA.

SHOULD I FIGHT THE SAMSHAPTAKAS OR ACCEPT ASHWATTHAMA'S CHALLENGE? TELL ME, O KRISHNA.

"IN RESPONSE, KRISHNA LED THE CHARIOT TOWARDS ASHWATTHAMA. A FURIOUS FIGHT ENSUED.

"SEEING ASHWATTHAMA GAINING AN EDGE OVER ARJUNA, KRISHNA SAID—

WHAT HAS COME OVER YOU? HAVE YOU LOST YOUR HOLD ON YOUR GANDEEVA?

SEE HOW THIS SON OF MY GURU IS TRYING TO KILL US. I WILL TAKE CARE OF HIM.

" THE FURY WITH WHICH ARJUNA THEN SHOT HIS ARROWS PIERCED NOT ONLY ASHWATTHAMA'S HORSES AND CHARIOT, BUT ALSO FELLED THE ELEPHANTS AND SOLDIERS WHO WERE FAR AWAY.

amar chitra katha

"GRIEVOUSLY INJURED, ASHWATTHAMA'S HORSES FLED THE FIELD, CARRYING THE CHARIOT AWAY WITH THEM.

"AS HE WAS LED AWAY FROM THE FIELD, ASHWATTHAMA REFLECTED.

KRISHNA AND ARJUNA ARE BOUND TO BE VICTORIOUS. I WILL NOT CONFRONT ARJUNA AGAIN. LET ME INSTEAD JOIN KARNA'S FORCES.

"KARNA WAS BUSY CONFRONTING NAKULA'S ONSLAUGHT.

O KARNA! THE GODS ARE INDEED PLEASED WITH ME TODAY. HOW I LONG TO KILL YOU, THE ROOT CAUSE OF ALL THIS ANIMOSITY!

BRAVE MEN DO NOT TALK; THEY ACT. LET ME PUT YOUR PRIDE IN ITS PLACE.

"KARNA ACTED OUT HIS THREAT AND UNABLE TO CONTAIN HIS ATTACK, NAKULA TRIED TO ESCAPE. KARNA LAUGHED AND SAID:

DO YOU REALISE YOU WERE BOASTING IN VAIN? RUN AWAY NOW.

"BY NOON WHILE KARNA CIRCLED THE BATTLEFIELD CAUSING HAVOC AND DESTRUCTION, SEVERAL DUELS WERE BEING FOUGHT.

"YUYUTSU FOUGHT ULOOKA.

"KRIPA CONFRONTED DHRISHTADYUMNA TO AVENGE THE DEATH OF DRONA.

"KRITAVARMA'S ARROW PIERCED SHIKHANDI'S ARMOUR AND, AS HE FAINTED, HE HELD ON TO THE FLAGPOST.

"ARJUNA WAS IN HIS ELEMENT DESTROY-ING THE SAMSHAPTAKAS WHO HAD ESCAPED HIS FURY EARLIER.

"DURYODHANA'S CONFRONTATION WITH YUDHISHTHIRA WAS IN KEEPING WITH A BRAVE KING. BUT NOT FOR LONG.

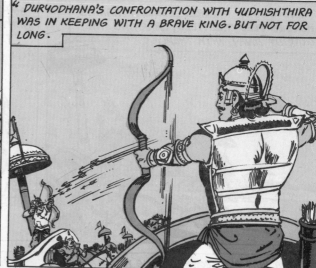

"WITH FOUR WELL-ARMED ARROWS, YUDHISHTHIRA KILLED DURYODHANA'S FOUR HORSES; WITH THE FIFTH ARROW, HE BEHEADED THE CHARIOTEER. WITH THE SIXTH, THE BANNER...

"...WITH THE SEVENTH, HE BROKE DURYODHANA'S BOW, AND WITH THE EIGHTH, HE SEVERED THE SWORD FROM DURYODHANA'S HAND.

"SEEING HIS PLIGHT, KARNA, ASHWAT-THAMA AND KRIPA RUSHED TO HIS AID. SOON THE FIGHT BECAME GENERAL.

"SO SWIFTLY DID ARJUNA SHOOT HIS ARROWS THAT THE SKY AS WELL AS THE EIGHT DIRECTIONS SEEMED TO BE FILLED WITH THE ARROWS RELEASED BY HIS GANDEEVA. HE SEEMED TO BE DANCING IN HIS CHARIOT.

amar chitra katha

"AFTER INFLICTING DEFEAT ON DURYODHANA, ASHWATTHAMA AND KRITAVARMA, ARJUNA TURNED TO KARNA.

"WHEN KARNA'S SHARP ARROWS FOUND THEIR MARK AND WOUNDED BOTH ARJUNA AND KRISHNA, THE PANDAVA WARRIORS GATHERED TO ATTACK HIM.

"AT SUNSET, THE SOLDIERS BEGAN TO RETURN TO THEIR CAMP.

LET US HOPE WE WILL NOT HAVE TO FIGHT AT NIGHT AGAIN.

"WHEN THE KAURAVA WARRIORS GATHERED TO DISCUSS THE STRATEGY FOR THE NEXT DAY, KARNA DECLARED—

ARJUNA IS CAREFUL, CLEVER AND DETERMINED. TODAY, WE FELL PREY TO HIS TACTICS. BUT TOMORROW I WILL SURELY MEET HIS CHALLENGE.

SO BE IT! COME, LET US ALL GET SOME REST NOW.

"ON THE DAWN OF THE SEVENTEENTH DAY OF THE BATTLE, KARNA CAME TO DURYODHANA.

TODAY I AM DETERMINED TO FACE ARJUNA IN A DUEL. I WILL KILL OR BE KILLED.

LIKE ARJUNA, I TOO HAVE ACCESS TO CELESTIAL WEAPONS. IN STRENGTH, SWIFT-NESS AND REACH, I CAN SURPASS ARJUNA.

MY BOW, VIJAYA IS EVEN BETTER THAN THE FAMED GANDEEVA OF ARJUNA—YET THERE ARE SOME POINTS IN WHICH I CANNOT EQUAL HIM.

HE HAS TWO INEXHAUSTIBLE CELESTIAL QUIVERS AND WHAT IS MORE, HE HAS KRISHNA AS HIS CHARIOTEER. IF ONLY SHALYA COULD DRIVE MY CHARIOT!

AS YOU WISH. I WILL ENSURE THAT YOU DO NOT RUN OUT OF WEAPONS OR CHARIOTS. I WILL TRY TO CONVINCE SHALYA ALSO.

"WHEN DURYODHANA REQUESTED SHALYA TO ACT AS KARNA'S CHARIOTEER, HE WAS LIVID WITH RAGE.

HOW CAN YOU INSULT A KSHATRIYA LIKE ME BY ASKING ME TO DO SUCH SERVILE WORK. I WILL GO BACK TO MY KINGDOM TODAY!

BUT, SHALYA, I DO NOT MEAN TO INSULT YOU AT ALL. I CONSIDER YOU TO BE SUPERIOR EVEN TO KRISHNA IN YOUR ABILITY TO HANDLE HORSES.

"SANJAYA NARRATED THE SCENE TO DHRITARASHTRA.

WHEN YOUR SON PUBLICLY PRAISED SHALYA AS BEING SUPERIOR TO KRISHNA, HE RELENTED AND AGREED TO BE CHARIOTEER TO KARNA ON CONDITION THAT THERE WOULD BE NO RESTRICTION ON WHAT HE COULD SAY.

"RESPLENDENT LIKE THE SUN AND FIRE ON A MIGHTY CLOUD, SAT KARNA AND SHALYA ON THE CHARIOT. ADDRESSING KARNA, DURYODHANA SAID—

O KARNA! THE TASK THAT THE GREAT BHEESHMA AND DRONA COULD NOT FULFIL IS YOURS TODAY. GO FORTH AND ANNIHILATE THE ENEMIES.

"KARNA SAID TO SHALYA—

LEAD ME TO THE PANDAVAS! I WILL KILL ALL FIVE OF THEM TODAY.

"SHALYA HAD CONSENTED TO THE TASK ON CONDITION THAT HE WOULD BE FREE TO SPEAK HIS MIND. SO HE SAID—

WAIT TILL YOU HEAR THE TWANG OF THE GANDEEVA, TILL YOU SEE BHEEMA OVERPOWERING ELEPHANT ARMIES, TILL YOU WITNESS THE SWIFT ARROWS OF YUDHISHTHIRA, NAKULA AND SAHADEVA.

OH! COME ON. LET US GO!

"AS THEY PROCEEDED TOWARDS THE BATTLEFIELD, SHALYA CONTINUED TO EXTOL ARJUNA'S VIRTUES.

LIKE THE SUN AND THE MOON ARE KRISHNA AND ARJUNA. YOU ARE A MERE FIREFLY IN COMPARISON.

I PROMISED TO ALLOW YOU TO SPEAK FREELY, OTHERWISE...

"BUT WHEN THEY CONTINUED TO EXCHANGE INSULTS DURYODHANA INTERVENED—

KARNA, PLEASE STOP ARGUING. SHALYA, I REQUEST YOU TO PUT AN END TO THIS FUTILE TALK.

"SEEING THE COMPLEX FORMATION OF THE KAURAVAS, YUDHISHTHIRA ASKED ARJUNA TO ARRAY THEIR FORCES IN A SUITABLE FORMATION.

ARJUNA, YOU ATTACK KARNA. BHEEMA WILL CONFRONT DURYODHANA. NAKULA WILL FACE VRISHASENA,* SAHADEVA WILL MEET SHAKUNI AND DHRISHTA-DYUMNA WILL FIGHT ASHWAT-THAMA. I WILL FIGHT KRIPACHARYA.

"WHEN THE SAMSHAPTAKAS CALLED OUT TO ARJUNA, HE ATTACKED THEM SINGLE-HANDED.

"AFTER THEIR NUMBERS BECAME DEPLETED, HE RAGED THROUGH THE KAURAVA FORCES LIKE FURY INCARNATE.

"KARNA TOO WAS IN HIS ELEMENT. HE RESEMBLED INDRA DEMOLISHING THE ASURAS.

* KARNA'S SON.

amar chitra katha

"YUDHISHTHIRA APPROACHED HIM.

LET ME SEE YOUR FAMED PROWESS. SHOW ME HOW POWERFUL YOU ARE.

I WILL BE TOO GLAD TO DO SO.

"ALTHOUGH SATYAKI AND OTHERS CAME TO HELP YUDHISHTHIRA, KARNA ROUTED THEM ALL. WHEN YUDHISHTHIRA'S ARMOUR WAS TORN ASUNDER, HE TURNED AWAY.

ARE YOU A TRUE KSHATRIYA? THEN HOW CAN YOU RUN AWAY? GO BACK TO ARJUNA OR KRISHNA. I WILL NOT KILL YOU IN THE BATTLEFIELD.

"BHEEMA WAS ENRAGED AT YUDHISHTHIRA'S INSULT. UNDER HIS ATTACK, KARNA FAINTED.

I WILL CUT OFF HIS TONGUE FOR INSULTING MY BROTHER AND KING.

RESTRAIN YOURSELF BHEEMA. REMEMBER, KILLING KARNA IS THE TASK OF ARJUNA.

"MEANWHILE ASHWATTHAMA CHALLENGED ARJUNA TO A DUEL AND COVERED HIM WITH ARROWS. KRISHNA EXCLAIMED—

WHAT HAS COME OVER YOU, ARJUNA? HAS YOUR GRIP LOOSENED? HAVE YOU LOST YOUR STRENGTH? THIS IS NO TIME TO BE CONSIDERATE TO A GURU OR HIS SON.

"KRISHNA'S TAUNTS HAD THE DESIRED EFFECT. WITH DIVINE WEAPONS, ARJUNA ATTACKED ASHWATTHAMA WITH SUCH FORCE THAT THE LATTER FAINTED AND HIS CHARIOT WAS DRIVEN AWAY FROM THE BATTLEFIELD.

"KRISHNA THEN DREW ARJUNA'S ATTENTION TO KARNA.

BEHOLD KARNA! HOW GRACEFULLY HE FIGHTS. THE FIELD IS STREWN WITH HIS VICTIMS. IT IS TIME YOU CONFRONTED HIM.

YES, I WILL. BUT WHERE IS YUDHISHTHIRA?

"BHEEMA TOLD HIM.

YUDHISHTHIRA, WOUNDED BY KARNA, HAS RETURNED TO THE CAMP.

"A WORRIED ARJUNA TOLD KRISHNA.

I MUST SEE MY BROTHER AT ONCE. THEN I WILL RETURN AND KILL KARNA.

"WHEN YUDHISHTHIRA SAW KRISHNA AND ARJUNA COMING, HE PRESUMED KARNA HAD BEEN KILLED.

AT LAST HE HAS BEEN KILLED! TELL ME, ARJUNA, WHICH ASTRA DID YOU USE TO KILL KARNA!

NO, I HAVE NOT KILLED HIM AS YET. I CAME TO ENQUIRE ABOUT YOUR HEALTH.

"YUDHISHTHIRA WAS FILLED WITH DESPAIR.

YOU HAVE DISAPPOINTED ME, ARJUNA. I WAS DEPENDING ON YOU TO SAVE OUR HONOUR. NOW SHAME ON YOU, YOUR CHARIOT AND YOUR MUCH VAUNTED STRENGTH.

"BEFORE ARJUNA COULD REPLY, KRISHNA INTERVENED AND PACIFIED HIM. WITH YUDHISHTHIRA'S BLESSINGS THEY RETURNED TO THE SCENE OF BATTLE.

REMEMBER, ARJUNA, KARNA IS NOT AN EASY ADVERSARY. HE IS A MATCHLESS ARCHER. YOU ALONE CAN KILL HIM.

WITH YOU AS MY PROTECTOR AND LORD, MY VICTORY IS ENSURED, KRISHNA.

"SHALYA'S EARLIER TAUNTS WERE NOW REPLACED WITH ENCOURAGEMENT AND ADMIRATION FOR KARNA.

HERE COMES ARJUNA. NOW YOU ALONE CAN KILL HIM.

TAKE ME TO HIM.

"BUT WHEN KARNA TRIED TO APPROACH ARJUNA, HIS PATH WAS BLOCKED BY FIVE PANDAVA WARRIORS.

"KARNA ROUTED THEM ALL IN A TRICE.

"IN THE GENERAL FIGHT THAT ENSUED, BHEEMA ENCOUNTERED DUHSHASANA.

COME DUHSHASANA! I HAVE WAITED LONG TO FIGHT WITH YOU. I HAVE AN ACCOUNT TO SETTLE.

I TOO REMEMBER A LOT, BHEEMA.

"WHEN HIS BOW WAS BROKEN, BHEEMA TOOK UP A HUGE MACE.

I REMEMBER HOW YOU HELD DRAUPADI'S HAIR WITH YOUR SINFUL HANDS.

I ALSO REMEMBER HOW SHAKUNI WANTED TO ENSLAVE HER ALONG WITH ALL OF YOU.

"AFTER HE KNOCKED DUHSHASANA OFF HIS CHARIOT, BHEEMA LET OUT A ROAR.

YOU REMEMBER, DO YOU? THEN YOU WILL REMEMBER HOW I HAD VOWED TO DRINK YOUR BLOOD.

"BHEEMA TURNED TO DURYODHANA.

I HAVE YOUR BROTHER AT MY MERCY. TRY AND SAVE HIM NOW.

"BHEEMA CUT OFF DUHSHASANA'S RIGHT HAND, RIPPED OPEN HIS CHEST AND TASTED HIS BLOOD.

"KARNA WAS GRIEF-STRICKEN. SHALYA COUNSELLED HIM.

DO NOT LOSE HEART, KARNA. YOU ARE DURYODHANA'S ONLY HOPE. COME LET US GO TO ARJUNA.

"KARNA'S SON VRISHASENA WAS TORMENTING NAKULA. BHEEMA CALLED TO ARJUNA FOR HELP.

I WILL KILL KARNA'S SON IN FRONT OF HIM.

"ARJUNA'S SHARP ARROWS FOUND THEIR MARK. KARNA SAW HIS SON BEING KILLED. ENRAGED HE SAID —

NOW I CANNOT WAIT TO KILL THIS ARJUNA. TAKE ME CLOSER, O SHALYA.

"AT LAST THE TWO HEROES WERE FACE TO FACE, WELL-MATCHED WITH THEIR SINEWY BODIES RUBBED WITH RED SANDALPASTE. BOTH WERE MOUNTED ON EXCELLENT CHARIOTS WITH WHITE UMBRELLAS AND WHITE HORSES.

"AS THEY WERE ENGAGED IN THE DUEL, THEIR MEN ENCOURAGED THEM WITH CHEERS AND THE BLOWING OF CONCH SHELLS.

"SOON, INSTEAD OF EARTHLY WEAPONS, THEY RESORTED TO CELESTIAL ONES. ARJUNA SENT OFF THE AGNEYASTRA AND KARNA COUNTERED IT WITH THE VARUNASTRA.

" IT WAS A TUSSLE BETWEEN EQUALS.

" KRISHNA SAID —

HOW COME KARNA IS ABLE TO DESTROY ALL YOUR WEAPONS TODAY? ROUSE YOURSELF!

I WILL USE THE BRAHMA- STRA NOW.

"THE BRAHMASTRA COVERED THE FIELD WITH ARROWS AND DEAD BODIES BUT KARNA'S ARROWS WERE ALSO COMING IN A CONTINUOUS STREAM.

" THE AIR RESOUNDED WITH THE TERRIBLE TWANGS OF THE GANDEEVA OF ARJUNA AND THE VIJAYA OF KARNA. THEY TWANGED TO LET FORTH A BARRAGE OF ARROWS. ELEVEN TIMES KARNA CUT ARJUNA'S BOW STRINGS. QUICK AS A FLASH, ARJUNA REPLACED THEM EVERY TIME. KARNA THEN DISCHARGED FIVE SNAKE-LIKE ARROWS. ARJUNA CUT EVERY ONE OF THEM INTO PIECES.

amar chitra katha

"SO NUMEROUS WERE THE ARROWS SHOT BY ARJUNA THAT NOTHING — NEITHER KARNA'S CHARIOT NOR THE SUN IN THE SKY — WAS VISIBLE FOR SOME TIME.

"SOON THE WARRIORS BEHIND KARNA FLED IN TERROR OF ARJUNA. KARNA AIMED THE NAGASTRA AT ARJUNA'S NECK.

ARJUNA! BID FAREWELL TO THE WORLD. THIS IS YOUR LAST MOMENT.

"JUST IN TIME, KRISHNA PRESSED HARD SO THAT THE HORSES BENT DOWN AND THE CHARIOT SUNK BY FIVE INCHES IN THE GROUND. NOW THE WEAPON SCRAPED PAST ARJUNA'S HEAD AND KNOCKED OFF HIS CROWN.

"ARJUNA GATHERED HIS CURLY TRESSES IN A WHITE KERCHIEF AND RESUMED FIGHTING. BY NOW EVEN KRISHNA AND SHALYA WERE WOUNDED.

"MEANWHILE, KARNA'S CHARIOT WHEEL WAS SINKING INTO THE GROUND. WHEN HE NOTICED IT, HE RECALLED HOW A BRAHMANA HAD ONCE CURSED HIM.

WHEN YOU ARE CONFRONTING YOUR BIGGEST ENEMY, YOUR CHARIOT WHEELS WILL SINK INTO THE GROUND. AS YOU KILLED MY POOR COW, YOU TOO WILL BE KILLED.

"BY NOW THE LEFT WHEEL WAS TOTALLY SUNK IN THE SOFT EARTH. KARNA WAS FORCED TO DESCEND.

ARJUNA, PLEASE STOP FIGHTING WHILE I RAISE THIS WHEEL. IT IS NOT FAIR TO FIGHT ME NOW WHEN I AM ON THE GROUND.

"KRISHNA WAS FURIOUS.

SO YOU WANT US TO BE FAIR. DID YOU THINK OF BEING FAIR AT THE GAME OF DICE? WERE YOU RIGHTEOUS WHEN YOU SURROUNDED AND KILLED ABHIMANYU?

"KARNA CLIMBED ONTO HIS CHARIOT AGAIN AND FOUGHT ARJUNA. WHEN HE MANAGED TO INJURE HIM, HE GOT OFF THE CHARIOT AGAIN. KRISHNA SAID—

HURRY, ARJUNA! KILL HIM BEFORE HE GETS UP ON HIS CHARIOT.

"ARJUNA INVOKED A DIVINE ASTRA, ANJALIKA, AND AIMED IT AT KARNA WHO WAS STILL STRUGGLING TO LIFT THE WHEEL.

IF I HAVE LIVED A DUTIFUL AND RIGHTEOUS LIFE, MAY THIS WEAPON DESTROY MY ENEMY.

LIKE THE SUN DESCENDING ON EARTH, THE HEAD OF THE GREAT KARNA FELL ON THE GROUND.

"THUS ENDS THE THIRTY-SEVENTH SESSION OF OUR RENDERING OF VYASA'S IMMORTAL ITIHASA MAHABHARATA.

amar chitra katha

Mahabharata-38
THE KURUS ROUTED

THUS ON THE AFTERNOON OF THE SEVENTEENTH DAY OF THE GREAT WAR, KARNA LAY DEAD ON THE BATTLEFIELD. THE SUN APPEARED TO MELLOW ITS RADIANCE FOR A WHILE AS IF MOURNING THE DEATH OF HIS BELOVED SON.

"A TEARFUL SHALYA DROVE THE CHARIOT BACK, DIVESTED OF BOTH ITS BANNER AND OWNER."

"HIS EARS WERE FILLED WITH THE TRIUMPHANT CRIES OF REJOICING EMANATING FROM THE PANDAVA FORCES CELEBRATING THEIR VICTORY.

"DHRITARASHTRA ASKED SANJAYA —

WHAT WAS THE STATE OF OUR ARMY AFTER THE FEARSOME DUEL BETWEEN KARNA AND ARJUNA?

OUR SOLDIERS WERE LIKE A HERD OF BULLS SHORN OF THEIR HORNS OR LIKE SERPENTS DEPRIVED OF THEIR FANGS. THE ARMY WAS IN TOTAL DISARRAY.

"TO RALLY HIS FORCES AGAIN, DURYODHANA HAD TO TAKE THE LEAD.

TAKE MY CHARIOT AHEAD. I WILL KILL ARJUNA, KRISHNA AND THAT CONCEITED BHEEMA, AND AVENGE THE DEATH OF KARNA.

"BHEEMA JUMPED DOWN FROM HIS CHARIOT AND WITH HIS MACE MERCILESSLY KILLED THE SOLDIERS ON FOOT...

...WHILE ARJUNA ATTACKED THE WARRIORS ON CHARIOTS.

"TORMENTED BY THE ARROWS OF DHRISHTADYUMNA, SHIKHANDI, NAKULA AND SAHADEVA, THE KAURAVA SOLDIERS BEGAN TO FLEE THE BATTLEFIELD.

"DURYODHANA ADDRESSED THE FLEEING SOLDIERS.

WHERE WILL YOU RUN? THE COWARD AND THE BRAVE ALIKE HAVE TO FACE DEATH ULTIMATELY. COME, MY BRAVE WARRIORS, CHOOSE TO DIE LIKE TRUE KSHATRIYAS.

"BUT THE WOUNDED AND FRIGHTENED SOLDIERS WERE IN NO MOOD TO HEAR HIS DISCOURSE. THEY RAN AS FAST AS THEIR FEET COULD TAKE THEM. SHALYA SAID TO DURYODHANA —

BEHOLD, O KING! THE FIELD IS STREWN WITH FALLEN SOLDIERS. COME, LET US RETURN TO CAMP. ALLOW THE SOLDIERS TO GO BACK.

"DURYODHANA COULD NOT CONTROL HIS TEARS AS THEY MADE THEIR WAY BACK TO THEIR CAMP. HE COULD NOT GET OVER KARNA'S DEATH.

OH! KARNA! KARNA!

"IN A JUBILANT MOOD, KRISHNA AND ARJUNA RETURNED TO THE CAMP.

"THEY RUSHED TO YUDHISHTHIRA'S TENT TO CONVEY THE NEWS OF KARNA'S DEATH.

"KRISHNA SAID—

IT IS INDEED FORTUNATE THAT ARJUNA, BHEEMA, NAKULA, SAHADEVA AND YOU HAVE EMERGED UNSCATHED IN THE BATTLE. COME, LET US HASTEN TO FINISH THE TASK IN HAND. YOU MUST PREPARE YOURSELF TO RULE THE EARTH NOW.

"YUDHISHTHIRA AFFECTIONATELY HELD KRISHNA'S HAND AND SAID —

WITH YOU ON OUR SIDE, OUR VICTORY WAS CERTAIN, O LORD! TONIGHT, AFTER THIRTEEN LONG YEARS, WE WILL SLEEP WITHOUT A WORRY.

"IN THE KAURAVA CAMP THE VENERABLE KRIPACHARYA COUNSELLED DURYODHANA.

TO FIGHT IN BATTLE IS INDEED THE PRIME DUTY OF A KSHATRIYA. BUT NOW BHEESHMA, DRONA, KARNA, JAYADRATHA AND ALL YOUR BROTHERS HAVE BEEN KILLED. EVEN YOUR SON LAKSHMANA HAS BEEN KILLED.

SEVENTEEN LONG DAYS OF DREADFUL BATTLE HAVE PASSED. LIKE A RAGING FOREST FIRE, ARJUNA HAS DESTROYED YOUR ARMY. MAKE PEACE WITH THE PANDAVAS. THIS IS MY SINCERE ADVICE TO YOU.

"FOR A WHILE, DURYODHANA SAT SILENT. THEN WITH A SIGH HE SAID —

I KNOW YOU MEAN WELL, BUT I CANNOT TAKE YOUR ADVICE. A MAN ON HIS DEATHBED DOES NOT RELISH MEDICINE.

HAVING RULED OVER THE ENTIRE EARTH, HOW CAN I BE A DEPENDANT OF THE PANDAVAS. TO DIE PEACE-FULLY IN BED IS SHAME-FUL FOR A TRUE KSHATRIYA. SO FIGHT I MUST AND DIE A GLORIOUS DEATH.

"HIS SOLDIERS HAILED HIS DECISION AND RESOLVING TO FIGHT THE NEXT DAY THEY ALL RETIRED FOR THE NIGHT.

"NEXT MORNING, DURYODHANA CONSULTED ASHWATTHAMA.

I SEEK YOUR ADVICE AS THE SON OF OUR GURU. WHO DO YOU SUGGEST SHOULD LEAD OUR ARMY NOW?

BRAVE SHALYA SHOULD BE OUR COMMANDER!

"DURYODHANA REQUESTED SHALYA TO TAKE CHARGE.

THIS IS A TESTING TIME FOR US. PLEASE TAKE COMMAND AND LEAD US TO VICTORY.

I SHALL DO MY BEST FOR YOU. EITHER WIN THE WAR OR DIE IN THE BATTLEFIELD.

"THE KAURAVAS THEN PLANNED THEIR STRATEGY—

REFRAIN FROM SINGLE COMBATS. WE WILL FIGHT NO DUELS TODAY. OUR WARRIORS WILL FIGHT IN UNISON AND PROTECT ONE ANOTHER.

"WHEN THE KAURAVA SOLDIERS LEARNT THAT SHALYA WOULD BE THEIR COMMANDER, THEY CHEERED SO LOUDLY THAT YUDHISHTHIRA COULD HEAR THEM.

I THINK SHALYA, THE ACE ARCHER, HAS BEEN PUT IN COMMAND. O KRISHNA, WHAT DO YOU SUGGEST WE SHOULD DO?

SHALYA IS INDEED SUPE-RIOR TO STALWARTS LIKE SHIKHANDI.

"KRISHNA CONTINUED —

YOU ALONE ARE CAPABLE OF KILLING SHALYA, O KING! FORGET THAT HE IS YOUR UNCLE AND FIGHT.

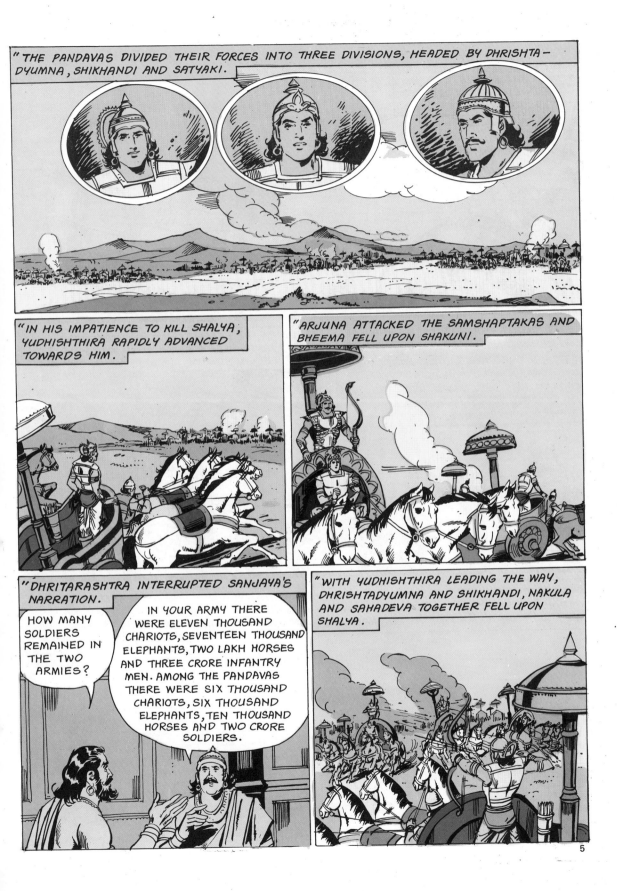

"THE KAURAVA SOLDIERS WERE FRIGHTENED OF THIS COMBINED ATTACK. BUT SHALYA WAS UNDAUNTED. HE TOLD HIS CHARIOTEER.

LEAD ME ON TO YUDHISHTHIRA AND WATCH ME IN ACTION TODAY.

"INDEED SHALYA ALONE WAS CAPABLE OF RESTRAINING THE SURGING PANDAVA FORCES.

"JUST THEN, NAKULA ATTACKED KARNA'S SON, CHITRASENA. BEING EQUALLY WELL-MATCHED IN PROWESS, THEIR DUEL WAS LONG DRAWN AND FURIOUS. NAKULA'S CHARIOT WAS DESTROYED. WITH HIS SWORD HELD ALOFT, HE ADVANCED TOWARDS CHITRASENA.

"SUDDENLY, HE LEAPED ONTO CHITRASENA'S CHARIOT, AND WITH A FATAL BLOW FROM HIS SWORD, BEHEADED HIM.

"CHITRASENA'S BROTHERS, SUSHENA AND SATYASENA ATTACKED NAKULA, BUT SOON MET WITH THE SAME FATE AS CHITRASENA.

"SEEING SHALYA BEING ATTACKED BY THE PANDAVAS, RRITAVARMA, KRIPA, SHARUNI AND ASHWATTHAMA CAME TO HIS HELP.

"AN ENRAGED KRITAVARMA INFLICTED A WOUND ON BHEEMA.

"KRIPACHARYA WORRIED DHRISHTADYUMNA WITH A VOLLEY OF ARROWS...

"...AND ASHWATTHAMA ATTACKED NAKULA AND SAHADEVA.

"WHEN BHEEMA'S HORSES WERE KILLED BY KRITAVARMA, HE JUMPED DOWN FROM THE CHARIOT, BRANDISHING HIS MACE.

"AFTER CHASING AWAY KRITAVARMA, BHEEMA TURNED TO SHALYA AND KILLED HIS HORSES. SHALYA SKILFULLY THREW A SPEAR AT BHEEMA.

"UNRUFFLED, BHEEMA CAUGHT THE WEAPON IN HIS HAND AND THREW IT BACK AT SHALYA'S CHARIOTEER SO SWIFTLY THAT HE FELL OFF.

"SHALYA THEN TOOK UP A MACE STANDING TALL LIKE A MOUNTAIN. THE TWO WARRIORS RESEMBLED TWO ENRAGED BULLS RARING FOR A FIGHT.

"SPARKS FLEW EACH TIME THEIR MACES CLASHED. WOUNDED AND BLEEDING PROFUSELY, THEY CIRCLED, REARED AND ATTACKED TILL BOTH OF THEM COLLAPSED SIMULTANEOUSLY.

"KRIPACHARYA QUICKLY PUT SHALYA ON HIS OWN CHARIOT AND TOOK HIM AWAY.

"ON RECOVERING, BHEEMA SPRANG UP WITH A ROAR, READY FOR THE FRAY AGAIN.

COME, SHALYA! FIGHT ME IF YOU DARE.

"THE ENTHUSED SOLDIERS FROM BOTH ARMIES SEEMED ALL EAGER TO EMBRACE DEATH. THE BATTLEFIELD RESOUNDED WITH THEIR BLOOD-CURDLING CRIES.

KILL, KILL!

SLAY HIM!

CUT HIM TO PIECES!

DESTROY!

"SHALYA AND YUDHISHTHIRA WERE ONCE AGAIN IN DIRECT CONFRONTATION; WHEN YUDHISH-THIRA CUT OFF SHALYA'S BANNER WITH A WELL-AIMED SPEAR, HE RETALIATED BY COVERING HIM WITH A CLOUD OF ARROWS.

amar chitra katha

"SATYAKI, BHEEMA, NAKULA AND SAHADEVA RUSHED TO YUDHISHTHIRA'S SIDE AND HARASSED SHALYA.

"BUT SHALYA TOOK GOOD CARE OF HIMSELF, ATTACKING SATYAKI, BHEEMA AND NAKULA WITH A SHOWER OF ARROWS.

"THE PANDAVAS TRIED VARIOUS WEAPONS ON SHALYA, BUT HE LIVED UP TO HIS REPUTATION OF A GREAT WARRIOR. HE QUELLED THEM ALL. A NIGGLING DOUBT BEGAN TO TORMENT YUDHISHTHIRA.

KRISHNA SAID WE WOULD BE VICTORIOUS. BUT SHALYA APPEARS TO BE CAPABLE OF DESTROYING MY WHOLE ARMY. ALL OF US TOGETHER CANNOT CONTAIN HIM.

"MEANWHILE, ARJUNA AND ASHWATTHAMA WERE LOCKED IN COMBAT. ARJUNA'S CHARIOT WAS BARELY VISIBLE UNDER THE ARROWS.

"NOTING SHALYA'S PROWESS, YUDHISHTHIRA CALLED HIS BROTHERS TOGETHER.

BHEESHMA, DRONA, KARNA AND OTHER WARRIORS FELL BECAUSE OF YOUR EFFORTS. NOW SHALYA ALONE REMAINS. LEAVE THIS TASK TO ME.

I WANT NAKULA AND SAHADEVA TO GUARD MY CHARIOT WHEELS. SATYAKI SHOULD BE ON MY RIGHT AND DHRISHTADYUMNA ON MY LEFT. BHEEMA, I WANT YOU TO BE AHEAD OF ME, AND ARJUNA BEHIND ME.

"READILY, THE BROTHERS AGREED. LIKE TWO HUNGRY LIONS POUNCING ON A PREY, YUDHISHTHIRA AND SHALYA LUNGED AT EACH OTHER.

"THE MILD AND CALM YUDHISHTHIRA APPEARED TO BE TRANSFORMED INTO A DETERMINED AND FORMIDABLE FOE.

"LIKE A STRONG GUST OF WIND DISPELLING CLOUDS, YUDHISHTHIRA PLAYED HAVOC WITH THE KAURAVA ARMY.

STAND STILL, SHALYA! HERE I COME!

"SO GALLANTLY DID YUDHISHTHIRA AND SHALYA FIGHT THAT IT WAS IMPOSSIBLE TO SAY WHO WOULD WIN IN THE DUEL.

TODAY, SURELY YUDHISHTHIRA WILL WIN THE WAR OR LOSE IT WITH HIS LIFE.

"SHALYA FIRED A HUNDRED ARROWS ON YUDHISHTHIRA WHO RETALIATED WITH THREE HUNDRED. SOON SHALYA'S REAR GUARDS WERE KILLED, HIS HORSES SLAIN AND BANNER FELLED.

"NOTING SHALYA'S PLIGHT, ASHWATTHAMA QUICKLY PUT HIM ON HIS OWN CHARIOT AND CARRIED HIM AWAY.

"YUDHISHTHIRA ROARED LIKE A LION AS HE SAW HIS ADVERSARY GETTING AWAY. BUT SOON SHALYA WAS BACK ON ANOTHER CHARIOT.

"BHEEMA, SATYAKI, NAKULA AND SAHADEVA FORMED A PROTECTIVE RING ROUND YUDHISHTHIRA AND CHALLENGED SHALYA TO FIGHT.

"UNDER YUDHISHTHIRA'S ATTACK SHALYA BECAME UNCONSCIOUS. HOWEVER, HE QUICKLY RECOVERED AND DISCHARGED A HUNDRED ARROWS AT YUDHISHTHIRA.

"WITH NINE WELL-AIMED ARROWS, YUDHISHTHIRA TORE OFF SHALYA'S ARMOUR. IN RETALIATION, SHALYA BROKE YUDHISHTHIRA'S BOW.

"SOON, SHALYA'S ARROWS RENT ASUNDER YUDHISHTHIRA'S GOLDEN ARMOUR AND KILLED HIS HORSES. KRIPA KILLED HIS CHARIOTEER.

" BHEEMA BEGAN TO HARASS SHALYA. WITH A SINGLE SWIFT ARROW, HE BROKE SHALYA'S BOW AND WITH ANOTHER KILLED THE CHARIOTEER. SOON THE FOUR HORSES TOO FELL.

" SHALYA NOW JUMPED DOWN, SWORD IN ONE HAND AND SHIELD IN THE OTHER.

" DHRISHTADYUMNA, SHIKHANDI AND SATYAKI SURROUNDED SHALYA WHILE BHEEMA BROKE HIS SHIELD TO PIECES AND KNOCKED HIS SWORD OFF.

" THE FRIGHTENED KAURAVA SOLDIERS RAN PELL-MELL IN ALL DIRECTIONS. SHALYA CHARGED TOWARDS YUDHISHTHIRA.

" YUDHISHTHIRA PICKED UP A FIERCE LOOKING GOLDEN JAVELIN, STUDDED WITH GEMS, AND THREW IT AT SHALYA'S BROAD CHEST.

" WITH HIS ARMS SPREAD OUT, SHALYA FELL DOWN. THE VERY EARTH APPEARED TO RISE TO WEL—COME HIM.

"IN HIS WARLIKE FERVOUR YUDHISHTHIRA CONTINUED TO ATTACK THE KAURAVA ARMY.

"SHALYA'S ARMY RALLIED TOGETHER TO ATTACK THE PANDAVAS.

"SHAKUNI ASKED DURYODHANA —

WHY DID YOU ALLOW SHALYA'S ARMY TO ATTACK THE PANDAVAS? HAD WE NOT ALL DECIDED TO FIGHT IN UNISON?

I DID TRY, BUT THEY DID NOT HEED ME. LOOK NOW, THEY HAVE ALL FALLEN AND LIE DEAD.

"SEEING HIS ARMY DEMORALISED BY THE FALL OF THEIR COMMANDER, DURYODHANA SAID TO HIS CHARIOTEER —

PLACE MY CHARIOT BEHIND OUR ARMY. I MUST PERSUADE THEM NOT TO FLEE.

"SEEING DURYODHANA TAKING CHARGE, TWENTY ONE THOUSAND KAURAVA SOLDIERS WERE INFUSED WITH CONFIDENCE AGAIN TO FACE THE ENEMY.

HERE COMES THE MIGHTY DURYODHANA TO LEAD US. LET US ATTACK THE PANDAVAS!

"BHEEMA SAW THE ROARING MASS APPROACHING, AND QUICKLY DESCENDED FROM HIS CHARIOT. WITH HIS MACE, HE SOON MANAGED TO KILL MOST OF THEM.

"THE KAURAVA KINGS TOO BEGAN TO FLEE. DURYODHANA CALLED OUT—

DO NOT RUN AWAY! YOU WILL SURELY BE KILLED IF ISOLATED. COME LET US FIGHT TOGETHER.

"PERSUADED BY DURYODHANA, THE KAURAVA KINGS PREPARED TO FACE THE ENEMY.

"ADDRESSING KRISHNA, ARJUNA SAID—

FOR EIGHTEEN DAYS, THIS BATTLE HAS BEEN GOING ON. TODAY I MUST DESTROY THE WHOLE KAURAVA ARMY AND PUT AN END TO IT.

"SOON, THE ARROWS, EMERGING IN A RAPID VOLLEY FROM THE GANDEEVA, COVERED THE ENTIRE BATTLEFIELD.

"TORTURED BY ARJUNA'S ARROWS, THE KAURAVA SOLDIERS WERE AGAIN READY TO FLEE.

"DURYODHANA TRIED TO REPEL DHRISHTADYUMNA WHO WAS ATTACKING THE ARMY.

14

amar chitra katha

"WHEN DHRISHTADYUMNA KILLED HIS HORSES AND CHARIOTEER, DURYODHANA RODE AWAY ON HORSEBACK.

"ASHWATTHAMA, KRIPACHARYA AND KRITAVARMA NOTED HIS ABSENCE.

WHERE IS KING DURYODHANA?

HE HAS GONE TOWARDS SHAKUNI.

HOW DOES IT MATTER? LET US CONCENTRATE ON THE FIGHT.

"SANJAYA NARRATED THE SUBSEQUENT EVENTS*

HARASSED BY ARJUNA'S ARROWS KRIPA, KRITAVARMA AND ASHWATTHAMA RAN TOWARDS SHAKUNI. DHRISHTA-DYUMNA SOON ADVANCED TO THAT SPOT. WITHOUT ANY THOUGHT FOR MY LIFE, I TOO JOINED THE FOUR WARRIORS IN THEIR BATTLE AGAINST DHRISHTADYUMNA. WE WERE DEFEATED. THEN SATYAKI ATTACKED ME AND CAPTURED ME AND I FAINTED.

"AFTER DESTROYING OUR ENTIRE ARMY OF ELEPHANTS, BHEEMA ATTACKED DURYODHANA'S BROTHERS.

"UNITED THEY TRIED TO REPEL HIS ATTACK, BUT SOON THEY WERE STRUCK DOWN BY HIS ARROWS AND FELL LIKE TREES UPROOTED ON A MOUNTAINSIDE IN A STRONG GALE.

"ON THIS EIGHTEENTH DAY OF THE TERRIBLE WAR, BHEEMA WAS IN HIS ELEMENT. AFTER PUTTING TO DEATH ALMOST ALL OF THE KAURAVA BROTHERS, HE TURNED TO THE REST OF THE ENEMY ARMY. SOON THE BATTLEFIELD AROUND HIM WAS STREWN WITH THE BODIES OF COUNTLESS ELEPHANTS, HORSES AND SOLDIERS THAT SUCCUMBED TO HIS MIGHTY MACE.

* SANJAY MIGHT HAVE NARRATED THIS AFTER THE DAY'S BATTLE

15

"KRISHNA SAID TO ARJUNA —

BEHOLD DURYO-DHANA AND SUDARSHANA AMIDST THE HORSEMEN. KILL THEM!

O, KRISHNA, ONLY THESE TWO REMAIN OF ALL DHRITARASHTRA'S SONS. THEY TOO WILL DIE TODAY; REST ASSUR-ED.

"ARJUNA THEN ATTACKED THE TRIGARTA ARMY, WHICH HAD BEEN HARASSING HIM ALL THESE DAYS.

"AT LAST HE KILLED SUSHARMA, THUS ENDING THE TRIGARTA SAGA.

" BHEEMA KILLED SUDAR-SHANA WITH SHARP ARROWS. DURYODHANA ALONE REMAINED AMONG THE KAURAVA BROTHERS.

"SHAKUNI AND HIS SON ULOOKA ATTACKED BHEEMA AND SAHADEVA.

"SO NUMEROUS WERE THE ARROWS SENT BY SAHADEVA IN RESPONSE THAT THEY COVERED THE SKY LIKE A SWARM OF LOCUSTS.

"ULOOKA SHOT SEVEN ARROWS AT BHEEMA AND SEVENTY AT SAHADEVA. SAHADEVA RETALIATED SUITABLY.

"HE BEHEADED ULOOKA WITH HIS SPEAR. SHAKUNI'S EYES BRIMMED OVER WITH TEARS. WITH A DEEP SIGH HE RECALLED VIDURA'S WORDS.

"AN ENRAGED SHAKUNI ATTACKED SAHADEVA WITH VARIOUS WEAPONS, BUT HIS ATTEMPTS WERE OF NO AVAIL.

"HIS DAGGER WAS CUT—

"HIS BOW WAS BROKEN—

"HIS MACE WAS FELLED—

"AND HIS SPEAR FELL LIKE LIGHTNING FROM THE SKY.

"FILLED WITH FEAR, SHAKUNI AND HIS MEN RAN AWAY. THE PANDAVAS REJOICED IN THEIR VICTORY.

"SAHADEVA CHASED THE FLEEING SHAKUNI.

OH FOOL! BE A KSHATRIYA! FIGHT LIKE A MAN! YOU EVIL SHAKUNI, COME, PAY FOR YOUR CUNNING MOVES IN THAT GAME OF DICE.

"DURYODHANA STOOD ALONE, WITHOUT AN ARMY OR A CHARIOT, FORLORN AND WOUNDED.

"THERE HE WAS, THE LONE WARRIOR FACING AN ARMY OF TWO THOUSAND CHARIOTS, SEVEN HUNDRED ELEPHANTS, FIVE THOUSAND HORSES AND TEN THOUSAND SOLDIERS WITH DHRISHTADYUMNA IN COMMAND. THE JOYOUS SOUNDS OF CELEBRATION REVERBERATED IN HIS EARS.

"WHEN HE LOOKED AROUND, HE SAW THE BATTLEFIELD STREWN WITH HIS FALLEN SOLDIERS. PETRIFIED WITH FEAR, HE TOOK TO HIS HEELS.

"A MIGHTY KING PROTECTED BY ELEVEN AKSHAUHINIS NOW HAD JUST A MACE OVER HIS SHOULDER TO DEFEND HIM. HE RECALLED VIDURA'S WORDS.

VIDURA, IN HIS WISDOM, HAD REALISED THE OUTCOME OF THIS BATTLE!

19

"RUNNING NORTHWARDS, HE CAME UPON A LAKE AND DECIDED TO IMMERSE HIMSELF IN IT.

"MEANWHILE, ON SAGE VYASA'S BIDDING, SATYAKI RELEASED SANJAYA AND LET HIM GO.

"WHILE SANJAYA WAS RETURNING TO THE CITY, HE ESPIED DURYODHANA, ALONE AND WOUNDED.

"SANJAYA RECALLED THE SCENE LATER.

I WAS DUMBSTRUCK WITH SHOCK AND SORROW AT HIS STATE. TO SEE A MIGHTY KING, WHOSE POMP AND GLORY WERE ONCE UNRIVALLED, REDUCED TO A PITIABLE CONDITION.

"SANJAYA NARRATED TO DURYODHANA THE TALE OF HIS CAPTURE AND SUBSEQUENT RELEASE.

VYASA TOLD ME THAT ONLY THREE MAHARATHIS* NOW REMAIN ON OUR SIDE.

"DURYODHANA SIGHED DEEPLY AND SAID —

THERE IS NO ONE BUT YOU WHOM I CAN CALL MY OWN NOW. CONVEY MY MESSAGE TO MY FATHER THAT I HAVE ENTERED THE DEPTHS OF THIS LAKE.

✱ THE HIGHEST HONOUR BESTOWED ON A WARRIOR.

"DURYODHANA THEN ENTERED THE POOL AFTER MAKING THE WATER STAND STILL. JUST THEN, ASHWATTHAMA, KRIPACHARYA AND KRITAVARMA ARRIVED ON THE SCENE.

"WOUNDED AND WEARY, THEY WERE SURPRISED TO SEE SANJAYA.

SANJAYA! HOW FORTUNATE TO SEE YOU STILL ALIVE. DO YOU KNOW WHERE DURYO-DHANA IS?

"SANJAYA GAVE THEM DURYODHANA'S MESSAGE. ASHWATTHAMA LOOKED TOWARDS THE LAKE AND SAID —

ALAS! THE KING DOES NOT KNOW WE ARE ALIVE. TOGETHER WE CAN STILL FACE THE PANDAVAS.

"THE THREE WARRIORS WAITED AWHILE, BEMOANING DURYODHANA'S DECISION. BUT WHEN THEY HEARD THE SOUND OF SOLDIERS APPROACHING, THEY WENT AWAY.

"ALONG WITH SANJAYA, THEY RETURNED TO THE CAMP. ON HEARING THE NEWS OF THE DEFEAT, THE GUARDS, ALREADY SHAKEN WITH WORRY, BROKE DOWN.

"THE OLDER MEN OF THE CAMP, WHO WERE LOOKING AFTER THE LADIES, MADE PREPARATIONS TO RETURN TO HASTINAPURA.

"CRYING AND WAILING, THE WOMEN WERE ESCORTED TO THE CITY BY THE SENTRIES AND THE OLD MINISTERS.

"UNABLE TO BEAR THE LONELINESS OF THE DESERTED CAMP, ASHWATTHAMA, KRIPA AND KRITAVARMA RETURNED TO THE LAKE SIDE.

"ON REACHING THE LAKE, THEY SOFTLY CALLED OUT TO DURYODHANA.

ARISE O KING! COME WITH US TO FIGHT YUDHISHTHIRA, WIN AND CONQUER, OR DIE IN GLORY.

YOU TOO HAVE DESTROYED MUCH OF THE PANDAVA ARMY. WE CAN EASILY SUBDUE THE REMAINING FEW, WOUNDED AND WEARY AS THEY ARE. COME, LET US FIGHT!

"DURYODHANA'S VOICE WAS HEARD FROM UNDER THE WATER.

I AM SO HAPPY YOU HAVE SURVIVED THIS FEARFUL WAR. JUST NOW, I AM EXHAUSTED AND WOUNDED. BUT TOMORROW, WE WILL CERTAINLY FIGHT AGAIN.

"DELIGHTED AT DURYODHANA'S DECISION TO FIGHT, ASHWATTHAMA DECLARED —

GLORY TO YOU, O KING! WE WILL SURELY DESTROY THEM. I SWEAR I WILL KILL THEM AS SOON AS DAY DAWNS!

"SOME HUNTERS WHO HAPPENED TO COME TO THE LAKE TO QUENCH THEIR THIRST OVERHEARD THE CONVERSATION.

"THEY CONCLUDED THAT DURYODHANA WAS HIDDEN IN THE LAKE AND WAS BEING INVITED TO FIGHT AGAIN. TALKING IN WHISPERS, THEY SAID —

IF WE TELL YUDHISHTHIRA THAT DURYODHANA IS HIDING HERE, WE WILL SURELY BE REWARDED.

COME, LET US GO FAST. MAYBE WE WILL GET SO RICH WE WILL NEVER HAVE TO WORK AGAIN.

"MEANWHILE, YUDHISHTHIRA REALISED THAT DURYODHANA WAS MISSING AND SENT HIS SPIES IN ALL DIRECTIONS.

"WHEN THEY RETURNED WITHOUT ANY CLUE OF DURYODHANA'S WHEREABOUTS, YUDHISHTHIRA WAS WORRIED INDEED.

"JUST THEN THE HUNTERS ARRIVED AT THE CAMP. IGNORING THE PROTESTS OF THE GUARDS, THEY FORCED THEIR WAY IN.

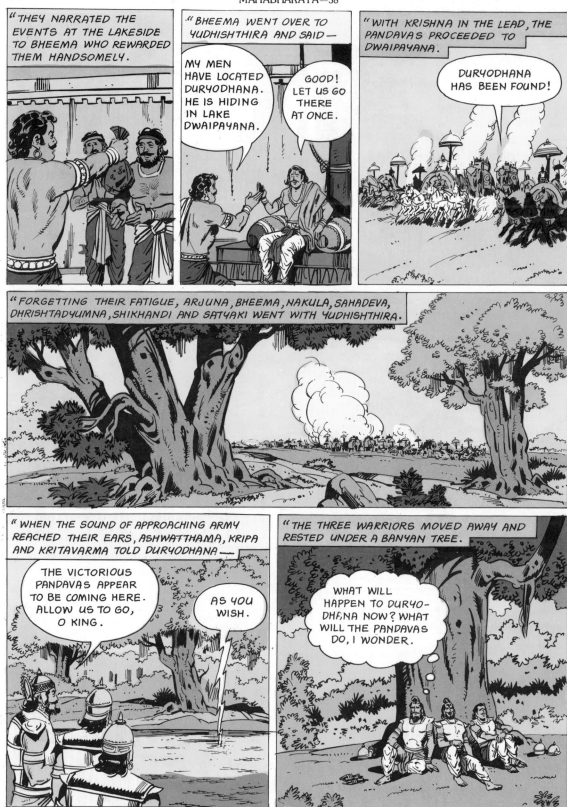

"THEY NARRATED THE EVENTS AT THE LAKESIDE TO BHEEMA WHO REWARDED THEM HANDSOMELY.

."BHEEMA WENT OVER TO YUDHISHTHIRA AND SAID—

MY MEN HAVE LOCATED DURYODHANA. HE IS HIDING IN LAKE DWAIPAYANA.

GOOD! LET US GO THERE AT ONCE.

"WITH KRISHNA IN THE LEAD, THE PANDAVAS PROCEEDED TO DWAIPAYANA.

DURYODHANA HAS BEEN FOUND!

"FORGETTING THEIR FATIGUE, ARJUNA, BHEEMA, NAKULA, SAHADEVA, DHRISHTADYUMNA, SHIKHANDI AND SATYAKI WENT WITH YUDHISHTHIRA.

" WHEN THE SOUND OF APPROACHING ARMY REACHED THEIR EARS, ASHWATTHAMA, KRIPA AND KRITAVARMA TOLD DURYODHANA —

THE VICTORIOUS PANDAVAS APPEAR TO BE COMING HERE. ALLOW US TO GO, O KING.

AS YOU WISH.

"THE THREE WARRIORS MOVED AWAY AND RESTED UNDER A BANYAN TREE.

WHAT WILL HAPPEN TO DURYO-DHANA NOW? WHAT WILL THE PANDAVAS DO, I WONDER.

"ON REACHING THE LAKE, YUDHISHTHIRA REMARKED —

LOOK, O KRISHNA, HOW THE WATERS HAVE BEEN STILLED BY DURYODHANA. LET HIM USE ALL HIS DEVIOUS WAYS, I WILL GET HIM IN THE END.

YOU TOO CAN USE ALL YOUR SKILLS AGAINST HIM.

"REASSURED BY KRISHNA, YUDHISHTHIRA CALLED OUT TO DURYODHANA.

YOU HAVE CAUSED THE DEATH OF ALL YOUR DEAR ONES, AND NOW YOU HIDE YOURSELF. WHERE IS YOUR PRIDE? YOUR VALOUR? YOUR PROWESS IN ARCHERY? ARISE AND FIGHT LIKE A KSHATRIYA, O KING!

"DURYODHANA RESPONDED FROM THE DEPTHS OF THE WATER —

I HAVE NO CHARIOT, NO WEAPON, NO ARMY. YET IT IS NOT FEAR OR SORROW THAT HAS BROUGHT ME HERE. I AM JUST TOO TIRED NOW. LET YOUR MEN REST AWHILE TOO. TOMORROW WE WILL RESUME FIGHTING.

"YUDHISHTHIRA REPLIED —

WE HAVE RESTED ENOUGH. COME OUT AND FIGHT. CONQUER US AND RULE, OR BE KILLED LIKE A WARRIOR.

"DURYODHANA SAID —

WITH ALL MY LOVED ONES DEAD, I HAVE NO DESIRE TO RULE. TAKE OVER THIS LAND. I WILL RETIRE TO THE FOREST IN BARK AND DEERSKIN.

"YUDHISHTHIRA SHOUTED IN ANGER —

DO NOT TWITTER USELESSLY LIKE A BIRD. WHAT RIGHT HAVE YOU NOW TO GIFT THIS LAND TO ME? WOULD A PROUD KSHATRIYA LIKE ME ACCEPT CHARITY? I WILL CLAIM THE KINGDOM BY DEFEATING YOU IN BATTLE. COME AND FIGHT.

"DURYODHANA FLAILED AROUND HIS ARMS IN FRUSTRATION, SIGHED REPEATEDLY, BUT REMAINED INSIDE. HE SAID —

YOU HAVE YOUR ARMY, CHARIOTS AND WEAPONS. I AM ALONE, OUTNUMBERED AND WITHOUT A CHARIOT. HOW CAN I POSSIBLY FIGHT...

...IT IS NOT FAIR FOR AN ARMY TO FIGHT AN ISOLATED, WEAPONLESS, ARMOURLESS, FATIGUED MAN. I CAN FIGHT ANY ONE OF YOU AT A TIME, I CAN EVEN KILL YOU IF WE FIGHT RIGHTEOUSLY LIKE TRUE KSHATRIYAS.

"YUDHISHTHIRA REPLIED SARCASTICALLY —

OH ! I AM GLAD TO HEAR YOU KNOW THE KSHATRIYA CODE OF CONDUCT. BUT ANYWAY, SINCE YOU ARE READY TO FIGHT, WE WILL ABIDE BY YOUR WISH. CHOOSE YOUR WEAPON AND FIGHT ANYONE OF US. THE REST WILL JUST BE SPECTATORS.

"DURYODHANA SAID —

IN THAT CASE, I CHOOSE MY MACE. LET ANYONE OF YOUR WARRIORS COME FORWARD TO OPPOSE ME.

COME, LET US SEE YOUR VALOUR, YOUR MANHOOD. I AM SURE THAT EVEN IF LORD INDRA COMES TO YOUR AID TODAY, YOU CANNOT ESCAPE ALIVE.

"THUS TAUNTED, DURYODHANA ROSE UP AND APPEARED ON THE SURFACE LIKE THE RISING SUN. HE HAD AN IRON MACE IN HIS HAND.

"THRILLED TO SEE DURYODHANA EMERGE AT LAST, THE PANDAVAS REJOICED AND CLASPED ONE ANOTHER'S HANDS.

"DURYODHANA DECLARED—

I WILL FIGHT ALL OF YOU BUT ONE AT A TIME. YOU RIGHTEOUS WARRIORS KNOW THE RULES OF CONDUCT.

BUT DID YOU NOT KNOW THE RULES OF CONDUCT WHEN YOU SURROUNDED ABHIMANYU? ONLY WHEN THEY FACE A PROBLEM THEMSELVES, DO MEN QUOTE FROM LAW BOOKS.

"YUDHISHTHIRA THEN MADE A MAGNANIMOUS OFFER—

YOU MAY CHOOSE ANY ONE OF US TO FIGHT WITH YOU. AND IF YOU KILL ONE OF US IN THE FIGHT, WE WILL ANOINT YOU KING.

"DURYODHANA PUT ON THE GOLDEN ARMOUR AND THE HEADGEAR OFFERED TO HIM.

"KRISHNA, WHO HAD BEEN WATCHING SILENTLY FOR A WHILE, SAID TO YUDHISHTHIRA WITH EXTREME ANGER—

HOW COULD YOU ASK HIM TO FIGHT ANY ONE OF YOU? ONLY BHEEMA IS POWERFUL ENOUGH TO FACE DURYODHANA IN A MACE COMBAT, BUT HE HAS NO PRACTICE. DURYODHANA HAS BEEN PRACTISING FOR THIRTEEN YEARS WITH AN IRON IMAGE OF BHEEMA...

...THIS IS GOING TO BE ANOTHER GAME OF DICE. YOU KNOW THAT PRACTICE IS MORE IMPORTANT THAN SKILL IN A DUEL. NO ONE CAN BEAT DURYODHANA IN A FAIR MACEFIGHT.

"BHEEMA CAME FORWARD AND REASSURED KRISHNA —

DO NOT WORRY, O KRISHNA. I WILL DEFINITELY KILL DURYODHANA TODAY.

"KRISHNA WAS OVERJOYED.

YES! BHEEMA. IT IS YOU WHO KILLED THE OTHER SONS OF DHRITARASHTRA. NOW KILL DURYODHANA AND PLACE THE WORLD AT YUDHISHTHIRA'S FEET. BUT TAKE CARE! DURYODHANA HAS BOTH SKILL AND EXPERIENCE.

"BHEEMA WENT UP TO DURYODHANA AND DECLARED —

RECALL ALL YOUR MISDEEDS, O DURYODHANA. THE TORTURES AND INSULTS YOU HURLED AT US. BECAUSE OF YOU, BHEESHMA, DRONA, KARNA AND SHALYA LAID DOWN THEIR LIVES. TODAY IT IS YOUR TURN.

WHAT IS THE USE OF BOASTING. COME AND FIGHT.

"THE FIGHT WAS ABOUT TO START, WHEN BALARAMA, WHO HAD BEEN AWAY ON A PILGRIMAGE, ARRIVED THERE. KRISHNA AND THE PANDAVAS RUSHED TO GREET HIM.

"KRISHNA SAID —

COME AND WATCH YOUR DISCIPLES IN ACTION.

I HAVE RETURNED AFTER FORTYTWO DAYS ON PILGRIMAGE. I AM ANXIOUS TO SEE MY PUPILS.

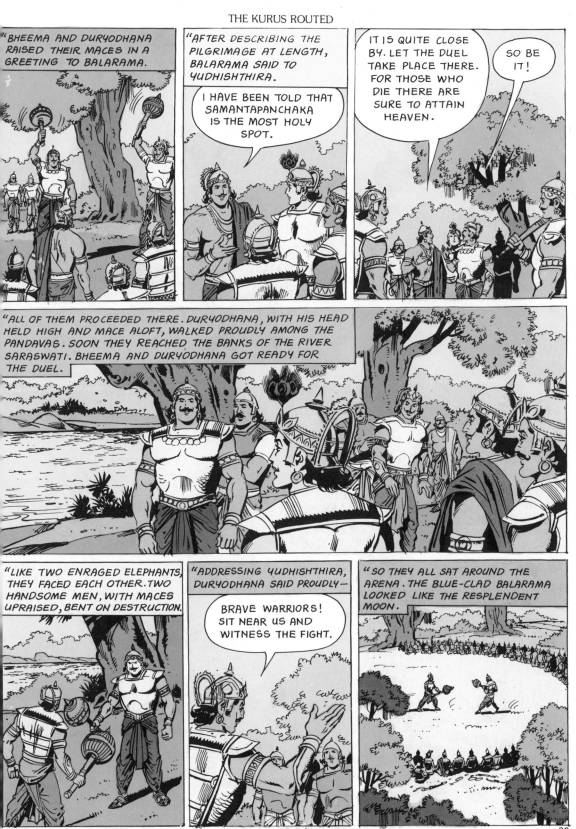

BHEEMA AND DURYODHANA RAISED THEIR MACES IN A GREETING TO BALARAMA.

"AFTER DESCRIBING THE PILGRIMAGE AT LENGTH, BALARAMA SAID TO YUDHISHTHIRA.

I HAVE BEEN TOLD THAT SAMANTAPANCHAKA IS THE MOST HOLY SPOT.

IT IS QUITE CLOSE BY. LET THE DUEL TAKE PLACE THERE. FOR THOSE WHO DIE THERE ARE SURE TO ATTAIN HEAVEN.

SO BE IT!

"ALL OF THEM PROCEEDED THERE. DURYODHANA, WITH HIS HEAD HELD HIGH AND MACE ALOFT, WALKED PROUDLY AMONG THE PANDAVAS. SOON THEY REACHED THE BANKS OF THE RIVER SARASWATI. BHEEMA AND DURYODHANA GOT READY FOR THE DUEL.

"LIKE TWO ENRAGED ELEPHANTS, THEY FACED EACH OTHER. TWO HANDSOME MEN, WITH MACES UPRAISED, BENT ON DESTRUCTION.

"ADDRESSING YUDHISHTHIRA, DURYODHANA SAID PROUDLY—

BRAVE WARRIORS! SIT NEAR US AND WITNESS THE FIGHT.

"SO THEY ALL SAT AROUND THE ARENA. THE BLUE-CLAD BALARAMA LOOKED LIKE THE RESPLENDENT MOON.

"WHILE BALARAMA PROUDLY WATCHED HIS PUPILS, ARJUNA ASKED KRISHNA ANXIOUSLY.

TELL ME, KRISHNA, WHO IS THE SUPERIOR OF THE TWO?

BOTH OF THEM ARE TRAINED BY MY BROTHER BALARAMA. BHEEMA IS MORE POWERFUL BUT DURYODHANA IS FAR AHEAD IN SKILL AND EXPERIENCE.

IT IS ALMOST IMPOSSIBLE TO BEAT DURYODHANA IN A FAIR FIGHT. BHEEMA MAY HAVE TO RESORT TO UNFAIR MEANS. REMEMBER HIS VOW TO BREAK DURYODHANA'S THIGHS?

"BHEEMA AND DURYODHANA WERE MEANWHILE FIGHTING FIERCELY. DURYODHANA SPRANG UP IN THE AIR TO DODGE A BLOW.

"CATCHING BHEEMA'S EYE, ARJUNA MEANINGFULLY STRUCK HIS OWN THIGH FORCEFULLY.

"CATCHING THE HINT, AND REMEMBERING HIS VOW, BHEEMA WAITED FOR A CHANCE. AFTER THE NEXT BOUT IN WHICH DURYODHANA ALMOST MADE HIM FAINT, BHEEMA TRIED TO ANTICIPATE HIS ADVERSARY'S NEXT MOVE.

"WHEN DURYODHANA JUMPED UP NEXT TIME, BHEEMA HIT OUT FORCEFULLY AT HIS THIGHS.

"WITH HIS THIGHS BROKEN, DURYODHANA COLLAPSED TO THE GROUND.

"THE ELATED PANDAVAS CAME CLOSER TO SEE THE FALLEN HERO. PROUDLY BHEEMA KICKED DURYODHANA'S CROWN AND PUT HIS FOOT ON HIS HEAD.

YOU WICKED MAN! YOU CHEAT! SUFFER FOR ALL THE INSULTS YOU HURLED AT US.

"YUDHISHTHIRA STEPPED FORWARD.

ENOUGH! BHEEMA. YOU HAVE FULFILLED YOUR VOW. DO NOT INSULT HIM SO. AFTER ALL HE IS OUR BROTHER, A KING AND THE LORD OF ELEVEN AKSHAUHINIS.

REPRIMANDING BHEEMA, YUDHISHTHIRA WENT TO DURYODHANA TO TELL HIM HOW LUCKY HE WAS TO DIE AND ATTAIN HEAVEN WHILE THEY WERE DESTINED TO LIVE ON IN A WORLD BEREFT OF SO MANY LOVED ONES. THUS THE RIGHTEOUS YUDHISHTHIRA BEMOANED THE FALL OF DURYODHANA.

"THUS ENDS THE THIRTY-EIGHTH SESSION OF OUR RENDERING OF VYASA'S IMMORTAL ITIHASA, MAHABHARATA.

* THE PLOUGH WAS BALARAMA'S PERSONAL WEAPON

"DHRITARASHTRA INTERRUPTED SANJAYA'S NARRATION.

HOW DID THE OTHER PANDAVAS REACT TO BHEEMA'S ACT?

DELIRIOUS WITH JOY, THEY BLEW LUSTILY THE CONCH-SHELLS, AND BEAT THE DRUMS.

"THEY SHOWERED BHEEMA WITH WORDS OF PRAISE.

BRAVO! WHO BUT YOU COULD DEFEAT THAT VALIANT DURYODHANA.

OUR HAIR STILL STANDS ON END WITH THE EXCITEMENT OF THAT DUEL.

YOUR FAME WILL SPREAD IN THE WHOLE WORLD NOW.

"KRISHNA INTERVENED—

ENOUGH! LET US NOT TRY TO KILL AN ENEMY WHO IS ALREADY VANQUISHED. COME, SIT ON YOUR CHARIOTS AND RETURN TO THE CAMP. FORGET ABOUT THIS MAN. HE IS BUT A PIECE OF DRY WOOD NOW.

"THEY FIRST WENT TO DURYODHANA'S QUARTERS, NOW DESERTED AND DESOLATE.

"THE OTHERS GOT DOWN FROM THEIR CHARIOTS. KRISHNA SAID TO ARJUNA —

REMOVE YOUR GANDEEVA AND THE CELESTIAL QUIVERS FROM THE CHARIOT AND COME DOWN.

"AS SOON AS KRISHNA DESCENDED FROM THE CHARIOT, THE MONKEY WHICH HAD ADORNED THE BANNER SO FAR SUDDENLY VANISHED.

"AND THE GREAT CHARIOT, WHICH HAD WITH-STOOD THE CELESTIAL WEAPONS OF DRONA AND KARNA, WENT UP IN FLAMES.

"IN AN INSTANT THE ENTIRE CHARIOT INCLUDING THE HORSES AND REINS WAS REDUCED TO ASHES.

"WHILE THE REST OF THE PANDAVAS WATCHED THIS MIRACLE WITH AWE AND FEAR, ARJUNA FELL AT KRISHNA'S FEET.

O KRISHNA! HOW DID THIS HAPPEN? HOW COULD THE CHARIOT SUDDENLY BE BURNT DOWN?

"KRISHNA GENTLY EXPLAINED —

THIS CHARIOT HAD ALREADY BEEN BURNT AND CHARRED BY THE REPEATED ONSLAUGHT OF THE ENEMY'S WEAPONS. BUT AS LONG AS I SAT IN IT, IT APPEARED TO BE INTACT.

NOW THAT YOUR MIGHTY TASK IS COMPLETED, I HAVE ABANDONED IT. SO THE CHARIOT IS NOW A HEAP OF ASHES.

"SMILING, KRISHNA THEN EMBRACED YUDHISHTHIRA AND SAID —

IT IS FORTUNATE THAT YOU HAVE EMERGED VICTORIOUS IN THIS WAR. REMEMBER HOW YOU HAD ASKED ME TO PROTECT ARJUNA? HERE HE HAS EMERGED UNSCATHED FROM THE TERRIBLE WAR AND IS SAFE AND SOUND WITH ALL HIS BROTHERS.

IT IS BY YOUR GRACE, O LORD, THAT WE HAVE WON THIS WAR.

7

VERILY THE SAGE VYASA HAD TOLD ME 'WHERE THERE IS DHARMA*, THERE IS KRISHNA. WHERE THERE IS KRISHNA THERE IS VICTORY?'

"LATER, AS THEY SAT AROUND RELAXED, KRISHNA SAID —

IT WOULD BE BETTER NOT TO RETURN TO OUR OWN CAMP TONIGHT.

WE WILL FOLLOW YOUR ADVICE.

" BEFORE NIGHTFALL, THEY ALL PROCEEDED TO THE BANKS OF THE RIVER NEAR BY.

"WHEN THEY WERE SETTLING DOWN FOR THE NIGHT, YUDHISHTHIRA REMARKED —

I FEEL, O KRISHNA, IT WOULD BE BEST IF YOU COULD GO TO HASTINAPURA AND PACIFY GANDHARI.

WITH YOUR REASONING AND PERSUASIVE TALK, YOU WILL SURELY CALM HER DOWN. THE VENERABLE SAGE VYASA WILL ALSO BE PRESENT THERE.

* RIGHTEOUSNESS

"KRISHNA READILY AGREED AND LEFT FOR HASTINAPURA ON HIS CHARIOT.

JANAMEJAYA INTERRUPTED VAISHAMPAYANA —

WAS IT NECESSARY TO SEND KRISHNA FOR THIS TASK?

YES, IT WAS. YUDHISHTHIRA REALISED HOW GANDHARI WOULD HAVE BEEN AFFECTED BY THE NEWS OF THE DEATH OF HER SONS. UNASSUAGED, THAT VIRTUOUS WOMAN'S ANGER COULD ANNIHILATE THE WHOLE WORLD. THAT IS WHY YUDHISHTHIRA REQUESTED THE LORD HIMSELF TO RUSH TO HASTINAPURA AND SAVE THE SITUATION.

"ON REACHING HASTINAPURA, KRISHNA WENT TO DHRITARASHTRA'S PALACE.

" BOWING RESPECTFULLY TO THE AGED KING, HE GREETED SAGE VYASA AND GANDHARI WHO WERE ALSO SEATED THERE.

"HOLDING DHRITARASHTRA'S HAND IN HIS OWN, KRISHNA WEPT IN SYMPATHY. THEN CONTROLLING HIS EMOTIONS, HE SAID AFTER A WHILE —

BELIEVE ME, THE PANDAVAS DID TRY THEIR BEST TO PREVENT THIS DESTRUCTION OF YOUR RACE.

THEY BORE ALL THE INSULTS HEAPED ON THEM BY THE KAURAVAS AND SPENT SO MANY YEARS IN THE FOREST.

9

I HAD REQUESTED YOU TO GIVE THE PANDAVAS JUST FIVE VILLAGES.

YOUR REFUSAL TOO IS IN A WAY RESPONSIBLE FOR THE SAD END OF THE KAURAVAS.

NOW ONLY THE PANDAVAS REMAIN TO CONTINUE THIS DYNASTY. SO DO NOT THINK ILL OF THEM. YOU KNOW IN WHAT HIGH ESTEEM AND REGARD YUDHISHTHIRA HOLDS YOU.

"TURNING TO GANDHARI, KRISHNA SAID—

DO YOU REMEMBER YOU HAD SAID TO DURYODHANA THAT THE RIGHTEOUS WOULD ALWAYS WIN. YOUR WORDS HAVE PROVED TRUE TODAY.

WITH THE POWER OF YOUR PENANCES, YOU ARE CAPABLE OF ANNIHILATING THE WHOLE WORLD. BUT PLEASE DO NOT LET ANY THOUGHT OF DESTROYING THE PANDAVAS ENTER YOUR MIND.

"GANDHARI REPLIED—

YOU GUESSED CORRECTLY, O KRISHNA, MY MIND WAS IN GREAT TORMENT. BUT YOUR WORDS OF WISDOM HAVE HELPED ME TO CONTROL MYSELF AND BANISH THE ANGER WITHIN.

"HAVING SAID THIS, GANDHARI BEGAN TO SOB INCONSOLABLY.

"KRISHNA SAT FOR A WHILE TRYING TO CONSOLE THE AGED KING AND THE DESOLATE MOTHER WITH HIS SOOTHING WORDS AND GENTLE MANNER.

"JUST THEN, HE DIVINED THE EVIL PLOT EVOLVING IN ASHWATTHAMA'S MIND. STANDING UP WITH A START, HE SAID TO SAGE VYASA.

I MUST TAKE YOUR LEAVE NOW. ASHWATTHAMA HAS THOUGHT OF A WICKED PLAN TO DESTROY THE PANDAVAS.

"BOTH GANDHARI AND DHRITARASHTRA ASKED HIM TO GO.

YES, YOU MUST GO AND PROTECT THE PANDAVAS. WE WILL MEET YOU LATER.

"KRISHNA THEN RETURNED TO THE PANDAVAS AND TOLD THEM WHAT HAD HAPPENED.

...SO WE MUST BE CAREFUL AND ALERT TONIGHT.

"MEANWHILE, ACCOMPANIED BY KRIPACHARYA AND KRITAVARMA, ASHWATTHAMA RUSHED TO SEE THE DYING DURYODHANA.

"THEY FOUND DURYODHANA BLEEDING PROFUSELY AND TOSSING AND TURNING HELPLESSLY IN AGONY.

"QUICKLY THEY GOT OFF FROM THE CHARIOT AND SAT BESIDE HIM.

"ASHWATTHAMA COULD NOT BEAR TO SEE THE KING IN THIS PATHETIC STATE. WITH TEARS IN HIS EYES, HE SAID—

OH! WHAT IS THIS WORLD WHERE A KING OF YOUR MIGHT AND STATURE CAN BE LEFT TO ROLL IN THE DUST.

WHERE IS YOUR GREAT ARMY, YOUR ROYAL UMBRELLA, YOUR POMP AND VALOUR? SURELY NOTHING IN THE WORLD CAN BE RELIED UPON. IT IS TRANSIENT AND EPHEMERAL.

"DURYODHANA TOO BROKE DOWN AT ASHWATTHAMA'S DISPLAY OF SORROW.

EVERYTHING IN THIS WORLD IS DESTINED FOR DESTRUCTION. APPARENTLY MY MOMENT OF DOOM HAS ALSO COME. HENCE YOU FIND ME IN THIS STATE.

YET I AM HAPPY THAT NEVER ONCE DID I TURN MY BACK IN WAR. IT WAS ONLY BY CHEATING THAT THE ENEMY COULD DESTROY ME. I HAVE BEEN TRUE TO MY DUTY AS A KSHATRIYA. SO DO NOT GRIEVE FOR ME, FRIENDS.

"THE TEARS IN DURYODHANA'S EYES FILLED ASHWATTHAMA WITH RAGE.

EVEN MY FATHER'S DEATH BROUGHT ABOUT BY DECEIT DID NOT HURT ME AS MUCH AS YOUR DESTRUCTION AT THE HANDS OF THOSE WICKED PANDAVAS...

CLENCHING HIS FISTS HE SAID —

...I SWEAR TO YOU BY EVERYTHING SACRED THAT I WILL SEND ALL THE PANCHALAS AND THE PANDAVAS TO DEATH TONIGHT. GIVE ME YOUR PERMISSION TO DO SO.

"DURYODHANA WAS TOUCHED. ADDRESSING KRIPA, HE SAID —

ACHARYA, PLEASE BRING WATER IN A VESSEL.

"WHEN KRIPACHARYA DID SO, DURYODHANA SAID FORMALLY —

I REQUEST YOU TO INSTALL ASHWATTHAMA AS THE COMMANDER OF OUR ARMY.

13

"KRIPACHARYA POURED THE WATER OVER ASHWATTHAMA AS A RITUAL OF THE CEREMONIAL BATH.

"ASHWATTHAMA EMBRACED THE PROSTRATE DURYODHANA IN FAREWELL AND THE THREE WARRIORS LEFT THE KING TO SPEND THE DARK NIGHT ALONE.

"SOON THEY SIGHTED THE CAMP, BUT WARY OF THE PANDAVAS, THEY HALTED IN A NEARBY FOREST.

"THEY RESTED FOR A WHILE. SOON THE JOYOUS SOUNDS OF CELEBRATION FROM THE PANDAVA CAMP PUT FEAR IN THEIR HEARTS AND THEY MOVED DEEPER INTO THE FOREST.

"SAFE IN THE HEART OF THE FOREST, THEY REFRESHED THEIR HORSES AND DECIDED TO REST UNDER A SPREADING BANYAN TREE.

"WEARY AND WOUNDED, KRITAVARMA AND KRIPA-CHARYA FELL ASLEEP AS SOON AS THEY LAY DOWN. BUT ASHWATTHAMA COULD NOT.

"ANGER AND VENGEFUL THOUGHTS HAD ROBBED HIS EYES OF SLEEP. LOOKING VACANTLY AROUND HIM, HE GAZED UP AT THE BANYAN TREE.

"MANY CROWS WERE PERCHED PEACEFULLY IN THEIR NESTS ON THE MYRIAD BRANCHES OF THE OLD BANYAN TREE. PEACE AND TRANQUILLITY REIGNED IN THE DARK FOREST. SUDDENLY THE SILENCE WAS PIERCED BY THE SCREECH OF A TERRIBLE-LOOKING OWL.

"HE SWEPT DOWN ON THE SLEEPING CROWS AND ATTACKED THEM WITHOUT MERCY.

"IN A MATTER OF MOMENTS, THE PLACE WAS STREWN WITH THE REMAINS OF A MYRIAD CROWS. THE OWL SEEMED PLEASED WITH HIMSELF.

"WATCHING THIS FROM BELOW, AN IDEA TOOK ROOT IN ASHWATTHAMA'S MIND.

THIS BIRD HAS INDEED SHOWED ME THE WAY. I KNOW WHAT I MUST DO NOW.

I HAVE VOWED BEFORE DURYODHANA TO KILL THE PANDAVAS. IF I USE FAIR MEANS, IT IS IMPOSSIBLE FOR ME TO KILL THEM. I MUST THEREFORE THINK OF A CUNNING PLAN.

IT IS WISER TO USE A FOOLPROOF THOUGH FOUL METHOD THAN TAKE A FOOLHARDY CHANCE TO DEFEAT THEM IN A FAIR FIGHT NOW. LIKE THIS OWL, I TOO WILL ATTACK THE UNSUSPECTING PANDAVAS WHILE THEY ARE ASLEEP.

"EXCITED AT THE PROSPECT, HE ROUSED KRIPA AND KRITAVARMA FROM THEIR SLUMBER.

LISTEN! I HAVE THOUGHT OF AN EXCELLENT IDEA. WE WILL ATTACK AND KILL THE PANDAVAS WHILE THEY ARE ASLEEP.

"HORRIFIED AT HIS SUGGESTION, THEY GAZED AT HIM SPEECHLESS WITH SHOCK. ASHWATTHAMA SAID—

A MIGHTY RULER OF ELEVEN AKSHAUHINIS LIES IN THE DUST. ONLY THREE OF US NOW REMAIN FROM THAT ARMY. WHAT DO YOU THINK WE CAN DO NOW TO SET MATTERS RIGHT?

"KRIPACHARYA TRIED TO COUNSEL THE EXCITED ASHWATTHAMA.

VALOUR AND VIRTUE ARE BOTH ESSENTIAL FOR A MAN. IT IS FUTILE MERELY TO THINK OF A GOOD DEED WITHOUT TAKING ANY ACTION. IT IS EQUALLY FOOLISH TO PLUNGE INTO ACTIVITY WITHOUT ANY CONSIDERATION OF RIGHT AND WRONG.

DURYODHANA WAS GREEDY AND ILL-ADVISED. CRUEL AND IMPATIENT, HE REFUSED TO LISTEN TO WELL-MEANING FRIENDS AND MADE ENEMIES OF THE PANDAVAS. WE FOLLOWED HIM AND HAVE REACHED THIS SORRY STATE.

MY OWN MIND NOW REFUSES TO FUNCTION. LET US NOW GO TO DHRITARASHTRA, GANDHARI AND VIDURA AND SEEK THEIR COUNSEL. THEY WILL SURELY GUIDE US PROPERLY.

"ASHWATTHAMA COULD NOT DENY THE WISDOM OF THE ACHARYA'S WORDS. YET HE WAS ADAMANT.

EVERYONE OF US FEELS CONVINCED THAT HIS WAY OF THINKING IS THE ONLY RIGHT AND PROPER ONE. I HAVE MADE UP MY MIND AND I WILL ACT ACCORDINGLY.

THE PANDAVAS WILL BE SLEEPING PEACEFULLY WITH THEIR ARMOURS CAST OFF. ONLY AFTER I HAVE KILLED ALL OF THEM WILL I FEEL I HAVE AVENGED THE DEATH OF MY FATHER.

"KRIPACHARYA SAID —

YOU SEEM TO HAVE MADE UP YOUR MIND. BUT, ANYWAY, SLEEP AWHILE AND REST YOURSELF. TOMORROW MORNING WE WILL BOTH COME WITH YOU TO ATTACK THE PANDAVAS. YOU WILL FEEL REFRESHED AFTER SOME REST.

"ASHWATTHAMA SAW THROUGH THE ACHARYA'S GENTLE PERSUASION. HE SHOUTED —

HOW CAN A MAN FILLED WITH ANXIETY, SORROW, ANGER OR DESIRE SLEEP? I AM TROUBLED BY ALL OF THESE. I CANNOT CONTROL MYSELF NOW. I WILL REST ONLY AFTER GETTING RID OF ALL THE ENEMIES.

"WHEN ASHWATTHAMA BEGAN TO HARNESS THE HORSES TO HIS CHARIOT, KRITAVARMA AND KRIPACHARYA TOO GOT UP.

WAIT! ASHWATTHAMA, WE TOO WILL COME WITH YOU.

THEN HURRY UP. DON YOUR ARMOUR AND TAKE UP YOUR WEAPONS.

"THE THREE OF THEM PROCEEDED TO THE PANDAVA CAMP.

"ASHWATTHAMA WHISPERED TO HIS COMPANIONS —

YOU GUARD THE GATE OF THE CAMP. I WILL ENTER THE CAMP NOW AND CREATE HAVOC. YOU TWO MAKE SURE NO ONE ESCAPES.

"AT THE GATE OF THE CAMP, A STRANGE SIGHT MET THEIR EYES. AN ENORMOUS MONSTER LOOMED LARGE IN THEIR PATH.

"UNAFRAID AND UNFLINCHING, ASHWATTHAMA RAINED A SHOWER OF ARROWS ON THE CREATURE.

"BUT THE MONSTER SWALLOWED UP ALL THE ARROWS EFFORTLESSLY.

"EVEN THE RATHASHAKTI SENT BY ASHWATTHAMA, FAILED TO MAKE ANY IMPACT. HE THEN TOOK UP HIS SWORD TO ATTACK.

"THE SWORD TOO DISAPPEARED INTO THE MOUTH OF THE MONSTER AS DID THE MACE THAT HE TRIED NEXT.

NOW ALL MY WEAPONS ARE EXHAUSTED. PERHAPS I SHOULD HAVE LISTENED TO KRITAVARMA AND KRIPACHARYA.

I CANNOT IMAGINE WHO THIS CREATURE IS. ALL I CAN DO NOW IS TO SEEK LORD SHIVA'S HELP.

"ASHWATTHAMA GOT DOWN FROM HIS CHARIOT AND STOOD RESPECTFULLY, PRAYING TO LORD SHIVA.

"WHEN HE MEDITATED FOR A WHILE, A GOLDEN ALTAR APPEARED BEFORE HIM. FROM IT EMERGED HUGE BEINGS WITH STRANGE FEATURES AND GROTESQUE LIMBS.

"THE GHASTLY CREATURES WHO DANCED AND ROMPED BEFORE HIM WERE ACTUALLY ATTENDANTS OF LORD SHIVA.

"REALISING THIS, ASHWATTHAMA CLIMBED INTO THE BLAZING ALTAR.

O LORD, I MAKE AN OFFERING OF MYSELF TO YOU. PLEASE ACCEPT MY GIFT.

"LORD SHIVA APPEARED BEFORE HIM, AND SAID WITH A LAUGH—

I WAS PROTECTING THE PANCHALAS FOR THE SAKE OF MY FAVOURITE DEVOTEE KRISHNA. BUT NOW THEIR LIFE IS AT AN END. HERE, TAKE THIS DAGGER.

"ASHWATTHAMA WENT STRAIGHT TO DHRISHTADYUMNA'S TENT.

" WITH A SWIFT KICK, ASHWATTHAMA ROUSED THE SLEEPING DHRISHTADYUMNA.

" HE WOKE UP WITH A START AND TRIED TO GET UP. ASHWATTHAMA PULLED HIM BY THE HAIR AND THREW HIM DOWN ON THE FLOOR.

"ASHWATTHAMA PRESSED DHRISHTADYUMNA DOWN WITH HIS FEET AND BEGAN TO RAIN BLOWS ON HIM.

AHHH! KILL ME WITH AN ARROW. LET ME DIE LIKE A A KSHATRIYA.

" HE LAUGHED CRUELLY AS HE STOMP- ED OVER DHRISHTADYUMNA.

YOU WRETCHED MURDERER OF YOUR GURU, YOU DO NOT DESERVE A HERO'S DEATH.

" THUS, AFTER KICKING AND CRUSHING DHRISHTADYUMNA TO DEATH, ASHWATTHAMA BEGAN ATTACKING THE OTHER WARRIORS.

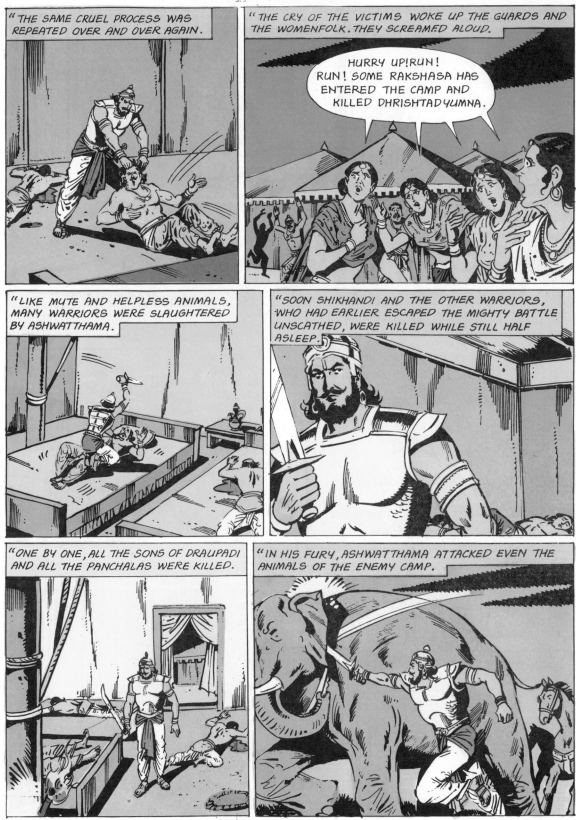

"THE SAME CRUEL PROCESS WAS REPEATED OVER AND OVER AGAIN.

"THE CRY OF THE VICTIMS WOKE UP THE GUARDS AND THE WOMENFOLK. THEY SCREAMED ALOUD.

HURRY UP! RUN! RUN! SOME RAKSHASA HAS ENTERED THE CAMP AND KILLED DHRISHTADYUMNA.

"LIKE MUTE AND HELPLESS ANIMALS, MANY WARRIORS WERE SLAUGHTERED BY ASHWATTHAMA.

"SOON SHIKHANDI AND THE OTHER WARRIORS, WHO HAD EARLIER ESCAPED THE MIGHTY BATTLE UNSCATHED, WERE KILLED WHILE STILL HALF ASLEEP.

"ONE BY ONE, ALL THE SONS OF DRAUPADI AND ALL THE PANCHALAS WERE KILLED.

"IN HIS FURY, ASHWATTHAMA ATTACKED EVEN THE ANIMALS OF THE ENEMY CAMP.

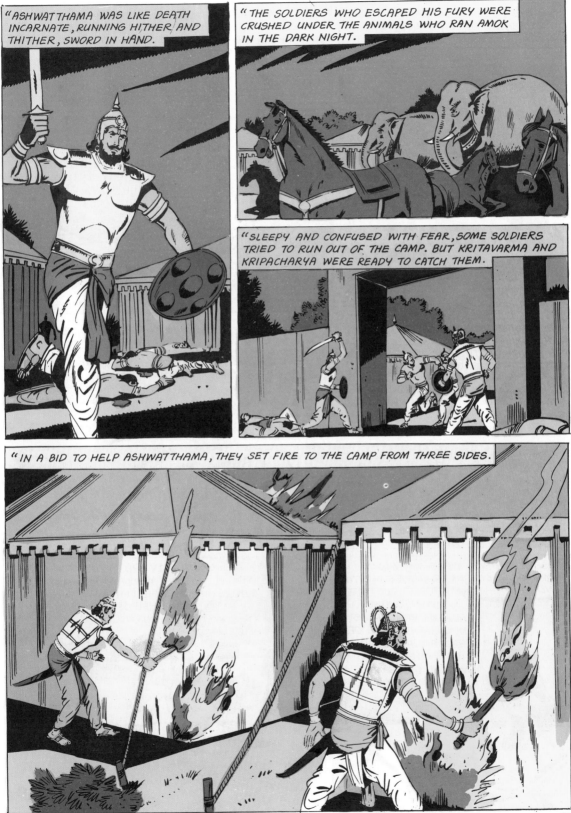

"ASHWATTHAMA WAS LIKE DEATH INCARNATE, RUNNING HITHER AND THITHER, SWORD IN HAND.

"THE SOLDIERS WHO ESCAPED HIS FURY WERE CRUSHED UNDER THE ANIMALS WHO RAN AMOK IN THE DARK NIGHT.

"SLEEPY AND CONFUSED WITH FEAR, SOME SOLDIERS TRIED TO RUN OUT OF THE CAMP. BUT KRITAVARMA AND KRIPACHARYA WERE READY TO CATCH THEM.

"IN A BID TO HELP ASHWATTHAMA, THEY SET FIRE TO THE CAMP FROM THREE SIDES.

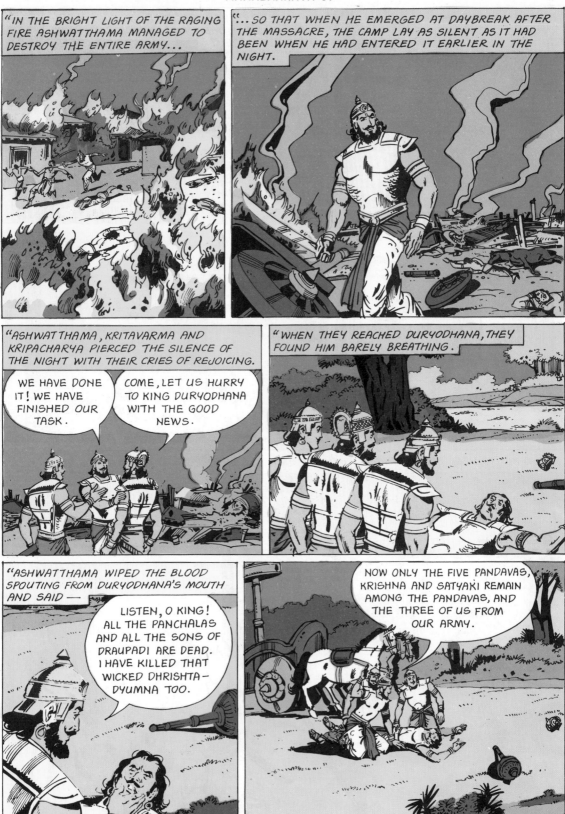

"IN THE BRIGHT LIGHT OF THE RAGING FIRE ASHWATTHAMA MANAGED TO DESTROY THE ENTIRE ARMY...

"...SO THAT WHEN HE EMERGED AT DAYBREAK AFTER THE MASSACRE, THE CAMP LAY AS SILENT AS IT HAD BEEN WHEN HE HAD ENTERED IT EARLIER IN THE NIGHT.

"ASHWATTHAMA, KRITAVARMA AND KRIPACHARYA PIERCED THE SILENCE OF THE NIGHT WITH THEIR CRIES OF REJOICING.

WE HAVE DONE IT! WE HAVE FINISHED OUR TASK.

COME, LET US HURRY TO KING DURYODHANA WITH THE GOOD NEWS.

"WHEN THEY REACHED DURYODHANA, THEY FOUND HIM BARELY BREATHING.

"ASHWATTHAMA WIPED THE BLOOD SPOUTING FROM DURYODHANA'S MOUTH AND SAID —

LISTEN, O KING! ALL THE PANCHALAS AND ALL THE SONS OF DRAUPADI ARE DEAD. I HAVE KILLED THAT WICKED DHRISHTA-DYUMNA TOO.

NOW ONLY THE FIVE PANDAVAS, KRISHNA AND SATYAKI REMAIN AMONG THE PANDAVAS, AND THE THREE OF US FROM OUR ARMY.

"THE NEWS REVIVED DURYODHANA LONG ENOUGH TO SAY—

ASHWATTHAMA! YOU HAVE DONE FOR ME WHAT BHEESHMA, DRONA OR KARNA COULD NOT DO. BLESS YOU! NOW WE WILL ALL MEET IN HEAVEN.

"WITH THESE WORDS, DURYODHANA BREATHED HIS LAST. THE MIGHTY WARRIOR WHO HAD BEEN THE FIRST TO ENTER THE BATTLEFIELD WAS AMONG THE LAST TO DIE.

"BRIEFLY EMBRACING THE DEPARTED KING DURYODHANA THE THREE WARRIORS LEFT THE PLACE.

"VAISHAMPAYANA CONTINUED HIS NARRATION—

WHEN SANJAYA HEARD THE NEWS OF DURYODHANA'S DEATH, HE LOST THE POWER OF THE DIVINE VISION BESTOWED ON HIM BY SAGE VYASA. MEANWHILE, DHRISHTADYUMNA'S CHARIOTEER HAD SOMEHOW ESCAPED THE MASSACRE AND RUSHED TO YUDHISHTHIRA WITH THE TERRIBLE NEWS.

"RELATING THE GRUESOME DETAILS OF THE MIDNIGHT MASSACRE, HE SAID—

O KING, I ALONE ESCAPED WHILE YOUR ENTIRE ARMY HAS BEEN DESTROYED.

"YUDHISHTHIRA FAINTED WITH SHOCK. SATYAKI CAUGHT HIM AS HE FELL.

"ON RECOVERING, YUDHISHTHIRA LAMENTED ALOUD—

ALAS! I HAVE LOST ALL AFTER WINNING THE WAR. MY WARRIORS WHO HAD ESCAPED THE ARROWS OF THE MIGHTY KARNA AND DRONA HAVE BEEN KILLED BY THEIR OWN CARELESSNESS.

"AFTER SENDING NAKULA TO FETCH DRAUPADI, YUDHISHTHIRA SORROWFULLY WENT TO HIS CAMP WITH HIS OTHER BROTHERS.

"HE COULD NOT BEAR TO SEE THAT AWFUL SIGHT AND, CRYING INCONSOLABLY FELL DOWN IN A SWOON.

"EVEN AS THE OTHER PANDAVAS TRIED TO CONSOLE HIM, NAKULA ARRIVED ON THE SCENE WITH DRAUPADI.

"AGITATED AS SHE WAS WITH THE NEWS, THE SCENE OF MASSACRE WAS TOO TRAGIC A SIGHT FOR HER. BHEEMA CAUGHT HER JUST IN TIME AS SHE FAINTED.

"WHEN SHE RECOVERED A LITTLE, SHE GLARED AT YUDHISHTHIRA, AND SAID—

SHOULD I CONGRATULATE YOU ON CONQUERING THE EARTH AFTER SACRIFICING YOUR SONS?

I AM BURNING WITH RAGE AT THIS MONSTROUS ACT. NOW YOU MUST AVENGE OUR DEAR ONES' DEATHS. I SWEAR I WILL NOT MOVE FROM HERE TILL YOU KILL THAT WICKED SON OF DRONA.

" SHE TOOK UP A POSE OF MEDITATION AND SAT DOWN RIGHT THERE ON THE BATTLEFIELD. YUDHISHTHIRA TRIED TO REASON WITH HER.

YOU KNOW THAT YOUR BROTHERS AND SONS HAVE DIED LIKE HEROES ON THE BATTLEFIELD. NOW ASHWATTHAMA HAS ESCAPED INTO THE FOREST.

EVEN IF WE DO MANAGE TO KILL HIM, HOW WILL WE CONVINCE YOU OF HIS DEATH ?

I KNOW THAT ASHWATTHAMA HAS A JEWEL ON HIS HEAD. BRING IT TO ME.

" TURNING TO BHEEMA, SHE SAID —

BHEEMA DEAR, I KNOW YOU ARE THE BRAVEST OF MEN. DO THIS FAVOUR FOR ME.

INDEED I WILL.

"AT ONCE BHEEMA MOUNTED HIS CHARIOT AND, WITH NAKULA AS HIS CHARIOTEER, SET OUT TO FOLLOW ASHWATTHAMA'S TRAIL.

" WHEN THEY LEFT, KRISHNA SAID TO YUDHISHTHIRA —

IT IS NOT SAFE TO LET BHEEMA GO ALONE. ASHWATTHAMA HAS IN HIS POSSESSION A POWERFUL WEAPON CALLED BRAHMASHIRA* WHICH CAN SET THE WORLD AFLAME.

✶ CELESTIAL WEAPON

DRONA HAD FIRST BESTOWED THIS WEAPON ON ARJUNA. ASHWATTHAMA PERSUADED HIS FATHER TO GIVE IT TO HIM TOO. I KNOW THAT ASHWATTHAMA CAN BE VERY DEVIOUS, CUNNING AND WILL STOP AT NOTHING. WHY, HE EVEN TRIED TO FLATTER ME TO GIVE HIM MY CHAKRA ONCE. WE MUST PROTECT BHEEMA NOW.

"KRISHNA ASCENDED HIS CHARIOT TAKING ARJUNA AND YUDHISHTHIRA WITH HIM."

"THE CHARIOT FLEW THROUGH THE AIR AND REACHED BHEEMA IN A MATTER OF MOMENTS."

"THEY FOUND ASHWATTHAMA CLAD IN BARK, SITTING AMIDST VYASA AND OTHER SAGES, ON THE BANKS OF THE RIVER GANGA."

"BHEEMA RAN UP TO HIM WITH HIS BOW AND ARROW.

COME ON NOW! ARISE AND FIGHT.

"ASHWATTHAMA PICKED UP A BLADE OF GRASS AND MEDITATED ON THE CELESTIAL WEAPON.

MAY THIS WEAPON DESTROY ALL THE PANDAVAS.

"NO SOONER HAD HE SAID THIS THAN ENORMOUS FLAMES BEGAN TO EMERGE FROM THAT BLADE OF GRASS.

"KRISHNA HAD READ ASHWATTHAMA'S MIND. HE SAID TO ARJUNA —

YOU TOO RECEIVED THIS WEAPON FROM DRONA. NOW IS THE TIME TO USE IT.

"JUMPING DOWN FROM THE CHARIOT, ARJUNA TOOK UP HIS BOW AND ARROW.

MAY THIS WEAPON COUNTER ASHWAT-THAMA'S WEAPON.

"THE ENTIRE WORLD APPEARED TO SHAKE AND TREMBLE WITH THE COMBINED EFFECT OF THE TWO POWERFUL WEAPONS.

"JUST THEN, THE SAGES VYASA AND NARADA, GOT UP AND STOOD BETWEEN ARJUNA AND ASHWATTHAMA.

NO ONE IN THE PAST HAS EVER DARED TO USE THIS WEAPON ON HUMAN BEINGS. HOW COULD BOTH OF YOU DO SO?

"ARJUNA SAID —

I USED IT TO COUNTER ASHWATTHAMA'S ATTACK. NOW I WILL CERTAINLY DO AS YOU SAY. I WILL TRY MY BEST TO RECALL IT.

"IT WAS NOT AN EASY WEAPON TO RECALL. HAVING OBTAINED IT AFTER SEVERE AUSTERITIES, ARJUNA HAD THE POWER AND ABILITY TO WITHDRAW IT.

"ASHWATTHAMA HOWEVER COULD NOT DO SO, MUCH AS HE TRIED. HE APPEALED TO VYASA.

I USED THIS WEAPON IN FEAR OF BHEEMA, SAYING, NOW MAY ALL PANDAVAS BE DESTROYED. BUT NOW I CANNOT WITHDRAW IT.

"SAGE VYASA SAID TO ASHWATTHAMA —

DO YOU KNOW THAT THE LAND WHERE SUCH TWO POWERFUL WEAPONS CLASH REMAINS RAINLESS AND PARCHED FOR TWELVE YEARS? THAT IS WHY ARJUNA DID NOT TRY TO DESTROY YOUR WEAPON.

THE PANDAVAS DO NOT WANT TO WIN BY UNFAIR MEANS. NOW TO COMPENSATE FOR YOUR WICKED ACT, GIVE THEM THE JEWEL FROM YOUR HEAD, AND ALSO RECALL YOUR WEAPON.

"ASHWATTHAMA REPLIED —

OH! THIS GEM IS MOST PRECIOUS TO ME. BUT I WILL GIVE IT UP IN DEFERENCE TO YOUR WISHES.

AS FOR THE WEAPON, I CANNOT RECALL IT. LET ITS EFFECT BE DIRECTED TO THE FUTURE PROGENY OF THE PANDAVAS IF NOT TO THEM.

"ASHWATTHAMA'S CURSE WOULD HAVE AFFECTED THE UNBORN BABY OF UTTARA, ABHIMANYU'S WIDOW. BUT KRISHNA INTERVENED IN TIME —

YOU WICKED ASHWATTHAMA, DESPITE YOUR CURSE, THIS SON OF UTTARA WILL BE REVIVED AT BIRTH.

NOT ONLY WILL HE SURVIVE YOUR CURSE, BUT WILL GROW UP TO BE A MIGHTY KING, AND CONTINUE THE PANDAVA DYNASTY.

I TOO BLESS THE BOY WHO WILL BE CALLED PAREEKSHIT.

"THE PANDAVAS RETURNED IN HASTE TO DRAUPADI WITH THE PRECIOUS JEWEL. ASHWATTHAMA WENT MOROSELY INTO THE JUNGLE.

" BHEEMA PRESENTED THE GEM TO DRAUPADI.

NOW ASHWATTHAMA IS DEFEATED AND DEMORALIS- ED. BEING OUR GURU'S SON, WE HOWEVER, SPARED HIS LIFE.

O YUDHISHTHIRA. LET THIS GEM ADORN YOUR FOREHEAD NOW.

AS YOU WISH.

THE BLIND KING DHRITARASHTRA FOUND IT DIFFICULT TO GET OVER THE GRIEF CAUSED BY THE DEATH OF ALL HIS SONS AND WEPT INCONSOLABLY. VIDURA, THE WISE, GENTLY BADE HIM TO CONTROL HIS SORROW.

"TRYING TO ASSUAGE HIS GRIEF, VIDURA SAID —

DO NOT GRIEVE FOR YOUR SONS, O KING! THEY DIED IN BATTLE LIKE BRAVE KSHATRIYAS AND HAVE SURELY ATTAINED HEAVEN. ARISE AND PREPARE YOURSELF FOR THE TASKS AHEAD.

"SANJAYA ADDED —

THOUSANDS OF KINGS FROM VARIOUS LANDS LAID DOWN THEIR LIVES FOR YOUR SON. IT IS NOW YOUR DUTY TO ARRANGE FOR THEIR FINAL RITES.

"AFTER MUCH PERSUASION, DHRITARASHTRA AGREED TO ACT ACCORDING TO THEIR COUNSEL.

LET MY CHARIOT BE PREPARED. SEND FOR GANDHARI, KUNTI AND THE OTHER LADIES OF THE ROYAL HOUSEHOLD.

"GANDHARI AND KUNTI SOON ARRIVED THERE, LAMENTING AND CRYING.

"WITH TEARS STREAMING DOWN THEIR FACES, THE WOMEN ASCENDED THE CHARIOTS. THESE LADIES OF THE ROYAL HOUSEHOLD WHO HAD NEVER BEFORE APPEARED IN PUBLIC NOW PASSED THROUGH THE MAIN STREET TO THE BATTLEFIELD, DRESSED IN MOURNING, UNADORNED BY JEWELS AND FINERY.

"ON THE OUTSKIRTS OF HASTINAPURA THEY MET KRIPACHARYA, KRITAVARMA AND ASHWATTHAMA.

"KRIPACHARYA SAID TO DHRITARASHTRA —

O KING, YOUR ENTIRE ARMY HAS BEEN DESTROYED. WE THREE ARE THE ONLY SURVIVORS.

"ADDRESSING GANDHARI, HE SAID —

YOUR SONS FOUGHT BRAVELY AND LAID DOWN THEIR LIVES LIKE TRUE WARRIORS. THEY MUST HAVE SURELY ATTAINED HEAVEN.

TO AVENGE DURYODHANA'S DEATH, WE ATTACKED THE ENEMY CAMP AT NIGHT. ALL THE PAN-CHALAS AS WELL AS DRAUPADI'S FIVE SONS HAVE BEEN KILLED.

BUT WE DARE NOT LINGER HERE ANY LONGER. THE PANDAVAS WILL SOON FOLLOW OUR TRACKS.

"BOWING RESPECTFULLY TO DHRITARASHTRA, THE THREE WARRIORS SPED AWAY TOWARDS THE BANKS OF THE RIVER GANGA.

"AND THERE THE THREE OF THEM PARTED: KRIPACHARYA PROCEEDED TO HASTINAPURA, KRITAVARMA WENT BACK TO HIS HOME, WHILE ASHWATTHAMA MADE HIS WAY TO SAGE VYASA'S HERMITAGE. BUT WOULD THEY BE SAFE THERE?

"WHEN YUDHISHTHIRA LEARNT THAT DHRITA-RASHTRA HAD LEFT FOR THE BATTLEFIELD, HE TOO HURRIED TO THE PLACE.

"ALONG WITH HIM WERE HIS BROTHERS BESIDES KRISHNA, YUYUTSU, SATYAKI AND DRAUPADI.

"WHEN YUDHISHTHIRA REACHED THE RIVER-SIDE NEAR THE BATTLEFIELD, HE WAS SURROUNDED BY THE BEREAVED WOMEN WHO WERE LAMENTING LOUDLY.

O KING! HOW COULD YOU KILL YOUR OWN KITH AND KIN?

WHERE IS YOUR FAMED RIGHTEOUS-NESS AND GENEROSITY?

"KEEN TO SPEAK TO HIS UNCLE DHRITARASHTRA, YUDHISHTHIRA WALKED PAST THEM...

"...AND WENT STRAIGHT TO DHRITARASHTRA. HE AND HIS BROTHERS PAID THEIR RESPECTS TO THE OLD KING. DHRITARASHTRA EMBRACED YUDHISHTHIRA. BUT THERE WAS NO AFFECTION IN THE GESTURE.

"THE BLIND KING APPEARED TO BE SEEKING SOMEONE. GUESSING HIS INTENTION KRISHNA QUICKLY PUSHED BHEEMA ASIDE.

"WITH A NIMBLE GESTURE, HE PLACED BEFORE DHRITARASHTRA AN IRON IMAGE OF BHEEMA.

"WITH SUCH FORCE DID DHRITARASHTRA CLASP THE IMAGE TO HIS BOSOM, THAT IT BROKE INTO PIECES.

amar chitra katha

GASPING FOR BREATH AND WITH BLOOD STREAMING OUT OF HIS MOUTH, DHRITARASHTRA COLLAPSED.

"THE FAITHFUL SANJAYA HELPED HIM TO GET UP AND SAID —

YOU SHOULD NOT HAVE DONE THIS, O KING!

"HIS ANGER ABATED, DHRITARASHTRA WAS NOW FILLED WITH REMORSE.

OH BHEEMA! OH BHEEMA!

"LORD KRISHNA CONSOLED HIM.

GRIEVE NOT, O KING. IT WAS NOT THE REAL BHEEMA YOU CRUSHED WITH YOUR MIGHTY ARMS BUT MERELY AN IRON IMAGE.

I HAD ANTICIPATED YOUR ANGER AND ARRANGED FOR THE IRON IMAGE OF BHEEMA TO BE BROUGHT HERE. IT WAS THE ONE THAT DURYODHANA HAD USED TO PRACTISE WITH THE MACE.

"AFTER DHRITARASHTRA HAD RESTED AWHILE AND REFRESHED HIMSELF, KRISHNA SPOKE TO HIM AT LENGTH.

HOW CAN A WISE AND INTELLIGENT PERSON LIKE YOU REACT THUS? HAD WE ALL NOT WARNED YOU EARLIER? WAS YOUR CONDUCT NOT UNJUST ALL THIS WHILE?

"DHRITARASHTRA ADMITTED —

YOU ARE RIGHT. I WAS UNDER DURYODHANA'S INFLUENCE. IT IS INDEED FORTUNATE THAT BHEEMA WAS SPARED. NOW I AM AT PEACE AND WOULD LIKE TO MEET ARJUNA.

"THE OLD KING THEN EMBRACED ARJUNA, BHEEMA, NAKULA AND SAHADEVA.

BLESS YOU! WITH MY SONS ALL DEAD, MY AFFECTION AND CONCERN WILL BE DIRECTED TO YOU, O SONS OF PANDU.

"RESPECTFULLY TAKING LEAVE OF DHRITARASHTRA, THE PANDAVAS AND KRISHNA WENT UP TO GANDHARI.

"BURNING WITH SORROW OVER THE LOSS OF ALL HER SONS, GANDHARI WAS ABOUT TO UTTER A CURSE ON THE PANDAVAS.

"READING HER MIND, SAGE VYASA INTERVENED IN TIME.

CALM YOURSELF. BEFORE YOU UTTER THE WORDS OF ANGER, HEAR WHAT I HAVE TO SAY TO YOU.

FOR THE LAST EIGHTEEN DAYS, YOUR SON DURYO-DHANA USED TO SEEK YOUR BLESSING BEFORE FACING THE ENEMY.

EACH DAY, YOU RIGHTLY TOLD HIM — WHERE THERE IS DHARMA*, THERE WILL BE VICTORY.

* RIGHTEOUSNESS.

amar chitra katha

DON'T YOU REALISE THAT THIS VICTORY OF THE PANDAVAS PROVES THE TRUTH OF YOUR STATEMENT THAT RIGHTEOUSNESS WILL PREVAIL?

"HIS WORDS OF WISDOM DID INDEED HAVE THE DESIRED EFFECT. GANDHARI SAID —

I BEAR NO ILL-WILL TOWARDS THE PANDAVAS NOR DO I REALLY WISH TO DESTROY THEM. BUT HOW CAN I CONTROL THE REST-LESSNESS OF MY HEART ON LOSING ALL MY SONS?

DURYODHANA, DUHSHASANA AND SHAKUNI ARE TO BE BLAMED FOR THE DESTRUC-TION OF THE KURU CLAN. THAT I DO REALISE. WHAT AGITATES ME IS BHEEMA'S UNFAIR ATTACK ON DURYODHANA.

"BHEEMA HEARD HER AND SAID —

DEAR MOTHER, I KNOW NOT WHETHER IT WAS RIGHT OR WRONG, BUT I HAD TO ATTACK HIM TO SAVE MY LIFE. I PLEAD YOUR FORGIVENESS.

WHO COULD DEFEAT YOUR MIGHTY DURYODHANA IN A FAIR FIGHT? BUT I HAD TO AVENGE THE INSULTS HE HAD HEAPED ON US. SURELY YOU TOO REMEMBER THAT DAY IN COURT.

PERHAPS YOU ARE RIGHT ABOUT DURYODHANA. BUT HOW COULD YOU DRINK DUHSHA-SANA'S BLOOD?

O MOTHER, NOT A DROP OF THAT BLOOD PASSED BEYOND MY LIPS AND TEETH. IT WAS JUST A GESTURE TO FULFIL MY VOW THAT I TOOK WHEN DUHSHASANA DRAGGED DRAUPADI BY HER TRESSES.

"BHEEMA TRIED HIS BEST TO PACIFY GANDHARI.

MOTHER GANDHARI, YOU DID NOT STOP YOUR SONS WHEN THEY TORMENTED US. NOW WHY DO YOU BLAME ME?

OH! WHY DID YOU NOT SPARE AT LEAST ONE SON OF MINE.

WE ARE BOTH OLD NOW, AND BEREFT OF OUR KINGDOM. EVEN ONE SON WOULD HAVE BEEN A SUPPORT FOR US AT THIS AGE.

"HER PAINFUL MEMORIES REVIVED WITH THIS EXCHANGE OF WORDS WITH BHEEMA. SHE CRIED OUT IN ANGER.

WHERE IS THAT KING YUDHISHTHIRA?

"WITH FOLDED HANDS AND TREMBLING WITH FEAR, YUDHISHTHIRA STEPPED AHEAD. IN HIS SWEET VOICE HE SAID —

HERE I AM, GUILTY OF THE DEATH OF YOUR SONS. GO AHEAD AND CURSE ME FOR I DESERVE TO BE CURSED.

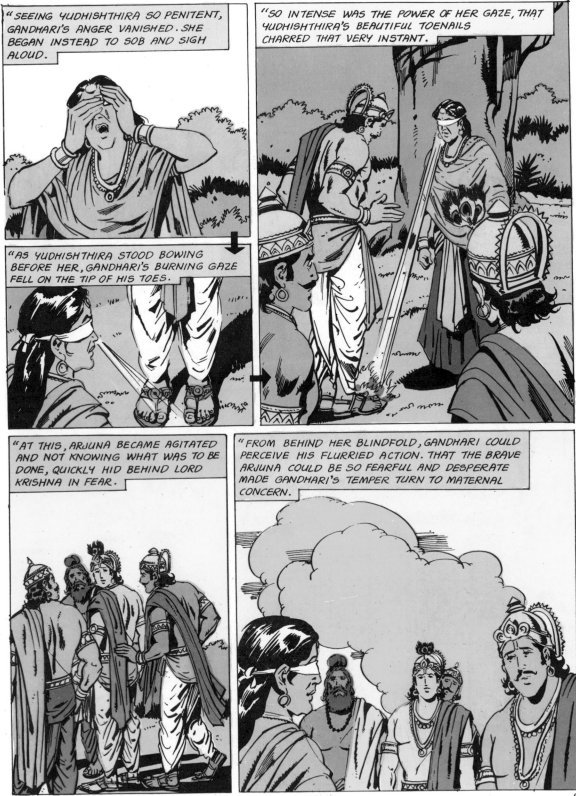

"SEEING YUDHISHTHIRA SO PENITENT, GANDHARI'S ANGER VANISHED. SHE BEGAN INSTEAD TO SOB AND SIGH ALOUD.

"AS YUDHISHTHIRA STOOD BOWING BEFORE HER, GANDHARI'S BURNING GAZE FELL ON THE TIP OF HIS TOES.

"SO INTENSE WAS THE POWER OF HER GAZE, THAT YUDHISHTHIRA'S BEAUTIFUL TOENAILS CHARRED THAT VERY INSTANT.

"AT THIS, ARJUNA BECAME AGITATED AND NOT KNOWING WHAT WAS TO BE DONE, QUICKLY HID BEHIND LORD KRISHNA IN FEAR.

"FROM BEHIND HER BLINDFOLD, GANDHARI COULD PERCEIVE HIS FLURRIED ACTION. THAT THE BRAVE ARJUNA COULD BE SO FEARFUL AND DESPERATE MADE GANDHARI'S TEMPER TURN TO MATERNAL CONCERN.

"WHEN THEY TOOK HER LEAVE TO GO TO THEIR MOTHER, SHE BLESSED THEM WITH AFFECTION.

"WHEN KUNTI BEHELD HER SONS AFTER MANY DAYS, HER EYES BRIMMED OVER WITH TEARS.

"GENTLY, SHE STROKED THEIR WOUNDS AND BEGAN LAMENTING FOR DRAUPADI, ALL OF WHOSE SONS HAD BEEN KILLED.

"SHARING THEIR GRIEF AND EMBRACING ONE ANOTHER, THEY WENT TO GANDHARI AGAIN.

"GANDHARI SAID TO DRAUPADI —

COME, DEAR DAUGHTER. SHED YOUR SORROW NOW. WHATEVER HAPPENED WAS INEVITABLE. I TOO HAVE THE SAME FEELING AS YOU HAVE. MY PLIGHT IS SIMILAR TO YOURS. WHO THEN WILL CONSOLE US?

"AS THEY ALL MADE THEIR WAY TO THE SITE OF THE BATTLE, GANDHARI BEHELD THE SCENE WITH HER DIVINE VISION.

"IT WAS INDEED A GRUESOME SIGHT WITH COUNTLESS BODIES STREWN ALL OVER.

"WIVES AND MOTHERS OF THE FALLEN SOLDIERS WERE SEEN WEEPING AND CRYING.

"AMIDST THEIR HEART-RENDING CRIES, GANDHARI SPOKE TO KRISHNA —

BEHOLD, O KRISHNA, THESE BEREAVED WOMEN RUNNING HERE AND THERE IN SORROW AND CONFUSION.

"WHEN SHE SAW DURYODHANA, GANDHARI COLLAPSED LIKE A FELLED TREE.

"ON RECOVERING, SHE HELD HIS LIFELESS FORM IN HER ARMS AND CRIED OUT.

OH, MY SON! OH, MY SON!

"KRISHNA STOOD BESIDE HER IN SILENCE. GANDHARI POINTED TO HIM THE VARIOUS WOEFUL SIGHTS.

SEE HOW DURYODHANA'S WIFE IS TORN BETWEEN GRIEF FOR HER SON AND FOR HER HUSBAND.

BEHOLD UTTARA LAMENTING THE DEATH OF HER BRAVE, YOUNG HUSBAND, ABHIMANYU. POOR THING, THEY WERE MARRIED JUST SIX MONTHS AGO.

"AS SHE DESCRIBED THE SCENES AROUND, GANDHARI'S ANGER SUDDENLY FLARED UP.

YOU, KRISHNA, ARE TO BE BLAMED FOR ALL THIS. HOW COULD YOU WATCH THE PANDAVAS AND KAURAVAS DESTROY EACH OTHER WHEN YOU COULD HAVE EASILY PREVENTED THEM.

YOU MUST ATONE FOR IT NOW. WITH ALL THE POWERS ATTAINED BY MY PENANCE, I CURSE YOU...

"GANDHARI SPELT OUT HER TERRIBLE CURSE.

...THIRTY-SIX YEARS FROM THIS DAY, YOUR FAMILY, YOUR MINISTERS, YOUR SONS, YOUR WHOLE CLAN WILL FIGHT AMONG THEMSELVES AND DIE.

FRIENDLESS AND ABANDONED, YOU TOO WILL WANDER ABOUT AIMLESSLY TILL YOU DIE AN INGLORIOUS DEATH.

JUST AS THESE WOMEN OF THE BHARATA RACE BEMOAN THE DEATH OF THEIR LOVED ONES, SO TOO WILL YOUR WOMEN-FOLK GRIEVE.

" BUT LORD KRISHNA MERELY SMILED, WHEN HE HEARD THIS HARSH PRONOUNCEMENT. HE SAID—

DEAR LADY, I KNOW THAT WHAT YOU SAID IS INEVITABLE. NO ONE BUT ME CAN CAUSE THE DESTRUCTION OF THE VRISHNI CLAN.

THE YADAVAS CANNOT BE KILLED BY MEN OR DEVAS. THEY MUST THERE-FORE DESTROY ONE ANOTHER.

"THE PANDAVAS WERE GREATLY DISTURBED AT THIS EXCHANGE OF WORDS. KRISHNA, HOWEVER, CONTINUED CALMLY.

ARISE, DEAR LADY, SHED YOUR SORROW WHICH MAKES YOU PUT ALL THE BLAME ON ME.

IS NOT ALL THIS YOUR FAULT? YOU KNOW WELL ENOUGH THAT YOUR SON DURYODHANA WAS WICKED, JEALOUS AND VAIN. YOU ARE INDEED GUILTY OF USING HIM AS A FRONT TO CAUSE THIS RUIN.

GANDHARI WAS SPEECHLESS AT KRISHNA'S TIRADE AGAINST HER. MEANWHILE DHRITARASHTRA REQUESTED YUDHISHTHIRA TO ARRANGE FOR THE LAST RITES OF THE THOUSANDS OF WARRIORS WHO HAD LAID DOWN THEIR LIVES IN THE BATTLE. YUDHISHTHIRA IN TURN ASSIGNED THIS TASK TO VIDURA, SANJAYA, YUYUTSU AND OTHERS.

"AFTER LIGHTING THE FUNERAL PYRES OF THOSE KILLED IN THE BATTLE, DHRITARASHTRA AND YUDHISHTHIRA PROCEEDED TO THE BANKS OF THE RIVER GANGA.

"THE MEN LAID ASIDE THEIR JEWELS AND SILKS TO OFFER OBLATIONS TO THE DEAD.

"THE WOMEN SHED COPIOUS TEARS AS THEY LIFTED THEIR PALMS TO OFFER OBLATIONS.

"JUST THEN, IN SOFT TONES, THE SORROWING KUNTI ADDRESSED HER SONS:

O PANDAVAS, THERE REMAINS ONE PERSON FOR WHOM YOU MUST MAKE OFFERINGS.

THE ONE WHO DEFIED ARJUNA, THE ONE WHO SHONE RESPLENDENT LIKE THE VERY SUN IN THE BATTLEFIELD, THE ONE WHO WAS UNRIVALLED IN STRENGTH AND VALOUR. KARNA, THE BRAVE: HIS RITES MUST BE PERFORMED BY YOU. HE WAS YOUR ELDER BROTHER. I GAVE BIRTH TO HIM, THE SON OF SURYA.

"THE PANDAVAS WERE ASTOUNDED TO HEAR HER SPEAK THUS. WITH A DEEP SIGH YUDHISHTHIRA ASKED HER —

HOW COULD KARNA BE YOUR SON, MOTHER? WAS HE REALLY OUR ELDER BROTHER?

HE WAS MY SON, DEAR YUDHISHTHIRA.

OH MOTHER! BY KEEPING THIS A DARK SECRET, YOU HAVE CAUSED US UNTOLD MISERY. OH, HOW I GRIEVE OVER KARNA. IT IS AS IF I AM PLACED IN A RAGING FIRE.

HAD WE KNOWN THIS EARLIER, WE WOULD HAVE STRIVEN HARD TO OWN HIM AS OUR BROTHER. PERHAPS THIS HORRENDOUS WAR COULD HAVE BEEN AVOIDED.

" WITH TEARS FLOWING DOWN HIS FACE, YUDHISHTHIRA OFFERED OBLATIONS TO KARNA.

" THE WOMEN AROUND HIM TOOK UP THE REFRAIN AND BEGAN CRYING AND WAILING. AMIDST THEIR CRIES YUDHISHTHIRA PRONOUNCED —

I HAVE CAUSED THE DEATH OF MY ELDER BROTHER BECAUSE OF THE SECRET KEPT BY MY MOTHER. FROM THIS DAY, MAY WOMEN OF THE WORLD NEVER BE ABLE TO KEEP A SECRET.

"WITH THESE WORDS, YUDHISHTHIRA STEPPED OUT OF THE WATER, FOLLOWED BY HIS BROTHERS.

"AFTER THE FUNERAL RITES WERE OVER, THE PANDAVAS DECIDED TO STAY AWAY FROM THE CITY FOR A MONTH. SO THEY SET UP CAMP ON THE BANK OF THE GANGA AND LIVED THERE.

"AT THIS TEMPORARY ABODE, YUDHISHTHIRA WAS VISITED BY SEVERAL SAGES INCLUDING VYASA, NARADA AND KANVA.

"SEVERAL SCHOLARS, BRAHMANAS AND HOUSEHOLDERS CAME TO VISIT YUDHISHTHIRA AND CONSOLE HIM IN HIS GRIEF. NARADA SPOKE FIRST —

BY. THE GRACE OF LORD KRISHNA AND THE VALOUR OF YOUR KINSMEN, YOU ARE NOW LORD OF THE EARTH. ARE YOU HAPPY NOW THAT YOU HAVE VANQUISHED YOUR FOES?

"YUDHISHTHIRA REPLIED —

INDEED THIS VICTORY HAS BEEN POSSIBLE DUE TO THE PROWESS OF SHRI KRISHNA AND THE VALOUR OF ARJUNA AND BHEEMA. BUT THE ONE SORROW THAT CONSTANTLY TORMENTS ME IS THAT MY DESIRE FOR THE KINGDOM CAUSED THE DEATH OF SO MANY DEAR ONES.

ANOTHER THOUGHT THAT BOTHERS ME IS THE REVELATION BY MY MOTHER KUNTI THAT KARNA WAS OUR ELDER BROTHER. EVEN UNKNOWINGLY, HOW COULD I HAVE MADE ONE BROTHER KILL ANOTHER?

"YUDHISHTHIRA'S THOUGHTS WENT BACK TO THE PAST.

I REMEMBER THAT DAY IN THE COURT AT HASTINAPURA. HOW MY ANGER VANISHED WHEN I BEHELD KARNA, ESPECIALLY WHEN I SAW HIS FEET. THEY REMINDED ME OF MOTHER KUNTI'S FEET AND I WAS PUZZLED BY THE SIMILARITY.

"YUDHISHTHIRA'S MIND WAS AGITATED WITH MANY QUESTIONS AND HE ASKED VYASA ABOUT THEM.

BUT WHY, DID KARNA'S CHARIOT WHEEL GET STUCK IN THE GROUND? DO TELL ME ALL THIS IN DETAIL.

"SAGE VYASA THEN NARRATED TO YUDHISHTHIRA THE STORY OF HOW KARNA CAME UNDER A CURSE.

YOU HAVE KILLED MY COW. I CURSE YOU THAT WHEN YOU FIGHT A CRUCIAL BATTLE, THE WHEELS OF YOUR CHARIOT WILL GET STUCK IN THE GROUND AND YOU WILL BE KILLED.

amar chitra katha

"YUDHISHTHIRA WAS HOWEVER PLUNGED IN A DEEPER GLOOM ON HEARING THE STORY FROM VYASA. KUNTI COULD NOT BEAR TO SEE HIM SO DESOLATE.

O BRAVE YUDHISHTHIRA, DO NOT GRIEVE SO FOR KARNA. BELIEVE ME, BOTH HIS FATHER, SURYA, AND I HAD TRIED TO EXPLAIN TO HIM THAT YOU PANDAVAS WERE HIS BROTHERS.

"YUDHISHTHIRA WAS TOO AGITATED AND UNHAPPY TO BE THUS CONSOLED. REPEATING HIS EARLIER CURSE ON WOMEN, HE SAT THERE SIGHING DEEPLY.

"TURNING TO ARJUNA HE SAID IN A SAD VOICE —

WE SHOULD HAVE BEEN CONTENT TO BEG FOR OUR LIVING. OF WHAT USE WAS THIS WAR IN WHICH NEITHER WE NOR THE KAURAVAS HAVE ATTAINED THEIR OBJECTIVE.

ONE CAN ATONE FOR ONE'S SINS BY CONFESSING, BY GOOD DEEDS, BY GIVING CHARITY AND BY MEDITATION. LET ME THEREFORE GO TO THE FOREST. I LEAVE THIS KINGDOM IN YOUR CARE, O ARJUNA.

"ARJUNA WAS STARTLED AS ONE ACCUSED OF WRONG-DOING. THEN TAKING A THEATRICAL STANCE, HE STOOD UP TALL AND SMILING.

IT IS SURPRISING THAT YOU WISH TO ABANDON THE KINGDOM YOU HAVE ACQUIRED AFTER SO MUCH EFFORT.

IF YOU WANTED TO GO AROUND WITH A BEGGING BOWL, WHY DID YOU LET SO MANY KINGS DIE IN BATTLE? BEGGING FOR ALMS IS ALL RIGHT FOR BRAHMANAS, BUT IT DOES NOT BEFIT A KSHATRIYA LIKE YOU.

DON'T DISCARD THIS HARD-EARNED WEALTH, O KING! THIS EARTH WHICH WAS RULED EARLIER BY DILIPA, NRIGA, NAHUSHA, AMBARISHA AND MANDHATA IS NOW IN YOUR CONTROL. COME PREPARE TO TAKE OVER THE REINS OF THE EMPIRE AND PERFORM THE ASHWAMEDHA YAJNA.

"BUT YUDHISHTHIRA WAS ADAMANT.

HEAR ME, O ARJUNA, I AM DETERMINED TO DWELL IN THE FOREST, EATING FRUITS AND ROOTS, WEARING DEERSKIN AND BARK AND WITH MY HAIR MATTED IN A KNOT. IN FASTING AND MEDITATION, I WILL SPEND MY REMAINING DAYS.

"BHEEMA, NAKULA AND SAHADEVA ALSO TRIED TO DISSUADE YUDHISHTHIRA FROM HIS RESOLVE, BUT HE REMAINED STUBBORNLY SILENT. THEN DRAUPADI ADDRESSED HIM IN HER SWEET VOICE —

LIKE THE "CHATAKA" BIRDS*, YOUR BROTHERS ARE REPEATEDLY BE-SEECHING YOU TO ACCEPT THE THRONE. WHY DON'T YOU LISTEN TO THEIR ENTREATIES?

THEY HAVE GONE THROUGH SO MUCH SUFFERING FOR YOUR SAKE. DID YOU NOT PROMISE THEM THAT YOU WOULD DEFEAT THE KAURAVAS IN BATTLE AND CONQUER THE EARTH? WHY DO YOU DIS-APPOINT US NOW?

"THEN VYASA SPOKE TO YUDHISHTHIRA AT LENGTH. WITH INSPIRING TALES AND WISE COUNSEL, HE TRIED TO PERSUADE HIM TO RETURN TO THE CITY AND TAKE UP HIS DUTIES AS A KING.

* A BIRD OF BLACKISH COLOUR REFERRED TO IN CLASSICAL POETRY

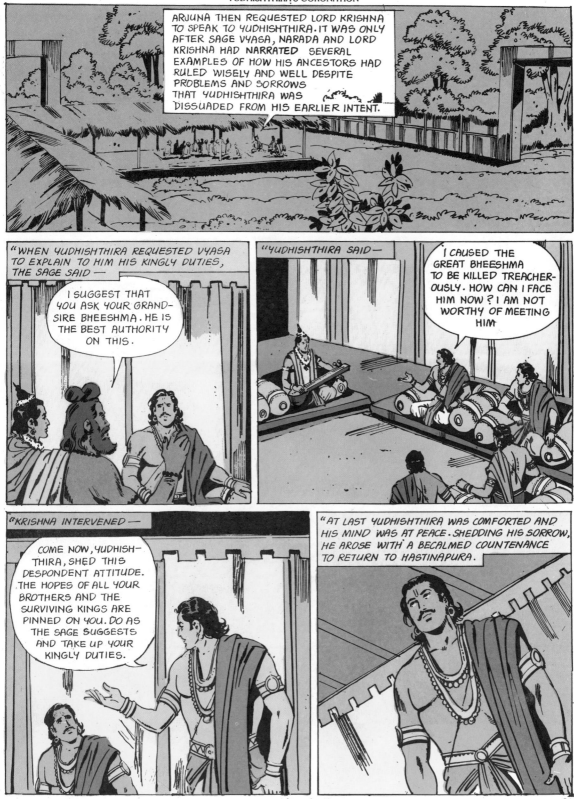

ARJUNA THEN REQUESTED LORD KRISHNA TO SPEAK TO YUDHISHTHIRA. IT WAS ONLY AFTER SAGE VYASA, NARADA AND LORD KRISHNA HAD NARRATED SEVERAL EXAMPLES OF HOW HIS ANCESTORS HAD RULED WISELY AND WELL DESPITE PROBLEMS AND SORROWS THAT YUDHISHTHIRA WAS DISSUADED FROM HIS EARLIER INTENT.

"WHEN YUDHISHTHIRA REQUESTED VYASA TO EXPLAIN TO HIM HIS KINGLY DUTIES, THE SAGE SAID —

I SUGGEST THAT YOU ASK YOUR GRAND-SIRE BHEESHMA. HE IS THE BEST AUTHORITY ON THIS.

"YUDHISHTHIRA SAID —

I CAUSED THE GREAT BHEESHMA TO BE KILLED TREACHER-OUSLY. HOW CAN I FACE HIM NOW? I AM NOT WORTHY OF MEETING HIM

"KRISHNA INTERVENED —

COME NOW, YUDHISH-THIRA, SHED THIS DESPONDENT ATTITUDE. THE HOPES OF ALL YOUR BROTHERS AND THE SURVIVING KINGS ARE PINNED ON YOU. DO AS THE SAGE SUGGESTS AND TAKE UP YOUR KINGLY DUTIES.

"AT LAST YUDHISHTHIRA WAS COMFORTED AND HIS MIND WAS AT PEACE. SHEDDING HIS SORROW, HE AROSE WITH A BECALMED COUNTENANCE TO RETURN TO HASTINAPURA.

"THEY RETURNED TO THEIR CAPITAL IN A MAGNIFICENT PROCESSION. AS THEY ENTERED THE GATES OF THE CITY, YUDHISHTHIRA MOUNTED A NEW CHARIOT DRIVEN BY SIXTEEN WHITE BULLOCKS, BHEEMA HELD THE REINS, AND ARJUNA A WHITE UMBRELLA, WHILE NAKULA AND SAHADEVA CARRIED CHAMARAS * ON EITHER SIDE OF THE KING. YUYUTSU, THE SOLE SURVIVING SON OF DHRITARASHTRA, FOLLOWED IN A WHITE CHARIOT. ON A GOLDEN CHARIOT WERE KRISHNA AND SATYAKI FOLLOWED BY A LONG RETINUE IN CHARIOTS AND PALANQUINS.

* WHISKS

amar chitra katha

"THE CROWDS THRONGED THE CITY GATES TO WELCOME THE KING.

"AMIDST THE CHANTING OF VEDAS AND MUSIC AND THE WELCOMING CHEERS OF THE CITIZENS, YUDHISHTHIRA ENTERED THE CITY.

"THE STREETS WERE GAILY DECORATED WITH WHITE BANNERS AND STREAMERS AND THE AIR WAS FILLED WITH THE FRAGRANCE OF FRESH FLOWERS AND INCENSE.

"AT THE ENTRANCE TO THE PALACE, THEY WERE GREETED CEREMONIOUSLY BY THE BRAHMANAS.

"YUDHISHTHIRA WAS MADE TO SIT ON A BEAUTIFULLY ADORNED THRONE OF GOLD. FACING HIM WERE SATYAKI AND KRISHNA SEATED ON GOLDEN SEATS. FLANKING THE KING, SAT ARJUNA AND BHEEMA ON BEJEWELLED SEATS. NAKULA SAT ON AN IVORY THRONE WHILE KUNTI SHARED A SIMILAR SEAT WITH HER FAVOURITE SON SAHADEVA.

"ON INSTRUCTIONS FROM KRISHNA, DHAUMYA, THE ROYAL PRIEST, CONSTRUCTED AN ALTAR AND REQUESTED YUDHISHTHIRA AND DRAUPADI TO SIT BESIDE IT.

"HOLDING ALOFT HIS CONCH-SHELL PANCHAJANYA, KRISHNA CEREMONIOUSLY POURED WATER ON YUDHISHTHIRA'S HEAD.

"WHEN THE CORONATION RITES WERE COMPLETED, YUDHISHTHIRA GAVE AWAY A THOUSAND GOLD COINS TO THE PRESIDING PRIESTS.

"THEY IN TURN SHOWERED HIM WITH PRAISE AND FELICITATION.

"HAVING TAKEN OVER AS THE KING, YUDHISHTHIRA THEN SET ABOUT ALLOCATING DUTIES TO HIS BROTHERS AND OTHERS. HE APPOINTED BHEEMA YUVARAJA.

"THE WISE VIDURA WAS MADE MINISTER. SANJAYA WAS PUT IN CHARGE OF FINANCE, NAKULA WAS ENTRUSTED WITH THE MAINTENANCE OF THE ARMY OF WHICH ARJUNA WAS NOW THE COMMANDER. TO SAHADEVA HE SAID —

YOU, SAHADEVA, MUST BE MY PERSONAL PROTECTOR, AND BE BY MY SIDE AT ALL TIMES.

"THE NEXT MORNING WHEN YUDHISHTHIRA WENT TO GREET KRISHNA, HE FOUND HIM IN A THOUGHTFUL MOOD. SAID YUDHISHTHIRA—

DID YOU SPEND THE NIGHT PEACEFULLY? YOU, THE CAUSE OF OUR VICTORY, O KRISHNA, ARE YOU FEELING WELL?

"BUT WHEN HIS QUERIES WERE MET WITH A PENSIVE SILENCE, YUDHISHTHIRA WAS PUZZLED.

LORD, WHAT MAKES YOU SO THOUGHTFUL?

MY THOUGHTS ARE WITH BHEESHMA WHO IS LYING ON A BED OF ARROWS IN THE BATTLEFIELD.

"KRISHNA CONTINUED—

WHEN THE VENERABLE BHEESHMA ASCENDS TO THE HEAVENS, HIS VAST KNOWLEDGE TOO WILL VANISH. HURRY THEREFORE TO HIS SIDE AND ASK HIM ABOUT WHATEVER YOU WISH TO KNOW WITH REGARD TO YOUR TASKS AND DUTIES AS A KING.

"YUDHISHTHIRA SAID—

I WILL INDEED DO AS YOU BID.

"KRISHNA THEN ORDERED HIS CHARIOT TO BE MADE READY, ACCOMPANIED BY THE PANDAVAS, HE WENT TO THE BATTLEFIELD.

"LYING ON HIS BED OF ARROWS, BHEESHMA WAS SURROUNDED BY SEVERAL SAGES.

"BOWING RESPECTFULLY TO BHEESHMA, THE PANDAVAS TOO SAT BESIDE HIM. KRISHNA SAID—

IF A NEEDLE AS MUCH AS PRICKS ME, I CANNOT BEAR THE PAIN. HERE YOU LIE CALMLY WITH ALL THOSE ARROWS PIERCING YOUR BODY. YOUR STRENGTH IS INDEED AMAZING. THERE IS NO ONE LIKE YOU IN THIS WORLD.

"KRISHNA THEN EXPLAINED THE REASON FOR THEIR VISIT.

YUDHISHTHIRA IS GREATLY DISTURBED BY THE DEATH OF SO MANY OF HIS KINSMEN. CONSOLE HIM, O BHEESHMA, WITH YOUR WORDS OF WISDOM.

"BHEESHMA RAISED HIS HEAD A LITTLE ON HEARING KRISHNA'S WORDS, AND GREETED HIM RESPECTFULLY. KRISHNA SAID—

NOW ONLY FIFTY-SIX DAYS REMAIN BEFORE YOUR SOUL ASCENDS TO HEAVEN. WITH YOU, ALL YOUR KNOWLEDGE TOO WILL DISAPPEAR. THEREFORE ALL THESE PEOPLE HAVE COME TO BE ENLIGHTENED BY YOU. WILL YOU INSTRUCT THEM IN DHARMA,* ARTHA** AND YOGA?

"BHEESHMA REPLIED WITH DUE MODESTY.

HOW CAN I TALK OF THESE THINGS WHILE YOU, THE ABODE OF ALL KNOW-LEDGE, ARE PRESENT HERE? BESIDES, MY WOUNDS ARE CAUSING ME IMMENSE PAIN AND I FEEL DRAINED OF ALL MY STRENGTH.

"KRISHNA THEN BLESSED HIM.

FROM NOW ON YOU WILL FEEL NO PAIN OR WEAKNESS. NEITHER HUNGER NOR THIRST WILL BOTHER YOU. YOUR MIND WILL BE UNCLOUDED AND YOUR BRAIN ALERT.

"WITH THESE WORDS, KRISHNA AND THE PANDAVAS TOOK LEAVE OF BHEESHMA.

* DUTY   ** ECONOMICS   amar chitra katha

"EARLY NEXT MORNING, DISPENSING WITH THEIR RETINUE OF SOLDIERS, THE PANDAVAS FOLLOWED KRISHNA TO THE BATTLEFIELD.

"NARADA, WHO WAS SEATED WITH THE OTHER RISHIS WHO WERE AROUND BHEESHMA, SAID —

YUDHISHTHIRA, PUT YOUR QUERIES AND DOUBTS BEFORE BHEESHMA. YOU MUST BE QUICK BECAUSE HE HAS VERY LITTLE TIME LEFT.

"AS THE SAGE SPOKE THUS, ALL THE PEOPLE SURROUNDING BHEESHMA DREW CLOSER, BUT NONE DARED TO SPEAK. THEN YUDHISHTHIRA SAID —

O KRISHNA, YOU ALONE CAN BEGIN THIS DISCUSSION ON OUR BEHALF.

"AFTER GREETING HIM WITH DUE RESPECT, KRISHNA REQUESTED BHEESHMA —

O BHEESHMA, YUDHISHTHIRA AND HIS BROTHERS ARE EAGER TO HEAR YOU SPEAK.

"BHEESHMA REPLIED —

YUDHISHTHIRA MAY ADDRESS HIS QUERIES TO ME ONE BY ONE. I WILL BE HAPPY TO TEACH HIM ALL I KNOW.

"KRISHNA SAID —

YUDHISHTHIRA IS TOO EMBARRASSED AND SCARED TO FACE YOU.

BUT SURELY HE HAS DONE NO WRONG. IT IS THE DUTY OF EVERY KSHATRIYA TO KILL HIS ENEMIES.

OVERWHELMED BY THESE WORDS, YUDHISHTHIRA TOUCHED BHEESHMA'S FEET RESPECTFULLY.

SIT DOWN, SON. DO NOT BE AFRAID. ASK ME ANYTHING YOU WANT.

"YUDHISHTHIRA SAID —

THE DUTIES OF A KING ARE SAID TO BE OF THE HIGHEST ORDER. PLEASE DESCRIBE THEM TO ME.

"BHEESHMA BEGAN —

A KING SHOULD DULY HONOUR THE DEVAS AND THE BRAHMANAS. HE SHOULD BE A MAN OF ACTION AND ALWAYS STRIVE FOR TRUTH. HE SHOULD BE JUST, HUMBLE, STRAIGHTFORWARD AND RIGHTEOUS...

"FOR LONG DID THE WISE BHEESHMA SPEAK TO YUDHISHTHIRA, ABOUT THE DUTIES OF A KING. THE SUN WAS ABOUT TO SET IN THE WEST, YET BHEESHMA'S NARRATION WAS NOT YET OVER. SUMMING UP HIS DAY-LONG DISCOURSE HE SAID —

THIS IS THE MERE ESSENCE OF KINGLY DUTIES. ASK ME ANY QUESTIONS YOU WANT, O YUDHISHTHIRA.

THANK YOU, O GRANDSIRE. THE SUN IS ABOUT TO SET AND I MUST TAKE YOUR LEAVE FOR TODAY.

"THE NEXT MORNING THE PANDAVAS EAGERLY RUSHED BACK TO BHEESHMA. YUDHISHTHIRA SAID —

COULD YOU EXPLAIN TO ME THE MEANING OF THE WORD 'RAJAN'. WHY IS A KING NECESSARY?

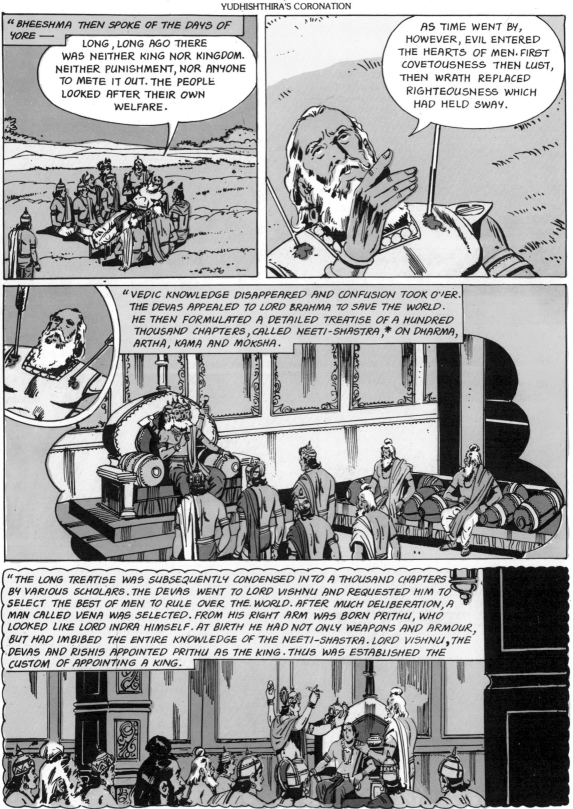

"BHEESHMA THEN SPOKE OF THE DAYS OF YORE —

LONG, LONG AGO THERE WAS NEITHER KING NOR KINGDOM. NEITHER PUNISHMENT, NOR ANYONE TO METE IT OUT. THE PEOPLE LOOKED AFTER THEIR OWN WELFARE.

AS TIME WENT BY, HOWEVER, EVIL ENTERED THE HEARTS OF MEN. FIRST COVETOUSNESS THEN LUST, THEN WRATH REPLACED RIGHTEOUSNESS WHICH HAD HELD SWAY.

"VEDIC KNOWLEDGE DISAPPEARED AND CONFUSION TOOK O'ER. THE DEVAS APPEALED TO LORD BRAHMA TO SAVE THE WORLD. HE THEN FORMULATED A DETAILED TREATISE OF A HUNDRED THOUSAND CHAPTERS, CALLED NEETI-SHASTRA,* ON DHARMA, ARTHA, KAMA AND MOKSHA.

"THE LONG TREATISE WAS SUBSEQUENTLY CONDENSED INTO A THOUSAND CHAPTERS BY VARIOUS SCHOLARS. THE DEVAS WENT TO LORD VISHNU AND REQUESTED HIM TO SELECT THE BEST OF MEN TO RULE OVER THE WORLD. AFTER MUCH DELIBERATION, A MAN CALLED VENA WAS SELECTED. FROM HIS RIGHT ARM WAS BORN PRITHU, WHO LOOKED LIKE LORD INDRA HIMSELF. AT BIRTH HE HAD NOT ONLY WEAPONS AND ARMOUR, BUT HAD IMBIBED THE ENTIRE KNOWLEDGE OF THE NEETI-SHASTRA. LORD VISHNU, THE DEVAS AND RISHIS APPOINTED PRITHU AS THE KING. THUS WAS ESTABLISHED THE CUSTOM OF APPOINTING A KING.

* A CODE OF CONDUCT

"THUS FOR SEVERAL DAYS DID BHEESHMA-CHARYA INSTRUCT YUDHISHTHIRA, ANSWERING HIS QUERIES, REMOVING HIS DOUBTS AND EXPLAINING THE CODE OF CONDUCT WITH STORIES AND NARRATIVES, DIALOGUES AND DISCUSSIONS FROM HIS VAST FUND OF KNOWLEDGE.*

"WHEN BHEESHMA LAY SILENT AFTER INSTRUCTING YUDHISHTHIRA, SAGE VYASA SAID—

NOW YUDHISHTHIRA'S CONFIDENCE HAS BEEN RESTORED. ALLOW HIM TO RETURN TO HASTINAPURA, O BHEESHMA.

"BHEESHMA SAID TO YUDHISHTHIRA—

YOU MAY GO BACK AND RULE YOUR KINGDOM LIKE THE GREAT KINGS BEFORE YOU. WHEN THE SUN BEGINS ITS NORTHWARD JOURNEY, COME BACK TO ME.

I WILL DO SO.

"BOWING RESPECTFULLY TO BHEESHMA, YUDHISHTHIRA RETURNED TO HASTINAPURA. FIFTY DAYS LATER, HE RECALLED BHEESHMA'S WORDS AND SENT FLOWERS AND INCENSE, SILKS AND SANDALWOOD IN PREPARATION FOR THE GRANDSIRE'S END.

"WITH GANDHARI AND DHRITARASHTRA LEADING THE WAY, YUDHISHTHIRA MADE HIS WAY TO THE BATTLEFIELD ACCOMPANIED BY HIS BROTHERS AND LORD KRISHNA TO PAY HIS LAST RESPECTS TO THE VENERABLE BHEESHMA.

"YUDHISHTHIRA SAID—

HERE I AM WITH MY BROTHERS AND LORD KRISHNA. KING DHRITARASHTRA, MINISTERS OF THE COURT ARE HERE TOO ALONG WITH THE CITIZENS OF HASTINAPURA. PLEASE OPEN YOUR EYES AND LOOK AT US.

* THIS INSTRUCTION OF BHEESHMA TO KING YUDHISHTHIRA IS THE FAMOUS SHANTIPARVA OF MAHABHARATA

"BHEESHMA OPENED HIS WEARY EYES AND SAID —

IT IS FORTUNATE THAT YOU HAVE ARRIVED HERE IN TIME. I HAVE BEEN LYING FOR FIFTY-EIGHT DAYS ON THIS BED OF SHARP ARROWS, BUT I FEEL I HAVE BEEN HERE FOR A HUNDRED YEARS. AT LONG LAST, THE SUN HAS TURNED HIS CHARIOT TOWARDS THE NORTH.

"TURNING TO DHRITARASHTRA, HE SAID —

WISE AND LEARNED AS YOU ARE, DO NOT GRIEVE OVER YOUR SONS. WHATEVER HAPPENED WAS INEVITABLE. CONSIDER THE PANDAVAS TO BE YOUR OWN CHILDREN.

"BHEESHMA THEN ADDRESSED KRISHNA —

ALLOW ME, O LORD, OF THE UNIVERSE, TO LEAVE THIS BODY OF MINE.

I GRANT YOU YOUR WISH, YOU HAVE THE POWER TO SUMMON DEATH AT WILL.

"BHEESHMA'S FACE SHONE WITH AN ETHEREAL SMILE. WITH HIS YOGIC POWERS, HE WILLED HIMSELF TO DIE. THE ONLOOKERS BEHELD A STRANGE PHENOMENON. AS EACH PART OF HIS BODY BECAME LIFELESS, THE ARROWS THEREIN FELL OFF AND THE WOUNDS WERE HEALED. WHEN THE LIFE FORCE FINALLY ESCAPED THROUGH HIS SKULL, THE HEAVENS RESOUNDED WITH CELESTIAL MUSIC AND SHOWERED HIM WITH FLOWERS.

WITH DUE HONOUR AND CEREMONY, BHEESHMA'S BODY WAS CONSIGNED TO THE FIRE. THUS DID THE VENERABLE BHEESHMA MEET HIS END AT WILL AT THE END OF A LONG AND ILLUSTRIOUS LIFE.

THUS ENDS THE FORTIETH SESSION OF OUR RENDERING OF VYASA'S IMMORTAL ITIHASA MAHABHARATA.

Mahabharata–41
THE ASHWAMEDHA YAJNA

AFTER CONSECRATING THE GRANDSIRE BHEESHMA'S BODY TO THE FIRE WITH DUE CEREMONY, DHRITARASHTRA AND YUDHISHTHIRA PROCEEDED TO THE BANKS OF THE HOLY GANGA. WHILE OFFERING OBLATIONS, YUDHISHTHIRA WAS ONCE AGAIN FILLED WITH REMORSE.

"SHATTERED BY GRIEF AND HIS EYES MOIST, HE STAGGERED OUT OF THE WATER WHILE BHEEMA STEADIED HIM.

"SEEING HIM SO DESPONDENT, THE OTHER PANDAVA BROTHERS TOO FELT HELPLESS AND FORLORN. ADDRESSING YUDHISHTHIRA, DHRITARASHTRA SAID —

COME, O KING, ARISE AND PREPARE FOR THE TASKS AHEAD. YOU HAVE WON THIS KINGDOM BY RIGHTFUL MEANS. ENJOY AND RULE OVER IT WITH YOUR BROTHERS AND WELL-WISHERS.

LOOK AT GANDHARI AND ME. WE HAVE LOST ALL OUR HUNDRED SONS. SURELY WE HAVE REASON TO BE SAD. I SEE NO CAUSE FOR YOUR GRIEF.

"WHEN YUDHISHTHIRA DID NOT REPLY, KRISHNA SAID —

YOU HAVE LEARNT SO MUCH FROM BHEESHMA AND OTHER WISE MEN. ACCORDING TO THEIR COUNSEL, YOU MUST NOW PREPARE YOURSELF TO RULE YOUR KINGDOM.

"YUDHISHTHIRA SAID —

IT IS I WHO WAS RESPONSIBLE FOR THE DEATHS OF BHEESHMA, DRONA AND KARNA. DO TELL ME HOW I MAY ABSOLVE MYSELF OF THIS SIN, O KRISHNA!

"SAGE VYASA THEN INTERVENED —

YOUR MIND IS STILL NOT AT REST, DESPITE THE LONG HOURS OF DISCUSSIONS YOU HAVE HAD. IS ALL OUR ADVICE IN VAIN? WHY DO YOU AGAIN AND AGAIN SINK INTO GLOOM?

HOWEVER, IF YOU ARE STILL GNAWED BY FEELINGS OF GUILT ABOUT THE WAR, I WILL SUGGEST A WAY TO PURIFY YOURSELF. PERFORM YAJNAS LIKE THE RAJASOOYA AND THE ASHWAMEDHA.

"YUDHISHTHIRA SAID —

NO DOUBT, THE ASHWAMEDHA YAJNA WILL SERVE TO PURIFY THIS ENTIRE EARTH. BUT I HAVE NO RESOURCES LEFT AT ALL. HOW CAN I UNDERTAKE THE YAJNA NOW?

"SAGE VYASA PONDERED FOR A WHILE AND SAID —

THERE IS A WAY OUT. FAR AWAY UNDER THE SLOPES OF THE HIMALAYAS LIES BURIED THE IMMENSE WEALTH OF KING MARUTTA. YOU MUST GO AND FETCH IT.

"YUDHISHTHIRA FELT PUZZLED.

BUT I DO NOT UNDERSTAND. HOW DID MARUTTA ACCUMULATE SO MUCH WEALTH? HOW CAN WE GET IT NOW?

I WILL TELL YOU THE STORY.

"ONCE UPON A TIME, WHEN KING MARUTTA OF THE IKSHVAKU DYNASTY, PLANNED TO UNDERTAKE A YAJNA, HE REQUESTED BRIHASPATI TO BE HIS PRIEST.

I HAVE MADE ALL PREPARATIONS. DO ME THE HONOUR OF PRESIDING OVER THE SACRIFICE.

I AM NOW THE PRIEST OF LORD INDRA. HOW CAN I BE THE GURU OF MERE MORTALS? GO AND FIND SOMEONE ELSE.

"KING MARUTTA WAS ADVISED TO FIND BRIHASPATI'S BROTHER SAMVARTA, WHO, TIRED OF BRIHASPATI'S ENVY AND THE HARASSMENT CAUSED BY HIM, HAD RETIRED TO THE FOREST.

YOUR BROTHER BRIHASPATI HAS REFUSED TO PERFORM THE YAJNA FOR ME. WILL YOU KINDLY COME TO MY HELP AND PERFORM IT FOR ME?

"WHEN KING MARUTTA MADE THE REQUEST REPEATEDLY, SAMVARTA AGREED.

I WILL TELL YOU A WAY TO OBTAIN INEXHAUSTIBLE WEALTH TO PERFORM THE YAJNA. AT THE SAME TIME, I WILL TEACH INDRA AND MY BROTHER, BRIHASPATI, A LESSON.

GO AND PRAY TO LORD SHIVA IN THE MANNER I WILL TELL YOU NOW.

I WILL DO SO AT ONCE.

"KING MARUTTA OFFERED PRAYERS TO LORD SHIVA AND OBTAINED FROM THE GOD IMMENSE WEALTH AS A BOON.

"KING MARUTTA THEN PREPARED FOR THE SACRIFICE. CRAFTSMEN WERE APPOINTED TO MAKE GOLD VESSELS AND POTS FOR THE CEREMONY, AND A SACRIFICIAL HALL WAS BUILT IN THE HIMALAYAS.

"WHEN BRIHASPATI CAME TO KNOW OF THE WEALTH ACQUIRED BY KING MARUTTA, HE BECAME THIN AND WAN WITH ENVY. INDRA ASKED HIM —

WHAT TROUBLES YOU? ARE YOU NOT LOOKED AFTER WELL BY YOUR ATTENDANTS?

I HAVE HEARD THAT MY BROTHER, SAMVARTA, IS GOING TO CONDUCT KING MARUTTA'S YAJNA. IT IS SOMETHING I CANNOT TOLERATE.

"INDRA WAS SURPRISED.

BUT YOU ARE THE PRIEST OF THE DEVAS THEMSELVES. WHAT CAN SAMVARTA DO TO YOU?

AH! WHO CAN BEAR TO SEE AN ENEMY PROSPER. PLEASE HAVE KING MARUTTA AND SAMVARTA CAPTURED.

"INDRA THEN SENT MESSENGERS TO KING MARUTTA, OFFERING THE SERVICES OF BRIHASPATI AS THE PRESIDING PRIEST. BUT THE KING WOULD NOT CHANGE HIS MIND.

SAMVARTA ALONE SHALL BE MY PRIEST.

"ENRAGED, INDRA DECIDED TO USE HIS CELESTIAL WEAPON ON MARUTTA. THE KING BEGGED SAMVARTA TO PROTECT HIM.

FEAR NOT, O KING. NO ONE CAN HARM YOU WHILE YOU ARE IN MY PROTECTION. TELL ME YOUR HEART'S DESIRE AND I WILL HAVE IT FULFILLED.

"KING MARUTTA SAID —

MAY LORD INDRA AND OTHER DEVAS ATTEND THIS YAJNA OF MINE.

SO BE IT.

"WITH HIS POWER OF PENANCE, SAMVARTA WAS INDEED ABLE TO INVOKE INDRA AT THE SACRIFICE. PACIFIED BY SAMVARTA, THE LORD OF THE DEVAS PARTICIPATED IN THE RITES AND BLESSED THE KING.

AFTER THE SACRIFICE WAS OVER, KING MARUTTA MADE GENEROUS GIFTS OF GOLD TO ALL THE BRAHMANAS. SO GREAT WAS HIS WEALTH THAT THERE STILL REMAINED ENOUGH TO FILL A BIG STOREHOUSE. LEAVING IT BURIED IN THE HIMALAYAS, KING MARUTTA RETURNED TO HIS CAPITAL. YOU MUST NOW ARRANGE TO FETCH THIS TREASURE FOR YOUR YAJNA.

" YUDHISHTHIRA'S GLOOM WAS DISPELLED BY THIS STORY AND HIS CHEER WAS RESTORED. TAKING ADVANTAGE OF HIS RECEPTIVE MOOD, KRISHNA SAID —

ONE WAR IS NOW OVER. WHAT REMAINS IS YOUR FIGHT WITH YOUR OWN SELF AND CONQUEST OF YOUR OWN MIND. ONCE YOU DO THAT, YOU WILL BE AT PEACE.

YOU MUST NOW PREPARE YOURSELF FOR THE PERFORMANCE OF SACRIFICES LIKE THE ASHWAMEDHA.

" YUDHISHTHIRA SAID —

I AM NOW AT PEACE WITH MYSELF. I WILL CERTAINLY DO AS YOU BID. SOON WE WILL GO TO THE HIMALAYAS.

" YUDHISHTHIRA AND HIS RETINUE RETURN-ED TO HASTINAPURA WITH DHRITARASHTRA LEADING THE WAY.

" PEACE AND PROSPERITY PREVAILED DURING KING YUDHISHTHIRA'S RULE. THE WELL-BEING OF THE PEOPLE WAS ASSURED, THERE WAS PLENTY EVERY-WHERE AND THE CATTLE WERE CONTENTED.

"ARJUNA AND KRISHNA REVELLED IN THE PEACEFUL SURROUNDINGS. TOGETHER THEY ROAMED THROUGH GARDEN AND GLADE, MOUNTAINS AND VALLEYS, REGALING EACH OTHER WITH TALES OF OLD. AFTER SPENDING MANY HAPPY DAYS IN EACH OTHER'S COMPANY, KRISHNA SAID —

HOW HAPPY AND TRANQUIL THESE PAST FEW DAYS WERE. BUT NOW I MUST TAKE YOUR LEAVE.

I MUST NOW RETURN TO DWARAKA. I HAVE NOT SEEN MY FATHER VASUDEVA FOR LONG. MY WORK HERE IS DONE. ALLOW ME TO GO, DEAR ARJUNA.

WILL YOU ALSO REQUEST YUDHISHTHIRA TO PERMIT ME TO LEAVE? I DARE NOT DO SO LEST I HURT HIS FEELINGS.

"WITH A HEAVY HEART, ARJUNA SAID —

AS YOU WISH, O KRISHNA. I WILL PERSUADE YUDHISHTHIRA TO ALLOW YOU TO GO.

"THE TWO FRIENDS THEN RETURNED TO HASTINAPURA AND TO THE PRESENCE OF DHRITARASHTRA.

I FEEL YOU HAVE SOMETHING TO SPEAK TO ME.

O KING, KRISHNA HAS BEEN WITH US FOR SO MANY DAYS. HE NOW LONGS TO SEE HIS FATHER. ALLOW HIM TO GO TO DWARAKA.

amar chitra katha

"YUDHISHTHIRA SAID —

INDEED HE MUST GO AND SEE HIS FATHER. YOU MAY LEAVE FOR DWARAKA TODAY, KRISHNA, IF YOU WISH. BUT DO NOT FORGET US WHEN YOU ARE THERE. YOU MUST ALSO RETURN HERE FOR THE ASHWAMEDHA YAJNA.

"AFTER BIDDING KUNTI, VIDURA AND OTHERS FAREWELL KRISHNA AND SUBHADRA LEFT HASTINAPURA.

"MEANWHILE ABHIMANYU'S YOUNG WIFE WAS STILL GRIEVING OVER HER HUSBAND'S DEATH. DIVINING HER STATE OF MIND, SAGE VYASA PAID HER A VISIT TO CONSOLE HER.

DO NOT GRIEVE SO. YOUR SON IS DESTINED TO BE A GREAT AND BRILLIANT KING.

"GOING TO YUDHISHTHIRA, SAGE VYASA SAID —

YOU MAY NOW PREPARE FOR THE ASHWAMEDHA YAJNA.

"RECALLING HIS EARLIER ADVICE, YUDHISHTHIRA PLANNED TO GO TO THE HIMALAYAS, CALLING HIS BROTHERS TOGETHER, HE SAID —

YOU TOO HAVE HEARD THE WISE COUNSEL GIVEN BY LORD KRISHNA AND SAGE VYASA.

OUR RESOURCES ARE DEPLETED. WE MUST GO AND FIND THE WEALTH LEFT BY KING MARUTTA, ABOUT WHICH SAGE VYASA TOLD US. WHAT DO YOU SAY, BHEEMA?

"BHEEMA REPLIED—

I AM HAPPY TO HEAR THIS. WITH SHIVA'S BLESSINGS, WE WILL FIND THE TREASURE OF KING MARUTTA.

"WHEN ARJUNA, NAKULA AND SAHADEVA TOO SUPPORTED YUDHISHTHIRA'S DECISION, HE SAID —

LET PREPARATIONS BE MADE FOR US TO LEAVE FOR OUR JOURNEY ON AN AUSPICIOUS DAY.

"LEAVING YUYUTSU TO LOOK AFTER DHRITARASHTRA, GANDHARI AND KUNTI, THE PANDAVAS STARTED ON THEIR JOURNEY TO THE HIMALAYAS.

"CROSSING NUMEROUS RIVERS AND LAKES, FORESTS AND VALLEYS, THE PANDAVAS FINALLY REACHED THEIR DESTINATION.

"THEY SET UP CAMP IN A SUITABLE SPOT. YUDHISHTHIRA ASKED THE ROYAL PRIESTS —

WHICH DAY IS SUITABLE TO BEGIN OUR WORK?

TODAY IS A GOOD DAY TO BEGIN ANY IMPORTANT WORK. WE MUST ALL FAST TONIGHT IN PREPARATION FOR TOMORROW'S TASK.

amar chitra katha

"DELIGHTED AT THE PROSPECT OF START- ING THEIR WORK SOON, THE PANDAVAS FASTED THAT NIGHT AND SLEPT PEACE- FULLY ON STRAW.

"NEXT DAY AT DAWN, THE PRIESTS SAID TO YUDHISHTHIRA —

NOW YOU MUST PRAY TO SHIVA BEFORE STARTING YOUR WORK.

AS YOU SAY.

"WITH APPROPRIATE RITES AND RITUALS, YUDHISHTHIRA OFFERED HIS PRAYER TO SHIVA.

"THEN THEY PROCEEDED TO THE SPOT WHERE THE TREASURE WAS BURIED. UNDER THE PANDAVAS' SUPERVISION, THEIR ARMY BEGAN TO DIG.

"SOON THEY BROUGHT OUT GLEAMING GOLD VESSELS OF ALL SHAPES AND SIZES.

"THESE WERE ARRANGED IN LARGE TRUNKS BROUGHT FOR THAT PURPOSE.

"THOUSANDS OF CAMELS AND HORSES AND HUNDREDS OF CHARIOTS AND ELEPHANTS WERE REQUIRED TO LOAD ALL THE TREASURE THAT WAS CARRIED TO HASTINAPURA.

"MEANWHILE, LORD KRISHNA AND HIS KINSMEN HAD ARRIVED AT HASTINAPURA FOR THE ASHWAMEDHA YAJNA.

"DHRITARASHTRA AND VIDURA MADE ARRANGEMENTS TO WELCOME THEM.

"DURING THEIR STAY THERE, ABHIMANYU'S WIFE UTTARA GAVE BIRTH TO A SON. WHEN THE SHOUTS OF JOY FROM THE PALACE SUDDENLY TURNED TO A DISQUIETING SILENCE, KRISHNA RUSHED TO THE INNER CHAMBERS.

"HE SAW KUNTI RUSHING OUT.

O KRISHNA, YOU ARE OUR ONLY HOPE NOW. UTTARA'S SON IS STILL-BORN. BRING HIM ALIVE. REMEMBER YOUR VOW TO REVIVE HIM.*

"WHEN KRISHNA REACHED THE INNER CHAMBERS, HE SAW SUBHADRA, DRAUPADI AND OTHER WOMEN IN TEARS.

"DRAUPADI RUSHED TO UTTARA AND SAID —

HERE HE COMES, LORD KRISHNA HIMSELF.

"HER VOICE CHOKING WITH TEARS, UTTARA SAID TO KRISHNA —

I BESEECH YOU, O LORD, REVIVE MY SON. IT SEEMS THAT THE BRAHMASTRA+ OF ASHWATTHAMA HAS HAD ITS EVIL EFFECT.

"TAKING SOME WATER IN HIS CUPPED HAND, KRISHNA DECLARED —

UTTARA, MY DEAR, MY WORDS CAN NEVER GO WRONG. I WILL FULFIL MY VOW AND SAVE THE CHILD.

"NULLIFYING THE EVIL INFLUENCE OF THE BRAHMASTRA, HE SAID —

IF I HAVE ALWAYS ADHERED TO TRUTH AND DUTY, MAY THIS CHILD COME ALIVE.

"NO SOONER HAD KRISHNA MADE THIS DECLARATION, THAN THE NEW-BORN INFANT BEGAN TO STIR WITH LIFE.

"JOY AND HAPPINESS PERCOLATED THROUGHOUT THE PALACE.

HAIL KRISHNA, OUR SAVIOUR.

PRAISES BE SHOWERED ON THE LORD.

"JOYFULLY, WITH HER SON CRADLED IN HER ARMS, UTTARA BOWED TO KRISHNA WHO SAID —

HE IS BORN AFTER THE KURU RACE HAS BEEN DESTROYED. LET HIM BE CALLED PAREEKSHIT.*

+ MAHABHARATA — 39   * PAREEKSHIN = DESTRUCTION

"JUST A FEW DAYS AFTER THEIR ARRIVAL, THE SAGE VYASA VISITED HASTINAPURA. YUDHISHTHIRA SAID —

WITH YOUR COUNSEL AND BLESSINGS, WE HAVE ACQUIRED THE TREASURE OF MARUTTA. I WOULD LIKE TO USE IT FOR THE ASHWAMEDHA YAJNA, IF YOU SO PERMIT.

"SAGE VYASA SAID —

I GRANT YOU PERMISSION TO CONDUCT THE YAJNA. IT WILL ABSOLVE YOU OF ALL YOUR SINS.

"YUDHISHTHIRA THEN APPROACHED KRISHNA.

LORD, I HAVE A REQUEST TO MAKE. IT IS DUE TO YOUR PROWESS THAT WE HAVE WON THIS KINGDOM. IT IS BUT RIGHT THAT YOU SHOULD PERFORM THE YAJNA ON OUR BEHALF.

"KRISHNA SAID —

O YUDHISHTHIRA, IT IS CHARACTERISTIC OF YOU TO BE SO GENEROUS. BUT I AM CONVINCED THAT YOU ARE THE RIGHT PERSON FOR THIS HONOUR. ASSIGN ME ANY TASK AND I PROMISE TO DO IT.

"SAGE VYASA SELECTED AN APPROPRIATE DAY FOR THE YAJNA. HECTIC PREPARATIONS WERE BEGUN.

CHOOSE A SUITABLE HORSE TO BE DESPATCHED TO ALL PARTS OF THE LAND. MAKE ALL OTHER PREPARATIONS AND SEE ME AFTER DOING SO.

amar chitra katha

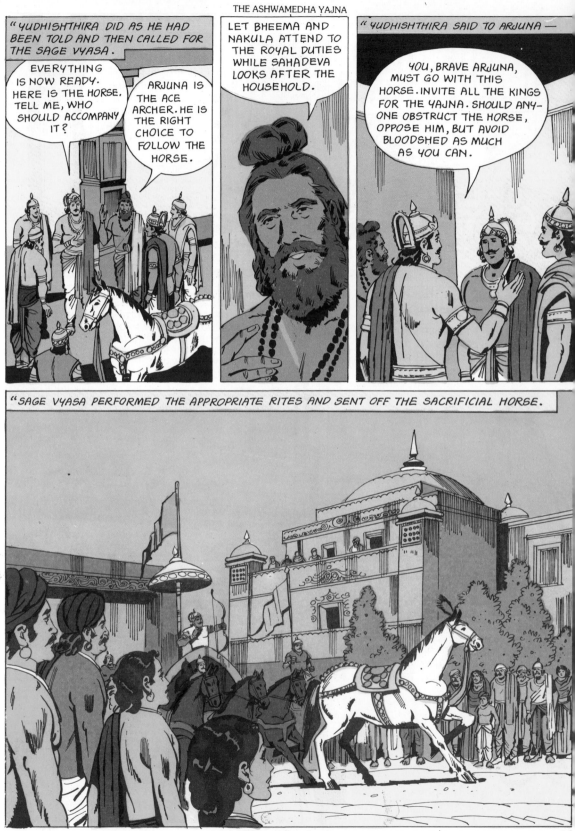

"YUDHISHTHIRA DID AS HE HAD BEEN TOLD AND THEN CALLED FOR THE SAGE VYASA.

EVERYTHING IS NOW READY. HERE IS THE HORSE. TELL ME, WHO SHOULD ACCOMPANY IT?

ARJUNA IS THE ACE ARCHER. HE IS THE RIGHT CHOICE TO FOLLOW THE HORSE.

LET BHEEMA AND NAKULA ATTEND TO THE ROYAL DUTIES WHILE SAHADEVA LOOKS AFTER THE HOUSEHOLD.

"YUDHISHTHIRA SAID TO ARJUNA —

YOU, BRAVE ARJUNA, MUST GO WITH THIS HORSE. INVITE ALL THE KINGS FOR THE YAJNA. SHOULD ANYONE OBSTRUCT THE HORSE, OPPOSE HIM, BUT AVOID BLOODSHED AS MUCH AS YOU CAN.

"SAGE VYASA PERFORMED THE APPROPRIATE RITES AND SENT OFF THE SACRIFICIAL HORSE.

"ARJUNA ACCOMPANIED THE HORSE, HAPPILY TWANGING HIS GANDEEVA, FOLLOWED BY SEVERAL PRIESTS AND SOLDIERS.

"MEANWHILE YUDHISHTHIRA SAT BEFORE THE SACRIFICIAL FIRE, LOOKING RESPLENDENT IN SILK GARMENTS AND GOLD ORNAMENTS, IN PREPARATION FOR THE INITIATION RITES OF THE YAJNA.

"ARJUNA FOLLOWED THE HORSE WHEREVER IT WENT. FIRST TO THE NORTH, THEN TO THE EAST. SEVERAL KINGS SOUGHT TO OBSTRUCT THE HORSE, BUT ARJUNA PROVED MORE THAN A MATCH FOR THEM. ONE BY ONE, THEY CONSENTED TO THE SUZERAINTY OF THE PANDAVAS AND AGREED TO ATTEND THE YAJNA.

"AFTER ACCOMPLISHING HIS TASK, ARJUNA MADE HIS WAY BACK TO HASTINAPURA. WHEN YUDHISHTHIRA HEARD OF THIS, HIS JOY KNEW NO BOUNDS.

BHEEMA, NAKULA! HAVE YOU HEARD? ARJUNA IS ON HIS WAY BACK.

THERE IS BARELY A MONTH LEFT FOR THE PREPARATIONS. BHEEMA, SELECT A SUITABLE PLACE FOR THE SITE.

"ELATED BY THE TIDINGS OF ARJUNA'S RETURN, BHEEMA WENT ABOUT FULFILLING HIS DUTIES WITH ENTHUSIASM.

"BEAUTIFUL PALACES, FITTED WITH GOLDEN PILLARS AND IMPOSING GATEWAYS, WERE SOON ERECTED. ONE BY ONE, THE INVITED GUESTS ASSEMBLED THERE.

"BEARING RICH GIFTS FOR YUDHISHTHIRA, KINGS FROM ALL PARTS OF THE LAND CAME FOR THE YAJNA.

"THE RICHLY DECORATED SACRIFICIAL HALL FILLED THEM WITH AWE AND ADMIRATION.

"EXCELLENT ARRANGEMENTS WERE MADE TO FEED AND HOUSE THE THOUSANDS OF GUESTS.

"AS YUDHISHTHIRA, WITH THE HUMILITY CHARACTERISTIC OF HIM, PERSONALLY SUPERVISED THE ARRANGEMENTS FOR THE COMFORT OF HIS GUESTS, A MESSENGER ARRIVED.

MY MASTER, ARJUNA HAS ARRIVED AT THE CITY GATES.

HERE IS YOUR REWARD FOR BRINGING THIS HAPPY NEWS.

amar chitra katha

"JUST THEN THE SACRIFICIAL HORSE GALLOPED INTO SIGHT FOLLOWED BY THE WEARY BUT VICTORIOUS ARJUNA.

"PEOPLE SHOWERED PRAISES ON HIM AS HE PROCEEDED TOWARDS THE YAJNA-ALTAR.

WHO BUT ARJUNA COULD RETURN VICTORIOUS LIKE THIS?

WE ARE FORTUNATE INDEED THAT HE HAS RETURNED SAFE.

"DHRITARASHTRA AND YUDHISHTHIRA HASTENED TO WELCOME HIM.

"WITH DUE CEREMONY, THE HORSE WAS SACRIFICED.

"YUDHISHTHIRA THEN OFFERED THE WHOLE EARTH AS A GIFT TO VYASA, WHO SAID—

I RETURN THIS GIFT TO YOU. WE BRAHMANAS PREFER A GIFT OF MONEY, NOT LAND.

"YUDHISHTHIRA WAS INSISTENT—

I CANNOT TAKE ANYTHING FROM BRAHMANAS. MY BROTHERS TOO WILL AGREE.

WE DO.

"THE PERFORMANCE OF THE ASHWAMEDHA REQUIRED THE GIFTING AWAY OF ALL THE LAND ACQUIRED DURING THE CONQUEST. BUT SELDOM WAS THIS ACTUALLY DONE. INSTEAD, GENEROUS GIFTS OF GOLD WERE MADE TO THE BRAHMANAS. SO VYASA PERSUADED YUDHISHTHIRA —

IT IS JUST LIKE YOU TO BE SO GENEROUS. BUT GIVE GOLD TO THE BRAHMANAS AND LET THE KINGDOM REMAIN IN YOUR HANDS.

"KRISHNA SAID TO YUDHISHTHIRA —

DO AS THE SAGE SAYS, O KING.

" KING YUDHISHTHIRA GIFTED TO THE ATTENDENT BRAHMANAS MILLIONS OF GOLD COINS AS WELL AS ALL THE GOLD VESSELS USED FOR THE CEREMONY.

LATER, AS YUDHISHTHIRA WAS BIDDING FAREWELL TO KRISHNA AND OTHER KINGS, A STRANGE THING OCCURRED. THERE APPEARED A BLUE-EYED MONGOOSE, HALF OF WHOSE BODY WAS SHINING GOLD. ADDRESSING THE GATHERING IN A HUMAN VOICE, HE SAID, "YOUR SACRIFICE IS NOT HALF AS MERITORIOUS AS THAT OF THE GENEROUS BRAHMANA OF KURUKSHETRA". THIS STRANGE CLAIM BY THE CREATURE, CAUSED BEWILDERMENT AMONG ALL THOSE PRESENT.

amar chitra katha

"THE PRIESTS SURROUNDED THE MONGOOSE AND ASKED HIM —

WHERE HAVE YOU COME FROM? WHO ARE YOU TO FIND FAULT WITH OUR SACRIFICE? WE HAVE DONE EVERYTHING ACCORDING TO THE SHASTRAS. WHAT MAKES YOU SCORN US?

"THE MONGOOSE LAUGHED AND SAID —

I DO NOT SPEAK OUT OF FALSEHOOD OR PRIDE, O BRAHMANAS. I REPEAT, YOUR SACRIFICE IS NOT EQUAL TO THE SEER OF PORRIDGE GIFTED BY THE POOR BRAHMANA OF KURUKSHETRA.

I WITNESSED THIS NOBLE ACT MYSELF AND, AS A RESULT OF HIS MERIT, HALF MY BODY HAS BECOME GOLD. LISTEN TO ME, O BRAHMANAS, WHILE I NARRATE THAT INCIDENT TO YOU.

LONG AGO, IN KURUKSHETRA, THERE LIVED A BRAHMANA WHO OBTAINED FOOD BY GLEANING GRAIN FROM NEARBY FIELDS. HIS FAMILY, CONSISTING OF HIS WIFE, SON AND DAUGHTER—IN—LAW, ATE ONLY ONCE IN THREE DAYS...

...AND SOMETIMES EVEN LESS FREQUENTLY. ONCE THERE WAS A TERRIBLE DROUGHT. THE LAND WAS PARCHED, THE FIELDS LAY BARE. THE FAMILY STARVED FOR DAYS ON END.

ONE DAY, AFTER WANDERING ABOUT FOR HOURS IN THE HEAT AND DUST, THEY MANAGED TO COLLECT A SEER OF GRAIN.

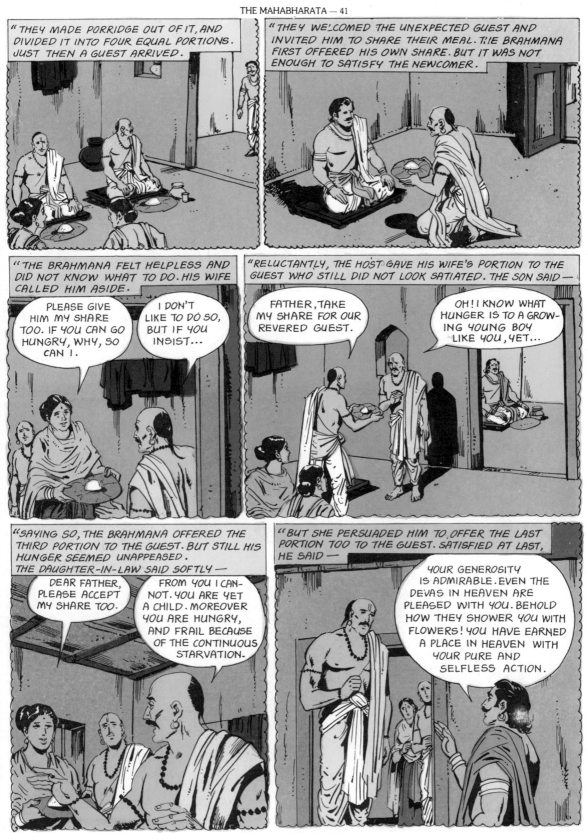

"THEY MADE PORRIDGE OUT OF IT, AND DIVIDED IT INTO FOUR EQUAL PORTIONS. JUST THEN A GUEST ARRIVED.

"THEY WELCOMED THE UNEXPECTED GUEST AND INVITED HIM TO SHARE THEIR MEAL. THE BRAHMANA FIRST OFFERED HIS OWN SHARE. BUT IT WAS NOT ENOUGH TO SATISFY THE NEWCOMER.

"THE BRAHMANA FELT HELPLESS AND DID NOT KNOW WHAT TO DO. HIS WIFE CALLED HIM ASIDE.

PLEASE GIVE HIM MY SHARE TOO. IF YOU CAN GO HUNGRY, WHY, SO CAN I.

I DON'T LIKE TO DO SO, BUT IF YOU INSIST...

"RELUCTANTLY, THE HOST GAVE HIS WIFE'S PORTION TO THE GUEST WHO STILL DID NOT LOOK SATIATED. THE SON SAID —

FATHER, TAKE MY SHARE FOR OUR REVERED GUEST.

OH! I KNOW WHAT HUNGER IS TO A GROWING YOUNG BOY LIKE YOU, YET...

"SAYING SO, THE BRAHMANA OFFERED THE THIRD PORTION TO THE GUEST. BUT STILL HIS HUNGER SEEMED UNAPPEASED. THE DAUGHTER-IN-LAW SAID SOFTLY —

DEAR FATHER, PLEASE ACCEPT MY SHARE TOO.

FROM YOU I CANNOT. YOU ARE YET A CHILD. MOREOVER YOU ARE HUNGRY, AND FRAIL BECAUSE OF THE CONTINUOUS STARVATION.

"BUT SHE PERSUADED HIM TO OFFER THE LAST PORTION TOO TO THE GUEST. SATISFIED AT LAST, HE SAID —

YOUR GENEROSITY IS ADMIRABLE. EVEN THE DEVAS IN HEAVEN ARE PLEASED WITH YOU. BEHOLD HOW THEY SHOWER YOU WITH FLOWERS! YOU HAVE EARNED A PLACE IN HEAVEN WITH YOUR PURE AND SELFLESS ACTION.

amar chitra katha

YOUR SACRIFICE IS EQUIVAL-ENT TO SEVERAL RAJASOOYA AND ASHWAMEDHA YAJNAS. THE CHARIOT TO TAKE YOU ALL TO HEAVEN IS WAITING FOR YOU AT YOUR DOOR.

JUST THEN I CAME OUT FROM MY HIDING PLACE. JUST BY THE SMELL OF THAT SANCTIFIED PORRIDGE AND THE TOUCH OF A FEW DROPS THAT HAD FALLEN ON THE GROUND, HALF MY BODY BECAME GOLD. SINCE THEN I VISIT EACH AND EVERY SACRIFICIAL HALL, IN THE HOPE OF TURNING THE OTHER HALF OF MY BODY TO GOLD.

BUT, ALAS, HERE TOO I AM DISAPPOINTED. YOUR YAJNA IS NOT EQUIVALENT TO A TINY PARTICLE OF THAT PORRIDGE.

AFTER NARRATING THIS TALE, THE MONGOOSE DISAPPEARED AS INEXPLICABLY AS HE HAD APPEARED. THE INCIDENT SHOULD NOT SURPRISE YOU, O KING. RIGHTEOUS CONDUCT, CONTENTMENT, SELF-CONTROL, GENEROSITY, TRUTHFULNESS AND AUSTERITIES — EACH OF THESE VIRTUES IS, INDEED, EQUIVALENT TO PERFORMING AN ELABORATE YAJNA.

"AFTER THE ASHWAMEDHA YAJNA WAS OVER, YUDHISHTHIRA RETURNED TO HIS ROYAL DUTIES.

"BUT EVEN AFTER HE WAS FORMALLY CROWNED HE SOUGHT DHRITARASHTRA'S ADVICE ON EVERY IMPORTANT MATTER.

"KRIPACHARYA AND VIDURA WERE DHRITARASHTRA'S CONSTANT COMPANIONS. SAGE VYASA TOO VISITED HIM REGULARLY AND REGALED HIM WITH STORIES.

"ONE DAY, YUDHISHTHIRA SAID TO HIS BROTHERS —

WE MUST DO OUR BEST TO MAKE HIM FORGET THE LOSS OF HIS SONS. LET NO EFFORT BE SPARED TO MAKE DHRITA-RASHTRA AND GANDHARI COMFORTABLE AND CONTENTED.

"ARJUNA, NAKULA AND SAHADEVA READILY COMPLIED. BUT NOT BHEEMA.

WHATEVER HAPPENED WAS THE RESULT OF DHRITARASHTRA'S EVIL MIND. I CAN NEVER FORGIVE HIM. NEVER!

"ALTHOUGH IN DEFERENCE TO YUDHISHTHIRA'S WISHES, HE WAS OUTWARDLY POLITE TO THE OLD COUPLE, HIS HEART WAS FILLED WITH BITTERNESS. ONE DAY, WHEN THEY WERE WITHIN HEARING, HE BOASTED TO HIS FRIENDS.

SEE THESE STRONG ARMS OF MINE.

amar chitra katha

"DISPLAYING HIS STRONG BICEPS, HE SAID —

WITH THESE VERY ARMS I CRUSHED TO DEATH ALL THE SONS OF THAT BLIND KING, DHRITARASHTRA.

"BHEEMA WENT ON TO GIVE A VIVID DESCRIPTION OF HOW HE HAD KILLED THE KAURAVAS, KNOWING VERY WELL HOW MUCH PAIN IT WOULD CAUSE TO THE OLD KING.

"FOR FIFTEEN YEARS, DHRITARASHTRA AND GANDHARI HAD LIVED AMICABLY WITH THE PANDAVAS, BUT BHEEMA'S CRUEL WORDS OPENED UP OLD WOUNDS. DHRITARASHTRA CALLED HIS FRIENDS TOGETHER.

YOU ALL KNOW WELL ENOUGH HOW THE KAURAVA CLAN WAS DESTROYED BECAUSE I IGNORED THE ADVICE OF MY WELL-WISHERS.

NOW, AFTER FIFTEEN YEARS, I HAVE BEGUN TO REALISE THE MANY SINS I COMMITTED. TO ABSOLVE MYSELF, I HAVE DECIDED TO FAST AND DO PENANCE.

" THEN ONE DAY, DHRITARASHTRA TOLD YUDHISHTHIRA —

GANDHARI AND I WOULD LIKE TO RETIRE TO THE FOREST AND SPEND THE REST OF OUR DAYS IN PRAYER AND PENANCE.

A KING IS LIKE A VENERABLE TEACHER FOR ALL HIS SUBJECTS. SO, WE REQUEST YOU TO GRANT US PERMISSION TO LEAVE.

"YUDHISHTHIRA WAS VISIBLY UPSET.

OH! WHAT A FOOL I HAVE BEEN NOT TO REALISE HOW UNHAPPY YOU ARE. HERE YOU ARE STARVING YOURSELF AND LIVING LIKE AN ASCETIC AND WE DID NOT EVEN KNOW ABOUT IT.

"DHRITARASHTRA TRIED TO EXPLAIN.

IT IS PROPER FOR US IN OUR OLD AGE TO LIVE IN THE FOREST. ALL OUR FOREFATHERS FOLLOWED THIS PRACTICE.

OH! BUT I CANNOT LET YOU GO. IF YOU INSIST ON GOING I SWEAR I TOO WILL FOLLOW YOU.

"FOR LONG DHRITARASHTRA TRIED TO PERSUADE YUDHISHTHIRA, WHO IN TURN PLEADED WITH HIM TO STAY ON. DHRITARASHTRA SAID—

SANJAYA! KRIPA! WILL ONE OF YOU EXPLAIN TO YUDHISHTHIRA THAT I AM WEARY AND NOW MY MOUTH IS DRY. I CANNOT TALK ANY LONGER.

"WITH THESE WORDS, DHRITARASHTRA, ALMOST FAINT WITH FATIGUE, TURNED TO GANDHARI FOR SUPPORT.

"YUDHISHTHIRA COULD NOT BEAR TO SEE HIM IN SUCH A STATE. HE TENDERLY WIPED THE OLD KING'S FACE WITH HIS HAND AFTER FIRST DIPPING IT IN COLD WATER.

OH! YOU, WHO COULD ONCE CRUSH THE IRON IMAGE OF BHEEMA, ARE NOW SO WEAK. IT IS ALL MY FAULT.

"DHRITARASHTRA EXPLAINED—

IT IS FOUR DAYS SINCE I LAST ATE. THAT IS WHY I AM SO WEAK. BUT YOUR SOOTHING TOUCH HAS REFRESHED ME. YOU MUST NOW ALLOW ME TO LEAVE.

I WILL DO WHAT IS DEAR TO YOU. BUT I REFUSE TO DISCUSS ANYTHING TILL I SEE YOU FED PROPERLY.

I WILL EAT ONLY AFTER I RECEIVE YOUR PERMISSION TO LEAVE FOR THE FOREST.

"JUST THEN, SAGE VYASA ARRIVED. HE SAID —

DO AS DHRITA-RASHTRA SAYS. ALLOW HIM TO RETIRE TO THE FOREST.

IF YOU SAY SO, I AGREE.

"AFTER ALL OF THEM HAD EATEN, DHRITARASHTRA AFFECTIONATELY GAVE YUDHISHTHIRA SOME PARTING ADVICE.

ALWAYS KEEP THE COMPANY OF WISE MEN AND TAKE THEIR OPINION ON IMPORTANT ISSUES.

"LATER GANDHARI ASKED DHRITARASHTRA —

NOW THAT SAGE VYASA HAS GIVEN YOU PERMISSION AND YUDHISHTHIRA TOO HAS AGREED, WHEN WILL WE LEAVE FOR THE FOREST?

SOON, VERY SOON. BUT BEFORE THAT I WOULD LIKE TO SPEAK TO THE PEOPLE.

"ARRANGEMENTS WERE MADE TO INVITE CITIZENS FROM ALL WALKS OF LIFE TO MEET DHRITARASHTRA. ADDRESSING THEM, HE SAID —

GANDHARI AND I HAVE DECIDED TO RETIRE TO THE FOREST. WE HAVE BEEN GRANTED LEAVE TO DO SO BY SAGE VYASA AND KING YUDHISHTHIRA.

BUT I SEEK YOUR PERMISSION TOO. I HAVE BEEN HAPPY DURING YUDHISHTHIRA'S REIGN, HAPPIER THAN I WAS WHEN DURYODHANA WAS KING. BUT I AM BLIND, OLD AND BEREAVED OF ALL MY SONS. SO ALLOW ME TO RETIRE NOW TO THE FOREST.

"DHRITARASHTRA'S HUMILITY BROUGHT TEARS TO THE PEOPLE'S EYES. HE CONTINUED —

IF I HAVE DONE ANY-THING WRONG, FORGIVE ME. MY SONS WERE SELFISH AND CONCEITED. I BESEECH YOU FOR FORGIVENESS ON THEIR BEHALF TOO.

"THERE WAS A WHISPERED CONSULTATION AMONG THE CROWD AND FINALLY A BRAHMANA CALLED SAMBA STEPPED FORWARD.

I HAVE BEEN SELECTED TO REPRESENT ALL THESE PEOPLE, O KING. YOU HAVE BEHAVED LIKE AN ELDER BROTHER TOWARDS US. NOW, WITH SAGE VYASA'S PERMISSION, IF YOU WISH TO GO TO THE FOREST, YOU MUST INDEED DO SO. WE WILL MISS YOU AND REMEMBER YOU ALWAYS.

"THE NEXT DAY, VIDURA APPROACHED YUDHISHTHIRA WITH A MESSAGE FROM DHRITARASHTRA.

ON THE NEXT FULL MOON DAY, KING DHRITARASHTRA WOULD LIKE TO LEAVE. BUT BEFORE THAT, HE WISHES TO ASK YOU FOR SOME MONEY TO PERFORM THE SHRADDHA* OF BHEESHMA, DRONA AND OTHER WARRIORS.

"ARJUNA AND YUDHISHTHIRA HAILED THIS IDEA OF THE OLD KING. BUT BHEEMA MUTTERED IN ANGER.

WE SHOULD NOT AGREE TO THIS. DO NOT GIVE HIM ANYTHING.

"ARJUNA GENTLY TOOK BHEEMA ASIDE.

BROTHER DEAR, HE IS OUR UNCLE AFTER ALL. YOU SHOULD NOT REFUSE HIM HELP. JUST THINK HOW TIMES HAVE CHANGED. TODAY DHRITARASHTRA HAS TO ASK US FOR HELP. ONCE WE WERE AT THEIR MERCY.

* RITES PERFORMED TO PLEASE THE DEAD ONES

"BHEEMA'S ANGER COULD NOT BE CONTAINED.

WE OURSELVES WILL PERFORM THE REQUIRED CEREMONIES. LEAVE THE OLD KING OUT OF IT.

"ONE BY ONE, BHEEMA BEGAN TO RECALL THE ACROCITIES HEAPED ON THEM BY THE KAURAVAS. YUDHISHTHIRA BECAME UNHAPPY.

KEEP QUIET, BHEEMA. THAT IS ENOUGH.

"THEN HE TURNED TO VIDURA AND SAID —

UNCLE, PLEASE TELL KING DHRITARASHTRA THAT HE CAN TAKE ANY AMOUNT OF MONEY AND MATERIALS FROM ME.

"VIDURA CONVEYED THIS NEWS TO DHRITARASHTRA WHO ARRANGED A TEN-DAY-LONG CEREMONY FOR THE SALVATION OF THE SOULS OF FALLEN WARRIORS.

"ON THE ELEVENTH DAY HE CALLED FOR THE PANDAVAS AND PREPARED TO LEAVE FOR THE FOREST.

"WHEN YUDHISHTHIRA SAW DHRITARASHTRA CLAD IN DEERSKIN, THE FINALITY OF THE DECISION STRUCK HIM.

OH! DO NOT LEAVE ME. DO NOT GO AWAY.

"ARJUNA COULD UNDERSTAND YUDHISHTHIRA'S EMOTIONAL STATE.

COME, BROTHER DEAR, DON'T BE SO RESTLESS.

"WHEN GANDHARI AND DHRITARASHTRA EMERGED FROM THE PALACE, YUDHISHTHIRA WAS SURPRISED TO SEE KUNTI LEADING THE WAY.

MOTHER, YOU ENCOURAGED US TO FIGHT AND WIN THIS THRONE. HOW CAN YOU LEAVE US NOW?

SON, WHATEVER I DID SO FAR WAS FOR YOUR SAFETY AND WELFARE. BUT NOW I MUST RETIRE TO THE FOREST.

"AS KUNTI, GANDHARI AND DHRITARASHTRA SLOWLY WALKED AWAY FROM THE PALACE, THEY WERE FOLLOWED BY A WEEPING AND SOBBING CROWD OF PEOPLE.

AND SO, ACCOMPANIED BY VIDURA, SANJAYA, KUNTI AND GANDHARI, DHRITARASHTRA LEFT HASTINAPURA TO SPEND THE REST OF HIS DAYS IN THE FOREST, IN PRAYER AND MEDITATION.

THUS ENDS THE FORTY-FIRST SESSION OF OUR RENDERING OF VYASA'S IMMORTAL ITIHASA, MAHABHARATA.

Mahabharata - 42
THE CELESTIAL REUNION

AFTER RETIRING TO THE FOREST, DHRITARASHTRA LEARNT THE RITES AND RITUALS OF FOREST LIFE FROM THE OTHER ASCETICS AND BECAME ACCUSTOMED TO A LIFE OF PRAYER AND MEDITATION.

"GANDHARI, KUNTI, VIDURA AND SANJAYA, WHO HAD ACCOMPANIED HIM, ALSO ADOPTED AN AUSTERE LIFESTYLE. MONTHS OF SEVERE PENANCE REDUCED DHRITARASHTRA TO SKIN AND BONES.

"DHRITARASHTRA AND THE OTHERS WERE VERY OFTEN REMEMBERED BY THE PANDAVAS.

I WONDER HOW THE OLD KING FARES IN THE FOREST.

OUR POOR DEAR MOTHER! HOW DOES SHE SPEND HER DAYS IN THE FOREST?

"READING THE ANXIETY AND RESTLESSNESS IN YUDHISHTHIRA'S MIND, SAHADEVA SAID—

I AM SO GLAD TO SEE THAT YOU TOO ARE AS ANXIOUS TO VISIT THE FOREST AS I AM. I WAS HESITATING TO ASK YOU...

"DRAUPADI SAID —

I TOO LONG TO SEE OUR DEAR MOTHER KUNTI. IN FACT, ALL THE LADIES OF THE INNER PALACE ARE WAITING FOR THE DAY THEY CAN MEET GANDHARI AND KUNTI.

"YUDHISHTHIRA SENT FOR HIS ARMY CHIEF.

PREPARE YOUR MEN. WE WILL LEAVE FOR THE FOREST TOMORROW. WE WISH TO VISIT KING DHRITARASHTRA. LET AN ANNOUNCEMENT BE MADE THAT ALL CITIZENS OF HASTINAPURA ARE WELCOME TO JOIN US.

"AT DAWN, A LONG CARAVAN OF CHARIOTS AND HORSES, ELEPHANTS AND CAMELS WAS SEEN WINDING ITS WAY OUT OF HASTINAPURA. BEHIND IT WERE MULES LADEN WITH GOODS.

"YUYUTSU AND THE ROYAL PRIEST DHAUMYA WERE LEFT IN CHARGE OF THE KINGDOM.

"LEAVING THEIR HORSES AND CHARIOTS AT A DISTANCE, THE PANDAVAS WALKED UP TO DHRITARASHTRA'S HERMITAGE.

amar chitra katha

"YUDHISHTHIRA ENQUIRED OF THE SAGES THERE—

WHERE IS OUR DEAR UNCLE DHRITA-RASHTRA?

YOU WILL FIND HIM ON THE BANKS OF THE YAMUNA, BATHING AND GATHERING FLOWERS.

"WHILE THE OTHERS WALKED LEISURELY TOWARDS THE RIVER BANK, SAHADEVA RAN AHEAD TO GREET KUNTI.

"HE FELL AT HER FEET AND SOBBED LOUDLY.

"AFTER GREETING THE ELDERS WITH DUE RESPECT, THE PANDAVAS HELPED THEM TO CARRY THE WATER POTS BACK TO THE HERMITAGE.

"DHRITARASHTRA SAID—

AH! HAVING ALL OF YOU AROUND ME MAKES ME FEEL I AM BACK IN THE PALACE.

"AT THE HERMITAGE, A CURIOUS CROWD HAD ALREADY GATHERED. SANJAYA INTRODUCED THE PANDAVAS TO THEM.

BUT I DON'T SEE THE VENERABLE VIDURA WITH YOU. WHERE IS HE?

HE IS DOING SEVERE PENANCE. HE IS REDUCED TO SKIN AND BONES.

"JUST THEN THEY SAW VIDURA COMING TOWARDS THE ASHRAM.

WHY THERE HE IS! BUT HE IS TURN-ING AWAY. I MUST SPEAK TO HIM.

"YUDHISHTHIRA RAN AFTER VIDURA.

STOP! STOP! I AM YOUR YUDHISH-THIRA! I HAVE COME TO MEET YOU.

"VIDURA PAUSED IN THE THICK OF THE FOREST, AND STOOD AGAINST A TREE, STARING INTENTLY AT YUDHISHTHIRA.

"IN A MOMENT YUDHISHTHIRA REALISED THAT HE WAS STARING AT VIDURA'S LIFELESS BODY.

"BUT WHEN IT CAME TO PERFORMING THE CREMATION OF THE BODY OF VIDURA, THERE WAS A HEAVENLY VOICE—

VIDURA WAS LIVING THE LIFE OF A SANYASI. THERE-FORE DO NOT CREMATE HIM.

✻ SANYASIS ARE BURIED, NOT CREMATED

4

"THE DEATH OF VIDURA TOOK EVERYONE BY SURPRISE. YUDHISHTHIRA AND HIS RETINUE SPENT THE NIGHT UNDER THE TREES.

"FOR A MONTH, YUDHISHTHIRA AND THE OTHERS STAYED IN THE FOREST VISITING VARIOUS ASHRAMAS AND BESTOWING GENEROUS GIFTS ON THE SAGES. THEN WITH THE PERMISSION AND BLESSINGS OF DHRITARASHTRA AND GANDHARI, THEY MADE THEIR WAY BACK TO HASTINAPURA.

"TWO YEARS AFTER THEIR VISIT TO THE FOREST, SAGE NARADA VISITED YUDHISHTHIRA. ANXIOUSLY YUDHISHTHIRA ASKED HIM —

DID YOU SEE THE VENERABLE DHRITA-RASHTRA? I HAVE HEARD THAT HE IS OBSERVING SEVERE PENANCE.

LISTEN CALMLY. I WILL GIVE YOU ALL THE NEWS.

AFTER YOU RETURNED TO HASTINAPURA, DHRITARASHTRA, GANDHARI, KUNTI AND SANJAYA ALL LEFT FOR HARI-DWAR*.

"YOUR UNCLE DHRITARASHTRA REDUCED HIMSELF TO A MERE SKELETON THROUGH STARVATION AND SEVERE PENANCE.

"GANDHARI, KUNTI AND SANJAYA ALSO SPENT THEIR DAYS IN FASTING AND PRAYER.

* A PLACE OF PILGRIMAGE IN THE HIMALAYAN FOOT HILLS, (NOW IN U.P.)

"ONE DAY WHEN DHRITARASHTRA WAS RETURNING TO HIS ASHRAMA AFTER HIS BATH, A STORM BROKE, AND WITH IT A FOREST FIRE. SOON, THE WHOLE FOREST WAS AFLAME.

"SO WEAK AND HELPLESS HAD THEY BECOME THAT DHRITARASHTRA, KUNTI AND GANDHARI COULD NOT RUN AWAY.

TAKE TO YOUR HEELS, SANJAYA. WE WILL MEET OUR ENDS IN THIS FIRE.

"PERSUADING SANJAYA TO ESCAPE, THE THREE OF THEM SAT DOWN.

SO WHILE THE THREE OF THEM WERE CONSUMED BY THE FOREST FIRE, SANJAYA WENT TO THE HIGHER HIMALAYAS.

"THE NEWS CAME AS A REAL SHOCK TO YUDHISHTHIRA AND HIS BROTHERS. THEY WERE REDUCED TO TEARS AND TRIED TO COMFORT ONE ANOTHER.

"YUDHISHTHIRA RETURNED TO HIS ROYAL DUTIES, BUT HIS HEART WAS NOT AT REST, FILLED AS IT WAS WITH SORROW. THE YEARS ROLLED BY UNEVENTFULLY. THIRTY-SIX YEARS AFTER THE GREAT WAR, ILL OMENS STARTED TO APPEAR.

"STORMS LASHED THE COUNTRYSIDE, METEORS STREAKED THROUGH THE SKY, THE SUN AND THE MOON TOO APPEARED TO BE SURROUNDED BY STRANGE RINGS.

"BUT WHEN THE NEWS OF THE DESTRUCTION OF THE VRISHNI CLAN REACHED THE PANDAVAS, THEIR GRIEF KNEW NO BOUNDS.

BUT HOW DID THAT HAPPEN? HOW COULD THE ENTIRE CLAN OF THE VRISHNIS BE SUDDENLY DESTROYED? WAS IT A RESULT OF SOME CURSE?

YES, IT HAPPENED MANY YEARS AGO WHEN SAGE VISHWAMITRA, KANVA AND NARADA HAD GONE TO DWARAKA FOR A VISIT.

"SOME MISCHIEVOUS YADAVA BOYS DRESSED UP SAMBA*AS A WOMAN AND TOOK HIM TO THE SAGES.

THIS IS BABHRU'S WIFE, AND SHE IS HOPING FOR A SON. YOU RISHIS ARE WISE MEN. TELL US WHETHER SHE WILL HAVE A BOY OR A GIRL.

WHAT DO THESE YOUNGSTERS THINK! HOW DARE THEY FOOL US THUS?

* A SON OF KRISHNA

amar chitra katha

"WITH RED-SHOT EYES, THE SAGES DECLARED —

YOU CRUEL, WICKED BOYS! THIS SON OF KRISHNA WILL GIVE BIRTH TO AN IRON PESTLE * WHICH WILL CAUSE THE DESTRUCTION OF ALL THE VRISHNI AND ANDHAKA RACES. ONLY BALARAMA AND KRISHNA WILL BE SPARED. BALARAMA WILL CONSIGN HIMSELF TO THE SEA, AND KRISHNA WILL BE KILLED BY A HUNTER WHILE HE IS LYING DOWN.

"SURELY ENOUGH THE NEXT MORNING, SAMBA GAVE BIRTH TO AN IRON PESTLE. HIS COMPANIONS RUSHED UP TO KING UGRASENA AND GAVE THE PESTLE TO HIM.

"AFRAID OF ITS ALLEGED POWER OF DESTRUCTION, THE KING ORDERED THE IRON PESTLE TO BE CRUSHED INTO POWDER, AND TO BE CAST INTO THE SEA. WITH A VIEW TO PREVENT DRUNKEN BRAWLS A PUBLIC PROCLAMATION WAS MADE THAT LIQUOR SHOULD NOT THEREAFTER BE PREPARED OR CONSUMED IN THE KINGDOM.

"IN COURSE OF TIME, THE DENIZENS OF DWARAKA FORGOT ABOUT THIS INCIDENT. BUT WHEN THIRTY-SIX YEARS AFTER THE GREAT WAR, ILL OMENS BEGAN TO APPEAR IN DWARAKA TOO, KRISHNA REALISED THE SIGNIFICANCE. GATHERING HIS PEOPLE TOGETHER, HE SAID —

I PERCEIVE ILL OMENS IDENTICAL TO THOSE WE PERCEIVED BEFORE THE GREAT WAR.

* TOOL USED FOR POUNDING IN A MORTAR.

8

"THEN HE PONDERED FOR A WHILE.

WHY! IT IS THIRTY-SIX YEARS SINCE THAT GREAT BATTLE. IT IS NOW TIME FOR GANDHARI'S CURSE TO TAKE EFFECT.

I FEEL IT IS BEST FOR ALL OF US TO GO ON A PILGRIMAGE. LET ALL OF US GATHER TOGETHER AT PRABHASA*.

"THE HEADS OF THE FAMILIES OF VRISHNIS AND ANDHAKAS WERE WILLING TO ABIDE BY HIS DECISION. HECTIC PREPARATIONS WERE SOON UNDER WAY.

"MOUNTED ON HORSES, ELEPHANTS AND CHARIOTS, THE ARMY TOO PREPARED TO LEAVE THE TOWN.

"ON REACHING PRABHASA, THEY SET UP CAMP AND SETTLED DOWN. THEN BEGAN THE FEASTING AND DRINKING IN WHICH KRISHNA, BALARAMA, SATYAKI AND KRITAVARMA ALSO JOINED.

* A PLACE OF PILGRIMAGE NEAR DWARAKA

"SATYAKI, QUITE DRUNK, TOOK IT TO HIS HEAD TO INSULT KRITAVARMA.

I HAVE YET TO SEE ANOTHER KSHATRIYA WHO WOULD KILL HIS HAPLESS ENEMIES WHILE THEY ARE ASLEEP. WHAT YOU DID WAS UNFORGIVABLE.

"WILD WITH FURY, KRITAVARMA RETORTED—

DIDN'T YOU KILL BHOORISHRAVA AFTER HE HAD LAID DOWN HIS WEAPONS? DO YOU THINK YOU WERE VERY BRAVE THEN?

"THE OTHERS BEGAN TAKING SIDES AND A DRUNKEN BRAWL WAS SOON ON.

"SATYAKI SPRANG UP WITH A LIVID FACE.

TODAY I SWEAR I WILL AVENGE THE DEATH OF DHRISHTADYUMNA AND THE OTHERS. I WILL KILL THIS WICKED KRITAVARMA WHO SLAYED THEM WITH THE HELP OF ASHWATTHAMA.

"SWIFTLY SATYAKI TOOK THE SWORD FROM KRISHNA AND IN AN INSTANT, CUT OFF KRITAVARMA'S HEAD.

"THEN, CRAZY WITH ANGER AND DRINK, HE BEGAN ATTACKING EVERYONE AROUND.

"KRISHNA HASTENED TO CONTROL HIM, BUT JUST THEN THE ANDHAKAS SURROUNDED SATYAKI. IN THEIR DRUNKEN STATE, THEY ATTACKED HIM WITH THE POTS AND PANS THAT WERE LYING AROUND.

"TO PROTECT SATYAKI, KRISHNA'S SON PRADYUMNA JUMPED INTO THE FRAY.

"THOUGH THEY WERE BOTH STRONG AND VALOROUS, SATYAKI AND PRADYUMNA WERE SOON OUT-NUMBERED AND KILLED.

"ENRAGED BY THE KILLING OF HIS SON AND FRIEND, KRISHNA PLUCKED A CLUMP OF ERAKA* GRASS.

"NO SOONER HAD THE GRASS TOUCHED HIS HAND, THAN IT TURNED INTO A FORMIDABLE IRON PESTLE.

✻ A TYPE OF GRASS BELONGING TO THE RUSH FAMILY

"HOLDING THE IRON WEAPON ALOFT, KRISHNA ATTACKED ALL THOSE WHO CONFRONTED HIM.

"THEREAFTER, WHOSOEVER PULLED UP A TUFT OF THAT GRASS, FOUND HIMSELF ARMED WITH A TERRIBLE WEAPON.

"DRIVEN BY DESTINY, THE VRISHNI CLAN ATTACKED ONE ANOTHER.

"WHILE THE FIGHT REACHED ITS CLIMAX, KRISHNA STOOD BY, WATCHING SILENTLY AS FATHER KILLED SON, AND BROTHER ATTACKED BROTHER WITH IRON RODS.

"SOON, HOWEVER, KRISHNA'S SONS SAMBA, CHARUDESHNA AND HIS GRAND-SON ANIRUDDHA WERE ALSO KILLED. ONLY DARUKA, KRISHNA'S CHARIOTEER, AND BABHRU, THE MINISTER OF THE YADAVAS, REMAINED ALIVE.

"DARUKA SAID —

ALL ARE DEAD NOW, O LORD, BUT BALARAMA IS NOT TO BE SEEN. COME, LET US GO AND LOOK FOR HIM.

"THEY SOON FOUND HIM NEAR THE SEA, SHORE.

"KRISHNA SAID —

DARUKA, GO AT ONCE TO HASTINAPURA AND TELL ARJUNA ABOUT THIS TERRIBLE CARNAGE. ASK HIM TO RUSH TO DWARAKA.

"DARUKA AT ONCE ASCENDED HIS CHARIOT AND LEFT. TURNING TO BABHRU, KRISHNA SAID —

GO TO DWARAKA TO PROTECT OUR WOMENFOLK.

"BEFORE HE COULD EVEN STIR, BABHRU WAS FELLED BY AN IRON ROD WHICH HAD GOT STUCK TO A HUNTER'S ARROW.

"KRISHNA SAID TO BALARAMA —

PLEASE WAIT HERE FOR ME WHILE I LEAVE THE WOMEN AND CHILDREN IN SAFE AND CAPABLE HANDS.

"KRISHNA RETURNED TO DWARAKA AND TO HIS FATHER VASUDEVA.

I HAVE CALLED FOR ARJUNA. PLEASE LOOK AFTER THE WOMEN OF OUR CLAN TILL HE ARRIVES. I MUST GO BACK TO BALA-RAMA. HE IS WAITING FOR ME AS WE BOTH INTEND TO DO TAPASYA* NOW. I CANNOT BEAR TO LIVE HERE ANY MORE.

"AS KRISHNA WAS ABOUT TO RUSH BACK, HE HEARD A LOUD WAILING AND CRYING.

"HE FOUND THE WOMEN AND CHILDREN HUDDLED TOGETHER, WEEPING HELPLESSLY. CONSOLING THEM, HE SAID —

CALM YOURSELF. ARJUNA WILL SOON BE HERE. HE WILL PROTECT YOU.

* MEDITATION AND AUSTERITIES   amar chitra katha   14

"WHEN KRISHNA RUSHED BACK TO BALARAMA, HE SAW A GREAT WHITE SERPENT EMERGING FROM HIS MOUTH.

"THE SNAKE THEN DISAPPEARED INTO THE OCEAN.*

"AFTER WITNESSING THE END OF BALARAMA, KRISHNA REALISED THAT HIS TIME TOO HAD COME. HE WANDERED OFF INTO THE FOREST DEEP IN THOUGHT.

"AFTER ROAMING AROUND AIMLESSLY, HE SAT DOWN AND REMEMBERED GANDHARI'S CURSE.

"WHEN HIS MIND TURNED TO THE PAST, KRISHNA DISCIPLINED HIS SENSES AND LAY DOWN IN A YOGIC POSE.

"JUST THEN A HUNTER CALLED JARA ARRIVED ON THE SCENE IN SEARCH OF A DEER.

* AS KRISHNA WAS THE INCARNATION OF VISHNU, BALARAMA WAS BELIEVED TO BE THE INCARNATION OF SHESHA, THE SERPENT ON WHICH VISHNU RECLINES

"CAMOUFLAGED BY THE FOLIAGE, HE MISTOOK THE SUPINE KRISHNA FOR A DEER, AND SHOT AN ARROW IN THAT DIRECTION.

"THE ARROW PIERCED THROUGH THE SOLE OF KRISHNA'S FOOT.

"WHEN JARA THE HUNTER CAME NEAR, HE REALISED HIS MISTAKE AND BEGGED FOR FORGIVENESS. AFTER CONSOLING THE HUNTER, KRISHNA'S SOUL DEPARTED FROM HIS BODY. THUS, LORD KRISHNA TOO MET HIS END IN THE MANNER PREDICTED BY GANDHARI.

"MEANWHILE DARUKA, WHO HAD REACHED HASTINAPURA, REPORTED TO THE PANDAVAS THE TERRIBLE EVENTS THAT HAD TAKEN PLACE.

"SHOCKED TO HEAR THIS TERRIBLE NEWS, ARJUNA ACCOMPANIED DARUKA BACK TO DWARAKA.

"IN DWARAKA THOUSANDS OF WOMEN, FORLORN AND DESERTED, LAMENTED ALOUD ON SEEING ARJUNA.

"EVEN THE STOUT-HEARTED ARJUNA COULD NOT BEAR TO SEE THEIR GRIEF. OVERCOME WITH SORROW AND SYMPATHY, HE FELL DOWN IN A SWOON.

"RUKMINI AND THE OTHER QUEENS RAN TO HELP HIM UP. THEY SEATED HIM ON A GOLDEN ASANA AND SAT BESIDE HIM IN SILENT SYMPATHY.

"ON RECOVERING, ARJUNA WENT TO MEET HIS UNCLE VASUDEVA. WHEN ARJUNA GREETED HIM, THE GRIEF-STRICKEN VASUDEVA CLASPED HIM TO HIS BOSOM.

OH ARJUNA! YOUR FAVOURITE PUPILS SATYAKI AND PRADYUMNA ARE NO MORE. IN FACT, THEY HAVE CAUSED THE DESTRUCTION OF THE ENTIRE VRISHNI CLAN.

BUT THEN WE CANNOT BLAME THEM. WHATEVER HAPPENED WAS AN OUTCOME OF THE CURSE OF THE RISHIS.

EVEN KRISHNA, WITH ALL HIS MIGHT AND POWER, WAS A SILENT WITNESS TO THIS MASS DESTRUCTION. PERHAPS HE DID NOT WANT TO OPPOSE THE CURSE OF GANDHARI AND THE RISHIS.

YOU, ARJUNA KNOW WELL THE GREAT PROWESS OF MY SON. YOUR GRANDSON PAREEKSHIT WAS REVIVED AFTER BEING KILLED BY ASHWATTHAMA. YET AFTER WATCHING ALL HIS KITH AND KIN BEING KILLED, HE DID NOTHING.

KRISHNA HAS GONE AWAY SOMEWHERE AFTER TELLING ME TO DO AS YOU BID. NOW TAKE CHARGE OF THIS PLACE AND PEOPLE. I HAVE NO WISH TO LIVE ANY LONGER.

"WITH A HEAVY HEART, ARJUNA SAID—

NOR CAN I BEAR TO SEE THIS WORLD BEREFT OF MY DEAR KRISHNA. AND I KNOW THAT MY BROTHERS AND DRAUPADI WILL FEEL LIKEWISE. AH! PERHAPS THE TIME HAS COME FOR YUDHISHTHIRA TO DEPART.

I WILL TAKE THE WOMEN AND CHILDREN AND THE AGED WITH ME TO INDRAPRASTHA. DARUKA, NOW I WANT TO MEET THE MINISTERS OF THE VRISHNIS.

" THE MINISTERS ARRIVED POST-HASTE. ADDRESSING THEM, ARJUNA SAID—

PREPARE YOUR CHARIOTS AND COLLECT ALL YOUR WEALTH TO COME WITH ME TO INDRAPRASTHA. ONCE THERE, KRISHNA'S GRANDSON, VAJRA WILL BE MADE YOUR KING.

SEVEN DAYS FROM NOW, WE WILL LEAVE AT DAWN. SO HURRY UP AND PREPARE TO LEAVE WITH ME.

"ARJUNA SPENT A SAD NIGHT IN KRISHNA'S PALACE.

"EARLY NEXT MORNING, VASUDEVA BREATHED HIS LAST.

"AFTER PERFORMING THE OBSEQUIES FOR VASUDEVA, ARJUNA WENT TO THE SPOT WHERE THE VRISHNIS HAD MET WITH THEIR DESTRUCTION.

"THERE TOO HE PERFORMED THE FINAL RITES FOR ALL THE DEAD. AFTER SEARCHING FOR KRISHNA AND BALARAMA, ARJUNA PRESUMED THEM TO BE DEAD, AND PERFORMED THE LAST RITES FOR THEM TOO.

"SEVEN DAYS LATER, ARJUNA LEFT DWARAKA. FOLLOWING HIM WERE NUMEROUS CHARIOTS OF THE CITIZENS OF DWARAKA.

"NO SOONER HAD THE SEA OF HUMANITY CROSSED THE LIMITS OF DWARAKA THAN THE CITY BEGAN TO SUBMERGE IN THE OCEAN.

HURRY! HURRY! THE SEA IS COMING CLOSER!

STRANGE ARE THE WAYS OF GOD!

"TRAVERSING THE VARIOUS MOUNTAINS AND RIVERSIDES, ARJUNA LED HIS RETINUE TO THE LAND OF FIVE RIVERS. WHEN THEY ESTABLISHED CAMP THERE, THEY WERE SET UPON BY A GROUP OF ROBBERS. WHEN ARJUNA TRIED TO USE HIS CELESTIAL WEAPONS TO COUNTER THEIR ATTACK, HE STOOD TRANSFIXED.

WHY, I CAN'T REMEMBER A THING. HOW CAN MY MEMORY FAIL ME AT THIS CRUCIAL MOMENT?

"WHILE THE DACOITS CONTINUED THE ATTACK...

...ARJUNA STOOD BY, HELPLESS. THEN HE TRIED TO ATTACK THE LOOTERS WITH ORDINARY WEAPONS. BUT SOON HIS QUIVERS, WHICH EARLIER HAD BEEN INEXHAUSTIBLE, BECAME EMPTY.

"GRADUALLY, REALISATION DAWNED ON ARJUNA.

ALL THIS IS SURELY DIVINELY ORDAINED. I CANNOT RECALL THE CELESTIAL WEAPONS; MY VERY LIMBS FEEL WEAK. AH! ALL THE KNOWLEDGE OF THE ARTS OF WAR I HAD ACQUIRED IS NOT TO BE RELIED UPON, AFTER ALL!

"HAPLESSLY, HE GATHERED TOGETHER THE PEOPLE WHO WERE LEFT AND TOOK THEM TO INDRAPRASTHA WHERE VAJRA, SON OF ANIRUDDHA, WAS LATER CROWNED KING.

"AFTER MAKING ALL THE REQUISITE ARRANGEMENTS, ARJUNA MADE HIS WAY TO VEDAVYASA'S ASHRAMA.

"WHILE ARJUNA GREETED HIM WITH DUE RESPECT, VYASA SHREWDLY DETECTED THE RESTLESSNESS IN HIS MIND.

IS ANYTHING THE MATTER, ARJUNA? WHY DO YOU LOOK SO CREST-FALLEN? WHAT HAS HAPPENED TO YOU?

THE LOTUS-EYED KRISHNA AND HIS BROTHER BALARAMA ARE NO MORE. THE ENTIRE CLAN OF VRISHNIS HAS BEEN DESTROYED.

AS IT IS, I CANNOT BEAR TO THINK OF THEIR MASS DESTRUCTION. AND HOW CAN I BELIEVE THAT KRISHNA IS DEAD. IF KRISHNA CAN DIE, WHY THEN, THE OCEANS CAN DRY UP, THE MOUNTAINS CAN SHAKE, THE SKIES TEAR APART, AND FIRE TURN COOL.

"VYASA SAID —

DO NOT GRIEVE OVER THE VRISHNIS. DUE TO THE CURSE OF THE BRAHMANAS THEIR DEATH WAS CERTAIN AND ORDAINED. ELSE WOULDN'T KRISHNA HAVE INTERVENED?

AIDED BY BHEEMA, NAKULA AND SAHADEVA, YOU TOO HAVE COMPLETED AN ONEROUS TASK, O ARJUNA. IT IS NOW TIME FOR YOU TO LEAVE THIS EARTH.

YOU NO LONGER NEEDED THE CELESTIAL WEAPONS, SO YOU LOST THEM AS SUDDENLY AS YOU HAD RECEIVED THEM EARLIER. SHOULD YOU EVER REQUIRE THEM, THE WEAPONS WILL BE RETURNED TO YOU. IT IS BEST NOW FOR YOU TO PREPARE TO DEPART FOR HEAVEN.

I THINK I UNDERSTAND WHAT YOU MEAN.

"ARJUNA RETURNED TO HASTINAPURA AND NARRATED ALL THE EVENTS TO YUDHISHTHIRA.

"YUDHISHTHIRA HEARD HIM AND SAID SOLEMNLY —

WE CAN ONLY SUBMIT TO FATE.

I TOO BELIEVE THAT.

"BHEEMA, NAKULA AND SAHADEVA ALSO AGREED. YUDHISHTHIRA SAID—

SINCE YOU AGREE, LET US ARRANGE THE CORONATION OF PAREEKSHIT. I WILL LEAVE YUYUTSU IN CHARGE OF MATTERS OF STATE.

"DISCARDING HIS SILKS AND JEWELS, YUDHISHTHIRA DONNED CLOTHES OF BARK. HIS BROTHERS AND DRAUPADI DID LIKEWISE. THEN ALL THE FIVE OF THEM, ALONG WITH DRAUPADI, SET OFF ON THE JOURNEY. A DOG FOLLOWED THEM.

"CROSSING RIVERS AND PLAINS, THEY TRAVELLED ACROSS THE COUNTRY. ARJUNA WAS STILL CARRYING WITH HIM HIS GANDEEVA AND QUIVERS. THE PANDAVAS MET AGNI ON THE WAY, AND HE ASKED ARJUNA TO GIVE AWAY THE GANDEEVA TO VARUNA."

"ARJUNA THREW AWAY HIS WEAPONS IN THE SEA NEARBY. NOW THE PANDAVAS TURNED WEST."

"AFTER VISITING THE SUBMERGED CITY OF DWARAKA, THEY WENT TOWARDS THE HIMALAYAS."

"THEY WERE ALL WALKING UP THE MOUNTAINS AT A FAST PACE. ON THE WAY, THEY SAW MOUNT MERU. AFTER A WHILE, DRAUPADI COULD NOT KEEP STEP WITH THE REST, AND FELL DOWN."

"BHEEMA ASKED YUDHISHTHIRA—

O KING! DRAUPADI HAS DONE NO WRONG IN HER LIFE. WHY DID SHE FALL DOWN NOW?

"YUDHISHTHIRA SAID—

IN HER HEART OF HEARTS, SHE WAS PARTIAL TO ARJUNA. THIS IS THE RESULT OF HER FAVOURITISM.

"WITHOUT PAUSING FOR A BACKWARD GLANCE, YUDHISHTHIRA MARCHED AHEAD. A LITTLE LATER, SAHADEVA FELL.

HE WAS SO SELFLESS AND HELPFUL. WHY DID SAHADEVA HAVE TO FALL, O YUDHISHTHIRA?

SAHADEVA THOUGHT THAT NO ONE WAS AS INTELLIGENT AS HE. HIS VANITY HAS BROUGHT ABOUT HIS FALL.

"NOW THE THREE BROTHERS AND THE DOG CLIMBED UP THE MOUNTAINS. BUT NAKULA COULD NOT ENDURE THE SEPARATION FROM SAHADEVA.

LOOK! NAKULA TOO HAS FALLEN. WHY IS IT SO?

NAKULA THOUGHT HE WAS THE BEST-LOOKING PERSON IN THE WORLD. IT IS HIS VANITY THAT CAUSED HIS DOWNFALL.

"SOON, ARJUNA COLLAPSED WITH APPARENT GRIEF. BHEEMA SAID—

ARJUNA HAS NEVER TOLD A LIE, NOT EVEN IN JEST. THEN WHY DOES HE MEET HIS END THUS?

ARJUNA HAD CLAIMED THAT HE WOULD ANNIHILATE HIS ENEMIES IN JUST ONE DAY. HIS BOASTING ABOUT HIS PROWESS HAS FELLED HIM.

"NONCHALANTLY YUDHISHTHIRA WALKED ON. BHEEMA CALLED OUT AS HE TOO FELL.

WHY ME, O BROTHER? WHY ME?

YOU ATE TOO MUCH BHEEMA AND BOASTED OFTEN ABOUT YOUR UNMATCHED STRENGTH. HENCE YOUR FALL.

BUT TO ABANDON A HELP-LESS CREATURE WHO HAS SOUGHT REFUGE IN YOU, IS A GREAT SIN. I WILL NOT LEAVE THIS POOR DOG.

"JUST THEN LORD DHARMA, WHO HAD BEEN TESTING YUDHISHTHIRA IN THE GUISE OF A DOG, SAID —

YOUR RIGHTEOUS BEHAVIOUR AND YOUR KIND AND GENEROUS NATURE TOWARDS ALL LIVING CREATURES, MAKE YOU THE GREATEST OF ALL KINGS.

ONCE, EARLIER TOO, I HAD TESTED YOU IN THE DVAITAVANA FOREST* THEN TOO YOU HAD DISPLAYED YOUR RIGHTEOUS-NESS. YOU ALONE DESERVE TO ENTER HEAVEN IN YOUR EARTHLY FORM.

"ON INDRA'S CHARIOT, YUDHISH-THIRA ROSE UP TO THE HEAVENS.

BEHOLD THESE NUMEROUS WORLDS OF THE DEVAS. FROM THE EARTH, THEY APPEAR TO BE TWINKLING STARS.

I WANT TO BE WITH MY BROTHERS, WHEREVER THEY MAY BE.

WHY DO YOU PERSIST IN RETAINING YOUR EARTHLY TIES NOW? YOUR BROTHERS CANNOT ACHIEVE YOUR STATUS.

"BUT THE TEMPTATIONS OF HEAVEN DID NOT LURE YUDHISHTHIRA.

NO, NO! I WANT TO BE WITH MY BROTHERS AND DRAUPADI.

"WHEN THEY REACHED SWARGALOKA,* YUDHISHTHIRA SAW DURYODHANA.

LOOK AT THIS! THE WICKED DURYODHANA IS SEATED ON A RESPLENDENT THRONE, ENJOYING ALL HEAVENLY DELIGHTS! I CANNOT BEAR TO SEE THIS.

"FILLED WITH RAGE ON THUS SEEING DURYODHANA, YUDHISHTHIRA TURNED BACK AND SAID—

THE ONE WHO IS RESPONSIBLE FOR THE DEATH OF OUR DEAR ONES, THE ONE WHO CAUSED THE DESTRUCTION OF THE EARTH, THE ONE WHO DRAGGED POOR DRAUPADI TO COURT, THAT VERY WICKED DURYODHANA IS HERE. I HAVE NO WISH TO BE WITH HIM. I DON'T EVEN WANT TO LOOK AT HIM.

"NARADA, WHO WAS AMONG THE ATTENDANT DEVAS, SAID WITH A LAUGH—

NO, DON'T SAY SO. BEFORE YOU COME TO HEAVEN, YOU MUST FORGET ALL YOUR OLD ANIMOSITIES.

"NARADA EXPLAINED—

DURYODHANA LIVED AND DIED LIKE A TRUE KSHATRIYA. THAT IS WHY HE DESERVED THIS HONOUR. FORGET ALL HIS WRONG DOINGS NOW.

YUDHISHTHIRA SAID—

IF THIS SINFUL DURYODHANA IS PLACED IN HEAVEN, WHERE ARE MY HONEST AND BRAVE BROTHERS? I WANT TO MEET THEM AS WELL AS KUNTI AND KARNA. WHERE ARE SHIKHANDI, VIRATA, DRUPADA, SATYAKI AND ABHIMANYU?

* HEAVEN, ACCORDING TO HINDU CONCEPT.

IF ONLY ALL THESE WARRIORS ARE HERE IN HEAVEN. WILL I CONSENT TO STAY HERE. ELSE I WILL GO WHEREVER THEY ARE AND LIVE WITH THEM.

"THE DEVAS ORDERED THEIR MESSENGER TO GO WITH YUDHISHTHIRA.

TAKE YUDHISHTHIRA TO MEET HIS DEAR ONES.

"THE DIVINE MESSENGER LED YUDHISHTHIRA ALONG A TREACHEROUS PATH — DARK, DISMAL AND GLOOMY.

"AN AWFUL STENCH FILLED THE AIR, AND THERE WERE THOUSANDS OF TERRIFYING CREATURES AROUND. YUDHISHTHIRA WAS PERPLEXED.

WHAT A TERRIBLE PLACE! I CAN HARDLY BEAR TO WALK THROUGH.

WHERE ARE WE NOW? WHERE ARE MY BROTHERS? HOW FAR DO WE HAVE TO GO?

JUST HERE. NOW WE MUST RETURN. I WAS TOLD TO TAKE YOU AHEAD TILL YOU GOT TIRED.

"YUDHISHTHIRA WAS QUITE WILLING TO GO AWAY FROM THERE. BUT AS HE TURNED, HE HEARD HUMAN VOICES CALLING OUT PITEOUSLY.

O YUDHISH-THIRA! HAVE PITY ON US! STAY HERE AWHILE!

YOUR PRESENCE IS SO SOOTHING. DON'T GO AWAY AS YET.

STAY JUST A FEW MOMENTS MORE.

"THE KIND-HEARTED YUDHISHTHIRA STOOD STILL.

OH, POOR THINGS! THEY SEEM TO BE SUFFERING A GREAT DEAL.

WHO ARE YOU? WHY DO YOU STAY HERE?

"NO SOONER HAD HE ASKED THAN HE HEARD THE VOICES ANSWER ALL AT ONCE.

I AM KARNA!

NAKULA!

ARJUNA!

I AM BHEEMA!

SAHADEVA!

"YUDHISHTHIRA THOUGHT TO HIMSELF—

WHAT IS THIS IRONY OF FATE. HOW COULD SUCH GOOD PEOPLE DESERVE TO BE IN THIS HIDEOUS PLACE, WHILE THE WICKED DURYODHANA REVELS IN HEAVEN? IS THIS JUST A DREAM?

"ALOUD, HE SAID TO THE MESSENGER—

GO BACK TO WHO-EVER SENT YOU. I AM NOT COMING WITH YOU. IF MY DEAR PEOPLE ARE HELPED BY MY PRESENCE, I WILL STAY RIGHT HERE.

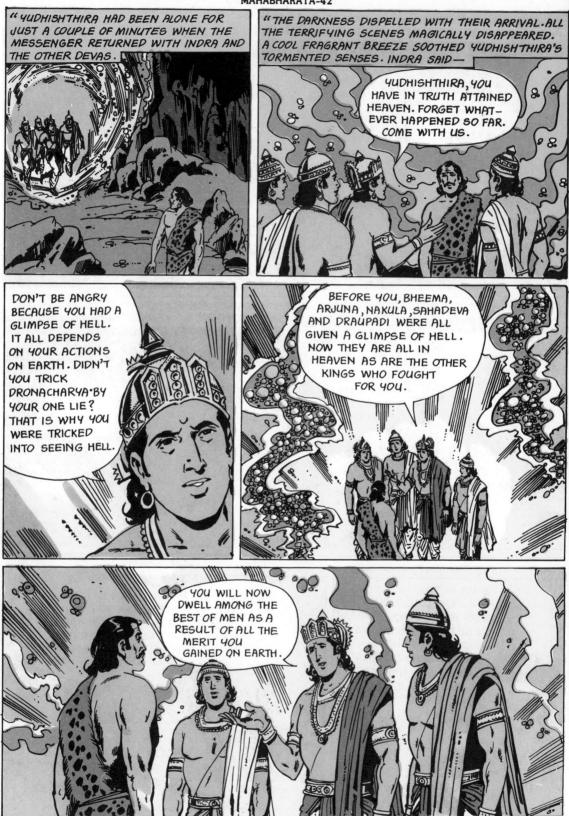

"YUDHISHTHIRA HAD BEEN ALONE FOR JUST A COUPLE OF MINUTES WHEN THE MESSENGER RETURNED WITH INDRA AND THE OTHER DEVAS.

"THE DARKNESS DISPELLED WITH THEIR ARRIVAL. ALL THE TERRIFYING SCENES MAGICALLY DISAPPEARED. A COOL FRAGRANT BREEZE SOOTHED YUDHISHTHIRA'S TORMENTED SENSES. INDRA SAID—

YUDHISHTHIRA, YOU HAVE IN TRUTH ATTAINED HEAVEN. FORGET WHATEVER HAPPENED SO FAR. COME WITH US.

DON'T BE ANGRY BECAUSE YOU HAD A GLIMPSE OF HELL. IT ALL DEPENDS ON YOUR ACTIONS ON EARTH. DIDN'T YOU TRICK DRONACHARYA BY YOUR ONE LIE? THAT IS WHY YOU WERE TRICKED INTO SEEING HELL.

BEFORE YOU, BHEEMA, ARJUNA, NAKULA, SAHADEVA AND DRAUPADI WERE ALL GIVEN A GLIMPSE OF HELL. NOW THEY ARE ALL IN HEAVEN AS ARE THE OTHER KINGS WHO FOUGHT FOR YOU.

YOU WILL NOW DWELL AMONG THE BEST OF MEN AS A RESULT OF ALL THE MERIT YOU GAINED ON EARTH.

"DHARMA, THE LORD OF RIGHTEOUSNESS, APPEARED AGAIN.

THIS IS THE THIRD TIME I TESTED YOU, SON. BUT NOTHING COULD SWAY YOU FROM THE PATH OF GOOD CONDUCT.

"YUDHISHTHIRA THEN BATHED IN THE CELESTIAL GANGA AND, ABANDONING HIS MORTAL BODY AT LAST, WENT TO MEET HIS KINSMEN. HE BEHELD THE RESPLENDENT KRISHNA WHOM ARJUNA WAS WORSHIPPING. BEDECKED WITH A GARLAND OF LOTUSES, DRAUPADI WAS RADIATING HER EXQUISITE BEAUTY. INDRA INTRODUCED YUDHISHTHIRA TO THE DEVAS ASSEMBLED THERE.

NOW I HAVE DESCRIBED IN DETAIL ALL THE EVENTS OF THE GREAT WAR BETWEEN THE KAURAVAS AND THE PANDAVAS. WHOEVER LISTENS TO THIS STORY OF THE MAHABHARATA WILL HAVE ALL HIS SINS WASHED AWAY, AND WILL SURELY GO TO THE ABODE OF VISHNU.

"THUS ENDS OUR RENDERING OF VAISHAMPAYANA'S RECITAL OF VYASA'S IMMORTAL ITIHASA, THE MAHABHARATA.

The History of The

The Mahabharata and the Ramayana, the two great epics of India, have had a profound impact on Indian thought and culture. They have captured the imagination of Indian people for many millennia.

Stories from the two epics permeate through the Indian consciousness and continuously unfold through folk art forms like the *Ramjet ka Phad* of the Rajasthan balladeers, or the shadow leather puppets of Orissa, through classical dances like *Kathakali* or new electronic media like television and films,

The core of the Mahabharata is the great battle that was fought on the field of Kurukshetra between the five sons of King Pandu and their allies on one side and the hundred Kaurava sons of King Dhritarashtra with their allies on the other side.

But besides the main story, there is a wealth of wisdom woven around the battle. Every digression in the main plot of

यदा यदा हि धर्मस
अभ्युत्थानमधर्मस्य त

Mahabharata

the Mahabharata is there to shed light on a central story. In fact, it is claimed that anything that happens anywhere is an echo of what is in the Mahabharata and also that what is not found in the Mahabharata will not be found anywhere in the world. The author of the Mahabharata is generally identified as Sage Veda Vyasa, also known as Krishna Dvaipayana. The text was originally called 'Jaya' and consisted of 8,800 verses that commemorated the victory of the Pandava princes over the wicked Kauravas. This was later revised by Vaishampayana, a disciple of Vyasa, to a work of 24,000 verses

A later edition was the work of Suta Ugrasrvas, which was recited at a sacrifice in the Naimisha forest by Sage Shaunaka. This edition had approximately 100,000 verses and was called Satasahasri Samhita. It was this edition that came to be called the Mahabharata.

The Mahabharata contains virtually all legend and lore, including the perennially favourite myths of the churning of the ocean of milk and the descent of the Ganges upon earth. It also has the romantic tales of Nala-Damayanti and Shakuntala Dushyanta, as well as puzzles and riddles, jokes and pranks. In it are also included codes of law- moral, ethical and natural.

The Mahabharata is therefore considered absolute literature in itself, containing a philosophy that has been an unfailing and perpetual source of spiritual strength to the people of India.

नानिर्भवती भारत ।
त्मनं सृजाम्यहम ॥

‖ Guru

The full moon day in the Hindu month of Ashad (July-August) is observed as the auspicious day of Guru Purnima, a day sacred to the memory of the great sage Veda Vyasa, and dedicated to all gurus. Guru Purnima is also known as Vyas Purnima in honour of Vyasa, who was one of the earliest gurus. He classified the Vedas, wrote the eighteen Puranas and the great epic Mahabharata.

‖ The Guru ‖

Traditionally, in India, people attach great importance to their guru, who is more than just a teacher. The guru is a preceptor, mentor and guide, and is responsible for moulding the personality of the student or shishya.

In ancient times, education in India was based on the *guru-shishya paramapara* where the student spent his formative years at the hermitage of his guru, the Gurukul. The importance of the guru is often equated with God, as the guru was always regarded as a link between the individual and the immortal. Just as the moon shines by reflecting the light of the sun, the disciples too can glow brilliantly like the moon by gaining knowledge from their gurus.

A Sanskrit *shloka*, which is still very popular and familiar to most people in India, equates the guru to the divine trinity of Gods (Brahma, Vishnu, Shiva) and also to the supreme power.

Purnima ||

|| Gurubrahma Guruvishnu Gururdevo Maheshwaraha ||
|| Guruhu Sakshaat Parambrahman Tasmai Shriguruve Namaha ||

"The guru is Brahma, Vishnu and Mahesh
Veneration to the Guru who is the manifestation of the supreme power"

Another popular couplet weaves this into a teasing riddle where the poet is confronted by God and his guru at once, and does not know whom he should greet first. He solves the dilemma by bowing to the Guru in gratitude for granting him a vision of God.

|| Guru Govind dono khade, kake laagu paay, ||
|| Balihari Guru aapne, Govind diyo milaye ||

"Guru and god stand before me, to whom should I bow first?
Thanks to you, Guru, you made me meet God"

|| Significance of Guru Purnima ||

Ashad Purnima, the full moon day of the start of the four months of the rainy season, heralds Chaturmas or the setting in of the eagerly awaited rains. It is a time to reflect and meditate and acknowledge the contribution of the Guru.

Just as the moisture soaked up by the clouds brings down rains that promise revival and fresh growth, so does Guru Purnima suggest a reawakening of one's spiritual quest.

This is a day to venerate your chosen Guru, and thank him/her for the role played in your life. It is suggested that on this day, one should partake of a simple meal of fruits and milk. Even if you cannot meet and greet your Guru, meditate, read, contemplate and pray.

Suppandi and his friends are all packed!

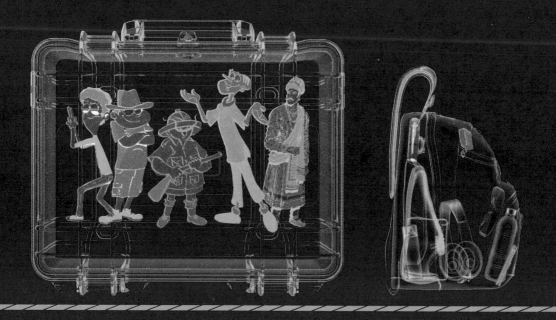

This time your favourite characters are bringing their (mis)adventures to your holiday. ACK Media introduces its special travel collection of Tinkle Digests, Amar Chitra Katha comics and Karadi Tales picture books (for the younger globetrotters), to make your travels more fun.

www.amarchitrakatha.com

Make sure you're packed. Log on to our website now to buy any comic or picture book with your special 25%* discount code: 'NGT 25', and have your favourite travel companions delivered straight to your doorstep.

Versus

*T&C app